Advances in Fluidics

Advances in Fluidics

Sponsored by:

Fluidics Committee
Fluids Engineering and Controls Divisions
The American Society of Mechanical Engineers

Presented at:

The 1967 Fluidics Symposium
Chicago, Illinois
May 9-11, 1967

Edited by:

FORBES T. BROWN,
Chairman
Fluidics Committee

THE AMERICAN SOCIETY OF MECHANICAL ENGINEERS

United Engineering Center   345 East 47th Street   New York, N.Y. 10017

EDITORS NOTE: *Numbers in brackets refer to the references listed at the end of each paper; numbers in parentheses denote equations.*

Library of Congress Number 67-23027

Foreword

THE recently coined word *fluidics* describes engineering systems in which fluid motion or displacement contains significant information as well as power. Probably the most common usage restricts the word to devices containing no moving mechanical parts, such as fluid jet amplifiers and logic elements, vortex valves and sensors, fluid diodes, capillarity relays, and so forth. Other usage describes this limited class with the term *fluerics*, allowing *fluidics* also to encompass other information-bearing devices, including traditional fluid power control walves.

The current spurt of invention and application of fluidic systems received its primary impetus in 1960 from disclosures by the Harry Diamond Laboratories (then Diamond Ordnance Fuze Laboratories), and agency of the U.S. Army, in Washington, D.C. A variety of prior sources also have been recognized. Since 1960 interest in the field has expanded continuously. Present estimates of annual expenditure in the United States are roughly $30 million, involving several hundred workers in over one hundred firms, universities and agencies. Interest in Europe, particularly in the United Kingdom, has become very keen in about the past three years; 49 papers were presented at the recent Granfield conference at Cambridge University (for a review of this conference, see p. 259). Russia first demonstrated fluidic amplifiers in 1960, but subsequent effort would appear to have been small.

The Harry Diamond Laboratories became an information center for fluidics partly by holding three-day general symposia in 1962, 1964, and 1965. The Laboratory felt that the value of future symposiums would be more useful if it were held under the ASME sponsorship. Hence, Joseph Kirshner, Chief of the Fluid Systems Branch, approached the Fluids Engineering Division of ASME.

ASME was no stranger to fluidics, having held a Symposium on Fluid Jet Control Devices in 1962, and having also published many other papers in the field. A Fluidics Committee was formed in May 1966 with Mr. Kirshner as its Chairman. The chairmanship descended to me in October upon Mr. Kirshner's decision to spend the year abroad. Other members of the committee are drawn from both the Fluid Engineering Division and Automatic Controls Division, as well as the field at large.

The Harry Diamond Laboratory has materially helped in the transition from HDL to ASME sponsorship. The present symposium appropriately can be called the Fourth HDL Symposium on Fluid Amplification. Future technical sessions will be sponsored by the Fluidics Committee at the ASME Winter Annual Meetings, the spring conferences of the Fluids Engineering Division, and the annual Joint Automatic Control Conference (JACC).

Uncontrolled publication was appropriate for an infant field. Adolescense is now approaching, however, and formal review procedures constitute the principal departure of the present symposium. Sixty-five manuscripts were submitted for review, of which twenty-five papers and nine Technical Briefs were finally accepted. The efforts of authors of rejected papers is deeply appreciated. In a large number of instances excellent future ASME papers can be based on extensions of the work.

The review process was excruciatingly difficult, and special thanks are due to the review Chairman, Dr. Turgut Sarpkaya of the University of Nebraska, and the Vice-Review Chairman, Dr. J. Lowen Shearer of the Pennsylvania State University.

Forbes T. Brown, *Chairman*
Fluidics Committee

Contents

An Experimental Study of Bounded and Confined Turbulent Jets

Richard D. Trapani, Capt. USA
Harry Diamond Laboratories
Washington, D. C.

Abstract

An experimental study was conducted to determine the characteristics of a turbulent bounded jet and a confined jet. These characteristics were compared with those of a two-dimensional turbulent free jet. For both bounded and confined jets the presence of solid boundaries was seen to alter their behavior. The bounded jet spread less rapidly than the free jet and the confined jet, spreading under the influence of an axial adverse pressure gradient, spread more rapidly than the free jet.

Nomenclature

A_R = nozzle aspect ratio (dimensionless)

$b_{.37}$ = ordinate of velocity profile where $V/U = .37$; (cm)

$b_{.50}$ = ordinate of velocity profile where $V/U = .50$; (cm)

$b_{.80}$ = ordinate of velocity profile where $V/U = .80$; (cm)

b_1 = bleed ratio (dimensionless)

C_R = channel ratio W/w (dimensionless)

p = static pressure (kN/m^2)

Re_w = Reynolds number $U_o w/\nu$ (dimensionless)

u = jet axial velocity (m/s)

U = jet centerline velocity (m/s)

U_o = jet centerline velocity at nozzle exit plane (m/s)

v = jet transverse velocity (m/s)

V = jet velocity, $\sqrt{u^2 + v^2}$ (m/s)

1

w = nozzle width (cm)

W = channel width (cm)

x = axial distance from apparent origin of fully developed jet (cm)

X = axial distance from nozzle exit plane (cm)

X_o = axial distance between nozzle exit plane and apparent origin of fully developed jet (cm)

y = transverse distance from jet centerline (cm)

z = vertical distance from x-y plane (cm)

σ = spread parameter of jet (dimensionless)

ν = kinematic viscosity (m^2/sec)

η = $\sigma y/x$, (dimensionless)

Introduction

Jets play an important role in the functioning of fluidic devices. This is particularly true for the confined jet (inclosed on the top, bottom, and sides) since many of the devices contain inclosed passages that induce a pressure gradient in the jet stream. Little information is available on the effect of this pressure gradient on the characteristics of a jet, particularly with regard to spreading. It was the purpose of this study to determine the effect of the presence of an axial adverse pressure-gradient on a jet to see how the characteristics were altered from those of the well-known, two-dimensional, turbulent free jet.

The presence of solid boundaries also affects the spreading of bounded jets (bounded by plates above and below). Hence, a bounded jet study was also conducted with some of the more significant results presented here to tie in with the confined jet results.

Apparatus and Instrumentation

The apparatus used in the confined jet study is drawn schematically in Fig. 1. The main parts consisted of a blower-supplied pressure chamber, nozzle, channel section, and traversing mechanism. To investigate the effect of an adverse pressure gradient on a jet, a means had to be provided to prevent the jet from attaching to one of the channel walls. Four hoses were used to connect together the regions on each side of the jet. However, it was necessary to provide, in addition, bleeding on each side of the jet before it would flow parallel to the channel walls.

Three configurations were used in the confined jet study involving changes in the nozzle aspect ratio A_R (height over width), channel ratio C_R (channel width over nozzle width), and bleed ratio b_1 (bleed opening over nozzle width). These are summarized in Table I

2

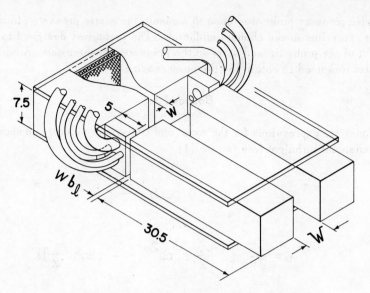

FIG. 1 SCHEMATIC DRAWING OF EXPERIMENTAL
APPARATUS SHOWING PERTINENT DIMEN-
SIONS IN CENTIMETERS.

TABLE I

w	A_R	W	C_R	b_1	Re_w	Bleed vel.
1.11	7	5.64	5	0.6	15,000	$0.11 U_o$
.49	15.5	5.64	12	2.1	8600	$0.13 U_o$
.49	15.5	3.81	8	2.1	8500	$0.17 U_o$

along with the approximate Reynolds number and bleed velocities given in terms
of the fraction of the jet centerline velocity at the nozzle exit plane.

The apparatus used for the bounded jet study was obtained by removing the
channel walls and hose support blocks shown in Fig. 1. A nozzle of aspect ratio
$A_R = 7$ was used, which discharged a jet of Reynolds number (based on nozzle
width and exit velocity) of $Re_w = 14,220$ between two horizontal Lucite sheets.
The nozzle contour consisted of circular arcs joined by straight lines. At the
exit plane, the tangents to the circular arcs were parallel to the jet axis. Two
200-mesh copper screens were placed in the nozzle to suppress air turbulence.

Velocity measurements were made with a constant-temperature hot-wire
anemometer. This instrument measured the absolute velocity, V, of the jet.
Hence, no true measurement of the axial velocity component, u, could be made
except at the jet centerline and points in the flow where the transverse component of velocity, v, vanished. In both the confined and bounded jet configurations, measurements were made in regions where the v component of velocity was
much smaller than the u component, except in the flow region near the bleed ports
in the confined jet. Profile measurements were made at the midplane between the
top and bottom plates.

3

A static pressure probe was used to measure the static pressure along the confined jet centerline at the channel midheight. The probe was designed to minimize the effect of the probe tip and stem on the pressure measurements. A micromanometer was used to obtain the pressure readings.

Bounded Jet

The analytic expressions for the axial and transverse velocity components for a two-dimensional turbulent free jet are [1]

$$u = U \operatorname{sech}^2 \frac{\sigma y}{x} \tag{1}$$

$$v = \frac{U}{2\sigma} \left[2 \frac{\sigma y}{x} \operatorname{sech}^2 \frac{\sigma y}{x} - \tanh \frac{\sigma y}{x} \right] \tag{2}$$

where

$$\frac{\sigma y}{x} = \eta \tag{3}$$

and

$$x = X + X_o \tag{4}$$

The location in a free jet where the y component of velocity is zero was found from equations (1) and (2) to correspond to $u = U$ and $u = 0.37U$. This was useful in minimizing the error in the measurement of u so that a more accurate value of the spread parameter, σ, could be obtained.

Upon substitution of equation (4) into equation (1), the following relationship was obtained between y and x:

$$y = \left[\frac{\operatorname{sech}^{-1}\sqrt{\frac{u}{U}}}{\sigma} \right] X + \left[\frac{\operatorname{sech}^{-1}\sqrt{\frac{u}{U}}}{\sigma} \right] X_o \tag{5}$$

This equation indicates that for a fixed ratio of u/U a linear relationship exists between y and x with slope

$$\left[\frac{\operatorname{sech}^{-1}\sqrt{\frac{u}{U}}}{\sigma} \right]$$

and y-intercept

$$\left[\frac{\operatorname{sech}^{-1}\sqrt{\frac{u}{U}}}{\sigma} \right] X_o.$$

This method was used to obtain the spread parameter of the bounded jet. Fig. 2 shows such a plot of y versus x for three fixed values of V/U^* from the potential

4

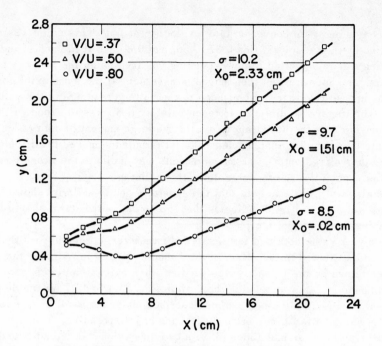

FIG. 2 SPREAD GROWTH OF BOUNDED JET

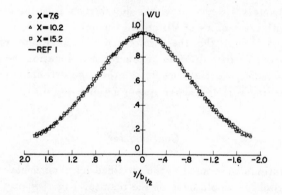

FIG. 3 DIMENSIONLESS VELOCITY PROFILES FOR
BOUNDED JET

core region to 19 nozzle widths downstream. Velocity ratios of 0.80, 0.50, and 0.37 were used to include the middle, center, and edge of the jet. The value of 0.37 was chosen specifically with the hope that a minimum error in the measurement of u would occur for the bounded jet. The values obtained for σ (8.5, 9.7, and 10.2) are higher than the Reichardt [1] value of 7.7. Weske and Pai obtained a value of $\sigma = 8.8$ for an aspect ratio of 12.2.

Fig. 3 shows the theoretical curve of equation (1) along with the data points for three axial locations. It is seen that there is good agreement between the curve and data.

A likely source of error can be traced to the manner in which the data in Fig. 2 were obtained. The hot-wire was set at an axial centerline position. The voltage was recorded and then converted into a velocity reading. This value was then multiplied by the velocity ratios 0.37, 0.50, and 0.80 and then each of these velocities was reconverted to corresponding voltages using the hot-wire calibration data. The hot-wire was then moved transversely at the same axial position, until the hot-wire voltage corresponded to the voltage readings of the velocity ratios. The transverse distance for each velocity ratio was recorded. Although this procedure has the advantage of yielding a large amount of data rather quickly, it has the disadvantage that, because the jet turbulence makes it difficult to measure the voltage output, the measurements may indicate the wrong position. This was especially true for large downstream distances.

It is also worthwhile to note that the generally good similarity shown by the experimental data in Fig. 3 indicates that the spread parameter σ should be constant across the width of the jet.

The higher value obtained for the spread parameter, compared with the free jet value, was attributed to the effect of the bounding plates in reducing the amount of air entrained by the jet. This was verified when extension plates were attached to the bounding plates increasing their width from 25.4 to 45.7 cm (an 80 per cent increase). By using the slope method described above for $u = 0.37U$, a value of 10.8 was obtained for σ indicating a decrease in jet spreading. A similar effect was observed by Foss and Jones [3] in a two-dimensional turbulent bounded jet study.

The potential core of the jet in the present study was found to become dissipated at approximately 4.5 nozzle widths downstream from the exit plane. This is in agreement with the results of Miller and Cumings [4]. The results from references [3, 5 and 6] show that the core region ends anywhere from 4 to 6 nozzle widths downstream. Difficulty was encountered in locating the point on the jet centerline where the potential core ended when the extension plates were used. However, in line with the above reasoning one would expect the core to be extended.

Confined Jet

Three configurations were used in the confined jet experiments to see what effect geometrical changes would have on the results. Fig. 4 shows the axial centerline static pressure distribution for the three configurations designated by the aspect ratio and channel ratio. It is seen that in each case the pressure distribution was not altered appreciably and the pressure gradient is positive for distances beyond 7 cm downstream. Most of the velocity measurements were made in the region of the adverse pressure gradient.

Fig. 5 shows the centerline velocity decay of the confined jet for the three configurations used. The decay curve for the bounded jet experiments is also included for comparison. The velocities of the confined jets are smaller than those of the bounded jet.

Since the bounded jet centerline velocity decays slower than that of the free jet because of smaller turbulent friction losses associated with less entrainment, one might on first thought expect the confined jet centerline velocity to be greater than that of the bounded jet.

On the other hand, the presence of the adverse pressure gradient and the resulting counterflow leads one to expect a more rapid centerline decay than for

6

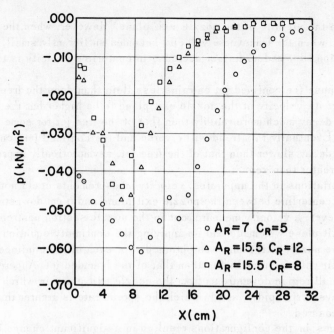

FIG. 4 CENTERLINE STATIC PRESSURE FOR THE
CONFINED JET CONFIGURATIONS

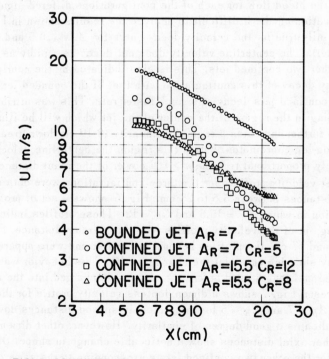

FIG. 5 CONFINED JET CENTERLINE VELOCITY DECAY

the free jet in the vicinity of the nozzle exit plane. However, when the jet fills the duct; i.e., when the transverse velocity becomes sufficiently small, we have essentially pipe flow and no further decrease in centerline velocity is to be expected.

Thus, because the confined jet entrains less fluid than does the free or bounded jet, we expect its velocity at the nozzle exit plane to be higher but the centerline velocity will decay much more rapidly than that of the free jet for some distance downstream. Eventually this trend will reverse and the confined jet centerline velocity will decay slower than that of the free jet, asymptotically approaching some value greater than zero.

Due to limitations in the apparatus, velocity measurements could not be made along the jet centerline between the nozzle exit plane and 6 cm downstream thereof. However, a velocity measurement in the nozzle section upstream from the nozzle exit plane was made and by applying the continuity equation the velocity at the nozzle exit plane was obtained. For each of the confined jets, the nozzle exit velocity was higher than that of the bounded jet. Apparently there is a rather small region downstream from the nozzle exit plane in which the velocity decays very rapidly, and in which the spread rate is greater than that in the region measured.

The changes in the configurations resulted in a significant change in the nozzle pressure only for the configuration in which $A_R = 7$ and $C_R = 5$. The nozzle pressures for the other configurations were approximately equal. It is also important to mention that the bleed openings for this configuration were also different from that of the other two configurations. Furthermore, the bleed velocity and consequently the bleed flow for each of the configurations differed significantly. These complications make it difficult to analyze the results shown in Fig. 5. This is especially true for the velocity decay curve for $A_R = 15.5$ and $C_R = 8$ (narrow channel). The centerline velocity does not decay as rapidly as in the case of the other two confined jets. This is also indicated by the nearly equal rate of velocity decay of this configuration with that of the bounded jet while the other two confined jets decay at a much faster rate. This was attributed to slower spreading in the region of the center of the jet which will be illustrated below. Fig. 5 further indicates a region of linearity (8-19 cm downstream) of U versus X on log-log coordinates. Within this region the centerline velocity varies inversely proportional to some $n > 1/2$ power of the axial distance.

Confined jet velocity profiles for the three configurations were obtained for downstream distances between 5.6 to 23 cm. Fig. 6 shows a set of profiles for the configuration in which $A_R = 15.5$ and $C_R = 12$. These profiles indicate a rapid flattening out of the velocity profiles with downstream distance. For axial distances beyond 17 cm, the profiles become rather flat and were apparently not affected by any shearing action at the channel walls. This behavior was attributed to the short channel length used before the air was discharged into the atmosphere 30 cm downstream. Fig. 7 shows a dimensionless velocity profile for the configuration in which $A_R = 7$ and $C_R = 5$ for three closely spaced distances downstream. The profile indicates a good degree of similarity. However, other dimensionless profiles for other axial distances show a noticeable change in shape. Dimensionless profiles for the other two confined jets corresponding to the same downstream distances "match" the profiles shown in Fig. 7. There is apparently an indication that the shape of the dimensionless profiles is a function of the axial dis-

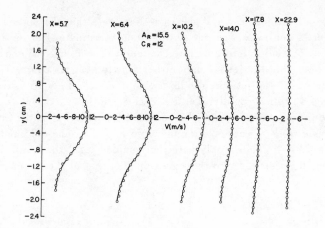

FIG. 6 CONFINED JET PROFILES FOR A_R = 15.5, C_R = 12

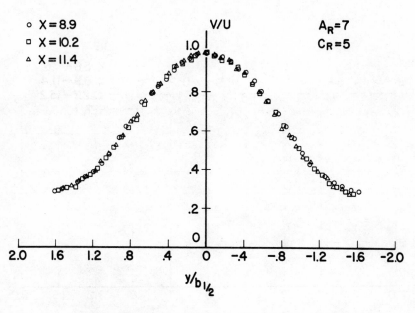

FIG. 7 DIMENSIONLESS CONFINED JET PROFILES FOR
A_R = 7, C_R = 5

tance and is not a function of the geometrical changes. This is indicated in Fig.
8 by the broken lines that pass through the data points of each configuration for
a limited downstream region. Also shown in the figure is the theoretical free jet
profile of equation (1). It is seen that only in the region from 8.9 to 11.4 cm downstream is there a good comparison between the confined jet data and the theoretical curve for the free jet. However, for values of $y/b_{1/2} > 1.2$, even this profile
deviates markedly from the free jet profiles. This deviation has been attributed to
a difference in spread growth characteristics, which is discussed below.

Figs. 9 through 11 show the spread growth of the confined jet for each configuration. Velocity ratios, V/U, of 0.80, 0.65, 0.50, and 0.37 were used so that
the spread growth could be observed at several locations from near the jet center-

9

line to the edge of the jet. Each of the figures reveals that the spread growth of the confined jet is nonlinear with the downstream coordinate. For the two cases in which the jet is issuing into a narrow channel ($A_R = 7$, $C_R = 5$ and $A_R = 15.5$, $C_R = 8$), it is seen that the jet spreads rather slowly near its center ($V/U = 0.80$). For the case in which the jet spreads in a wide channel ($A_R = 15.5$, $C_R = 12$, Fig. 10) it does so rather rapidly over its entire width.

To compare the spread growth of the confined jet with that of the bounded jet, a graph was made of $b_{1/2}$ versus X as shown in Fig. 12. The confined jet data for all configurations is shown only with the bounded jet data. In all configurations the confined jet spread growth is greater than that of the bounded jet.

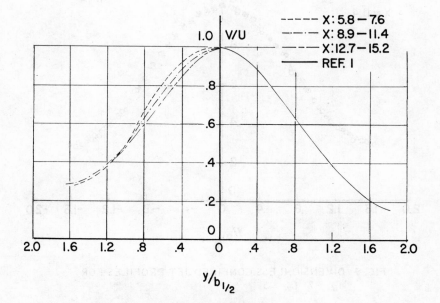

FIG. 8 COMPARISON OF THE CONFINED JET PROFILES
WITH THAT OF THE TWO-DIMENSIONAL TURBULENT
FREE JET

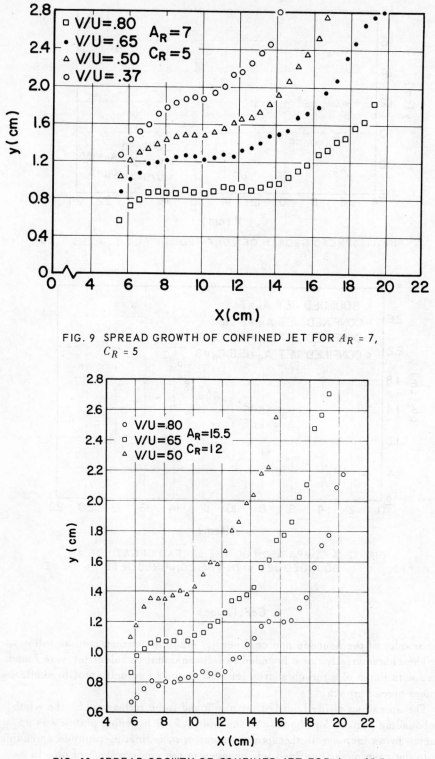

FIG. 9 SPREAD GROWTH OF CONFINED JET FOR $A_R = 7$, $C_R = 5$

FIG. 10 SPREAD GROWTH OF CONFINED JET FOR $A_R = 15.5$, $C_R = 12$

11

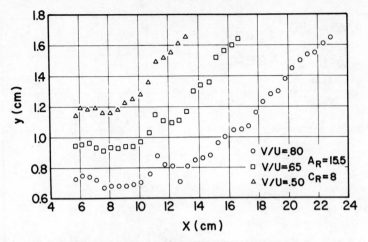

FIG. 11 SPREAD GROWTH OF CONFINED JET FOR A_R = 15.5,
C_R = 8

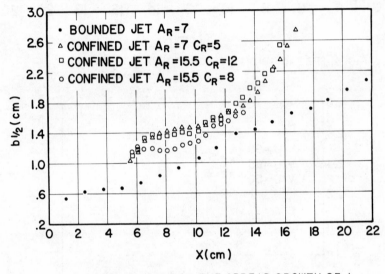

FIG. 12 A COMPARISON OF THE SPREAD GROWTH OF A
BOUNDED JET WITH THE CONFINED JETS

Conclusions

The results of the bounded and confined jet study are summarized as follows:

1) The characteristics of a bounded two-dimensional turbulent jet were found to agree with those of a turbulent free jet with regard to velocity profile similarity and linear spread growth.

2) The spreading of the bounded jet was found to be influenced by the width of the bounding plates. An increase in the width of the bounding plates was accompanied by an increase in the spread parameter σ, indicating retarded spreading.

3) In the case of the confined jet, changes in the configuration of nozzle aspect ratio and channel ratio did not change the pressure gradient significantly.

12

This is not surprising since the configurations used were the only ones (within small dimensional tolerances) in which the jet did not attach to one of the channel walls. In other words, if the channel ratio was changed while the aspect ratio was left unchanged, the jet "locked on" to one of the channel walls. If the bleed spacing was not increased for a particular configuration, the jet would also "lock on" to a channel wall. In each of the configurations, the jet filled the channel at approximately 8 to 10 cm downstream from the nozzle exit plane. The presence of low pressure regions close to the nozzle exit caused the jet to spread quickly.

4) Within the downstream region measured, the centerline velocity of the confined jet decayed more rapidly for all the configurations than did the bounded jet. This trend is expected to reverse itself for distances farther downstream.

5) For the confined jet, the centerline velocity obeys an inverse power law with downstream distance over a smaller region downstream than do the centerline velocities of the bounded and free jets.

6) Over the region measured, the confined jet profiles do not match the Görtler profiles of the two-dimensional turbulent free jet. Moreover, there is a change in shape of the dimensionless profiles as the jet moves downstream.

7) In each of the configurations and within the regions measured, the confined jet spreads more rapidly (using the ordinate $b_{1/2}$ as a criterion) than does the bounded jet. In the configurations in which the jet issued into a narrow channel ($C_R = 5$ and $C_R = 8$), spreading in the center region of the jet was retarded. For the configuration in which the jet spread into a wide channel ($C_R = 12$), spreading over the entire width of the jet was enhanced. One would expect that as the width of the channel is increased an increase in spreading would occur if the bubble pressure remains constant (which it nearly did in the experiments) due to easier recirculation caused by larger recirculation regions. A large rate of spreading apparently occurred upstream of the region of measurements, which unfortunately our apparatus did not allow us to measure.

References

[1] H. Schlichting, "Boundary Layer Theory," McGraw-Hill Book Co., Inc., 1960, pp. 605-608.

[2] S. J. Pai and R. Weske, "Two-Dimensional Wall Jet," Institute for Fluid Dynamics and Applied Mathematics, Final Report for the Harry Diamond Laboratories, TR-1087, Dec. 1962.

[3] J. F. Foss and J. B. Jones, "A Study of Incompressible Turbulent Bounded Jets," Purdue Research Foundation, Project No. 3728, Report for Harry Diamond Laboratories, October 1964.

[4] D. R. Miller and E. W. Cumings, "Static Pressure Distribution in the Free Turbulet Jet," *Journal of Fluid Mechanics*, Vol. 3, Part 1, October 1957, pp. 1-16.

[5] M. J. Albertson, Y. B. Dai, R. A. Jensen, and H. Rouse, "Diffusion of Submerged Jets," *Proc. ASCE*, December 1948, pp. 1571-1596.

[6] R. E. Olson and D. P. Miller, "Aerodynamic Studies of Free and Attached Jets," Fluid Amplification Report 6, Harry Diamond Laboratories, October 1963.

Experiments on the Separation of a Fluid Jet From a Curved Surface

D. W. McGlaughlin

IBM Corp.
Poughkeepsie, N.Y.

I. Greber

Case Institute of Technology
Cleveland, Ohio

Abstract

Results are reported of experiments examining the mechanism of separation of a fluid jet from a curved wall. Conditions under which laminar separation, turbulent separation, and enclosed separated regions occur are discussed. The existence of hysteresis in the variation of separation angle with Reynolds number, and the existence of regions of unstable oscillations are pointed out. Some effects of wall heating on the separation phenomena are indicated.

Nomenclature

H = Channel Height

L = Channel Length

P = Pressure

Q = Volume Flow

R = Curved Wall Radius

Re = Reynolds Number

T = Temperature

Ta = Ambient Temperature

Tw = Wall Temperature

u = Component of Velocity in ϕ Direction

v = Component of Velocity in y Direction

V = Average Jet Velocity

W = Channel Width

14

y = Coordinate Perpendicular to Curved Wall

θ = Departure Angle

ν = Kinematic Viscosity

ρ = Density

ϕ = Coordinate along Curved Wall

ϕ_s = Separation Angle

Introduction

This paper reports the results of experiments performed to elucidate some features of the mechanism of separation of a fluid jet from a curved wall. The experiments were performed as part of a program of work on fluid amplifiers.

It is a common observation that a fluid jet impinging tangentially on a curved surface will flow along the surface for some angle before leaving the surface. The curved surface thus deflects the jet. This "attachment" is frequently called the Coanda effect and is easily observed by placing one's finger under a faucet of running water.

Considerable research has been done on two-dimensional jets or sheet flow over curved surfaces [1, 2, 3, 4]. Newman [5] conducted experiments to relate the separation of two-dimensional (high aspect ratio) turbulent jets from a circular surface with the geometry of the surface and the Reynolds number of the jet. Kadosch [6] investigated the separation of low aspect ratio turbulent jets from a circular wall. The development of fluid amplifiers employing jet separation from a curved surface requires additional information on the relationship of geometry and Reynolds number to the separation phenomenon, especially at low Reynolds number and low aspect ratio.

To help clarify the effects of Reynolds number and geometry on laminar to turbulent separation and on the transition from laminar to turbulent separation, some simple experiments were performed on low-speed air jets.

The major results are qualitatively as follows:

At low Reynolds numbers, one observes a laminar jet which separates from the curved surface after only a relatively short length of run on the surface. The separated jet becomes turbulent some distance downstream of the separation point. As the Reynolds number is increased, the transition to turbulence occurs closer to the separation point. At some critical Reynolds number, the turbulent jet reattaches to the surface. One then has an enclosed separation "bubble"; that is, the jet leaves an enclosed region of circulating flow between the jet and the wall. The reattached *turbulent* jet again separates at a point downstream of the bubble. As the Reynolds number is further increased, the reattachment point moves upstream, but the separation points do not change much. The bubble size decreases with increasing Reynolds number; finally the bubble vanishes. For still higher Reynolds numbers, the transition to turbulence occurs closer and closer to the jet exit.

If the Reynolds number is then decreased, the events are reversed. A separation bubble appears, the bubble grows larger, the turbulent jet detaches. However, the critical Reynolds number for occurrence of different phenomena may be lower than for this occurrence with increasing Reynolds number; that is, hysteresis is observed.

15

The critical Reynolds numbers, and the presence and amount of hysteresis, depend on the length ratios, and particularly upon the ratios of transverse distance to a length in the representative plane. (The ratio of transverse length to the nozzle mouth opening is called the aspect ratio.) Note that large aspect ratio implies a more two-dimensional flow than small aspect ratio.

The following sections discuss the details of the experiments and the quantative results.

Geometry and Basic Definitions

The geometry of the experimental apparatus is shown in Fig. 1. The basic apparatus is a Plexiglas "wind tunnel." Air from a settling chamber passes through a constant area straight section. At the end of the straight section, the issuing jet is allowed to flow over a circular arc, forming what is sometimes known as a "wall jet." The circular arc is carefully located to be tangent to the straight wall of the initial straight section. The channel height is denoted by "H", the channel length by "L", and ϕ is the polar angle measured from the channel exit. The separation angle ϕ_s is defined in the usual two-dimensional description as the angle where $\dfrac{\alpha u}{\alpha y}\bigg|_{y=0} = 0$, where u is the component of velocity in the x direction and y is the radial distance from the wall. θ, the departure angle, is the angle between the jet maximum velocity direction after separation and the center line of the channel. θ then is a measure of the direction of the separated jet.

The Reynolds number used herein is $Re = Q/\nu H$ where Q is the volume flow rate. This is a Reynolds number based on channel width and average velocity in the channel, as can easily be seen by rewriting as follows:

$$R = \frac{Q}{\nu H} = \frac{VWH}{\nu H} = \frac{VW}{\nu}$$

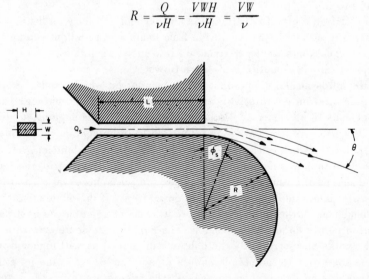

FIG. 1 GEOMETRY CONSIDERED

16

Experimental Procedure

Two models were used in the experiments. Each had a fixed channel height and an adjustable channel width. The smaller model had a fixed channel length and the larger provided two channel lengths. Each model provided three radii of curvature. The values are tabulated below in inches:

L	H	W	R	Model
1.75	.22	0–.500	½, ¾, 1	smaller
7.30, 11.50	.94	0–1.10	2, 3, 4	larger

The smaller model was used to measure the departure angle of the jet. The model was mounted on a turn table which allowed an impact pressure probe to be pivoted around the element to determine the jet departure angle. The departure angle was measured at the point of highest impact pressure at a position several inches downstream of the jet separation point.

The larger model was used for the static pressure measurements along the curved wall, velocity profile measurements at the channel exit, and smoke jet observations.

The static pressure measurements were made using surface pressure taps located at 5 degrees intervals flush with the curved surface midway between the top and bottom cover plates.

The velocity profile measurements were taken approximately 1/16 in. from the channel exit midway between the cover plates. A micromanometer was used for both the static and impact pressure measurements.

All the data shown in this paper were taken with air as the fluid medium.

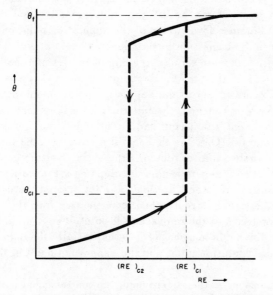

FIG. 2 TYPICAL PLOT OF DEPARTURE ANGLE VS.
REYNOLDS NUMBER

Effect of Reynolds Number on Departure Angle

It is useful to discuss the effect of Reynolds number on departure angle θ for constant geometry. A qualitative plot of departure angle vs. Reynolds number for a small width-to-radius ratio ($W/R < 0.3$) is shown in Fig. 2. As the Reynolds number is increased from some critical value of Reynolds number, the departure angle increases virtually discontinuously; we designate this critical Reynolds number Re_{c1}. For Reynolds numbers higher than Re_{c1}, the departure angle θ is nearly independent of Reynolds number. If the Reynolds number is decreased from values above Re_{c1}, there is a discontinuous decrease in θ at some critical Reynolds number Re_{c2}; after this decrease, the small Reynolds number curve is retraced. The critical Reynolds number for the departure angle drop, Re_{c2}, is less than the critical Reynolds number for the departure angle increase Re_{c1}; that is, a hysteresis phenomenon occurs. This hysteresis occurs for some combinations of geometrical parameters, as will become clearer when geometrical effects are discussed.

Flow Visualization

The flow patterns were observed using air mixed with kerosene vapor. The kerosene vapor was obtained from a Chelmsford smoke generator that generates kerosene vapor by heating liquid kerosene. Air is passed through the generator, mixing with the vapor. The mixture is then passed through the experimental model. The amount of vapor mixed with the air can be controlled by the air flow or the temperature of the heater.

A series of photographs of the flow are shown in Fig. 3 for fixed geometry ($H/W = .234$, $W/R = 0.055$) and varying Reynolds number. Photographs (a) through (e) are for increasing Reynolds number. Considering first increasing Reynolds number less than Re_{c1} (photographs (a), (b), (c)), one notes that the jet is laminar up to and for same distance downstream of the separation point on the curved wall. One also notes the transition to turbulence some distance downstream of the separation point, with more rapid spreading of the jet and the appearance of "vortices" at the edge of the jet. As Reynolds number is increased, the transition to turbulence occurs closer to the separation point. When the first critical Reynolds number Re_{c1} is reached, the turbulent jet makes contact with the curved wall. The incipient attachment and the attached configuration are shown in photographs (d) and (e). One has the mental picture that the initial contact blocks flow from downstream after reaching the vicinity of the separation point. As a result, a decreased pressure region develops near the wall. There is brought into existence a centripital force "driving" the jet against the curved wall.

One notes that the turbulent reattached jet separates from the curved wall some distance downstream of the reattachment point. The jump in departure angle at the first critical Reynolds number Re_{c1} is essentially the angular difference between the laminar separation point and the separation point of the reattached turbulent jet.

If the Reynolds number is then decreased, the reattachment point moves downstream, as seen in photograph (f). When the reattachment point has moved downstream to coincide with the second (turbulent) separation point, as in phtograph

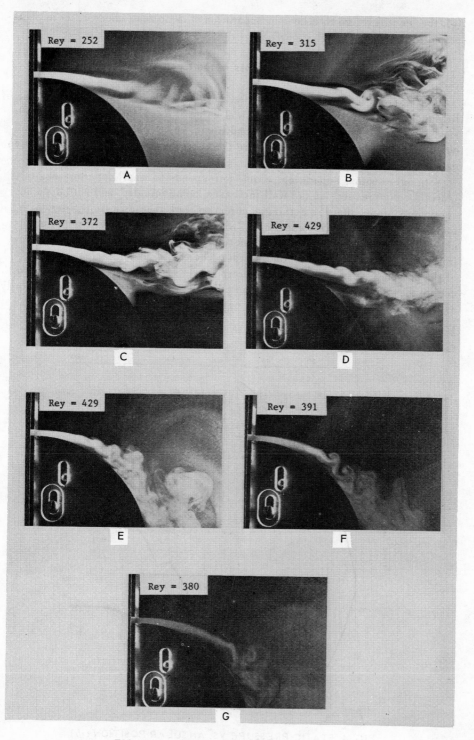

FIG. 3 PHOTOGRAPHS OF SMOKE JET

19

(g), the jet will return to a laminar separation with no reattachment, as in photograph (c).

Pressure Measurements in the Hysteresis Region

Fig. 4 shows the static pressure distribution on the curved wall for a value of Reynolds number between the two critical values, Re_{c1} and Re_{c2}, for both the small and the large departure angle conditions. The departure angles are 14 degrees and 70 degrees, which also are the approximate separation point angles as observed with smoke visualization.

With only laminar separation, which corresponds to small departure angle (curve 1), the pressure on the wall increases monatonically, and with apparent continuous slope; there is nothing apparent to mark the separation point. With turbulent reattachment and separation, which corresponds to large departure angles (curves 2), both the laminar and turbulent separation points are apparent from the pressure distribution on the wall. There are sudden increases in slope of the pressure curve at both the separation points. The pressure *decreases* with ϕ up to the vicinity of the first separation point, for reasons that we do not yet fully understand. The apparent decrease in pressure in the vicinity of $\phi = 85$ degrees is probably spurious.

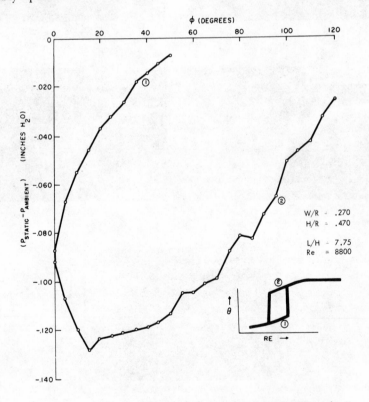

FIG. 4 STATIC PRESSURE VS. ANGULAR POSITION (ϕ)

20

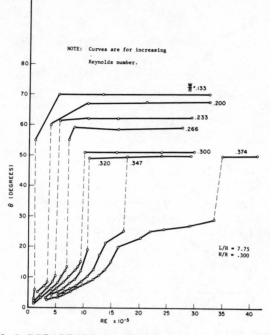

FIG. 5 DEPARTURE ANGLE VS. REYNOLDS NUMBER

Geometrical Effects

There are four pertinent lengths, and hence three length ratios in these experiments. The lengths are the channel length, width, height (L, W, H respectively), and the radius of curvature R of the wall. The jet profile at the channel exit is controlled by the Reynolds number, the geometrical ratios L/W and H/W, and of course the channel entrance conditions. For a given profile at the channel exit, the succeeding flow depends on the Reynolds number and the length ratios L/W and W/R. Note that in most of these experiments L and H were held fixed. It is, therefore, convenient herein to use the alternative triplet of length ratios L/H, H/R and W/R with $L/H = 7.75$ for most of the experiments.

In all of the experiments reported herein, the channel length to width ratio L/W was too small for fully developed flow at the channel exit. This would also be true in the motivating problem of fluid amplifier application. Correspondingly, the aspect ratio H/W is sufficiently small so that three-dimensional effects are very important.

Fig. 5 shows the variation of the departure angle θ with Reynolds number for *increasing* Reynolds number, for H/R and L/H fixed, and for different value of W/R. It is seen that as W/R is increased (relatively smaller radius of curvature), the critical Reynolds number Re_{c1} increases, the jump in departure angle θ at Re_{c1} decreases, and the final asymptotic departure angle for large Reynolds number decreases. The same data are replotted in Fig. 6 to show the variation with W/R of the final asymptotic value of departure angle (θ_f) and the value of the laminar departure angle at the critical Reynolds number (θ_{c1}). Note that θ_{c1} increases and as mentioned above θ_f decreases with increasing W/R up to

21

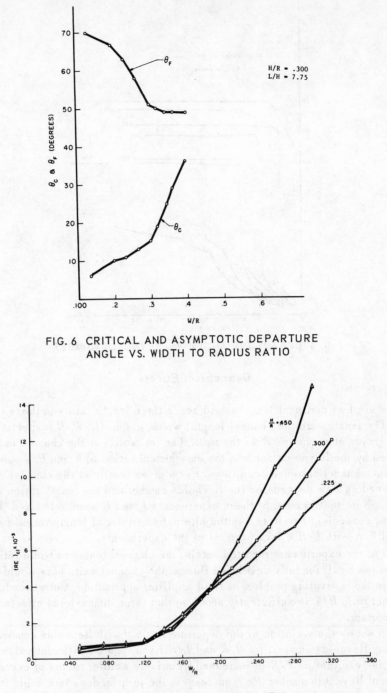

FIG. 6 CRITICAL AND ASYMPTOTIC DEPARTURE
ANGLE VS. WIDTH TO RADIUS RATIO

FIG. 7 CRITICAL REYNOLDS NUMBER $(Re)_{cl}$ VS.
WIDTH TO RADIUS RATIO

22

$W/R \approx 0.45$. For larger W/R, θ_{c1} and θ_f coincide, and both decrease with increasing W/R. Corresponding to the coincidence of θ_{c1} and θ_f, there is no discontinuity in the departure angle Reynolds number curve at the higher value of W/R ($W/R > 0.45$) instead, the asymptotic value of departure angle is reached smoothly.

In Newman's [5] experiments, departure angles in excess of 200 degrees were observed. The aspect ratio used in those experiments ranged between 1200 and 2000. The maximum value of departure angle (θ_f) in the experiments reported herein is approximately 70 degrees at an aspect ratio of 2.4 (Fig. 6). The lower departure angles for turbulent flow observed in the author's experiments are due to the three-dimensional effects associated with the low aspect ratios of the jet.

An interesting instability is observed in the region in which the departure angle exhibits a discontinuity, but no hysteresis.

In this region ($0.3 < W/R < 0.45$) either the small or the large value of departure angle can occur, and at times, the jet appears to switch randomly from one value of departure angle to the other. It is completely plausible that small disturbances can cause switching from one side of the discontinuity to the other. (This instability may have serious bearing on observed oscillations of fluid amplifiers under load. Experiments to elucidate this point are being performed by one of the authors, I. Greber.) Many of the graphs are terminated at a value of W/R corresponding to the beginning of instability. This value is tabulated below:

L/H	H/R	(W/R) crit.
7.75	0.450	0.290
7.75	0.300	0.320
7.75	0.225	0.330

Fig. 7 shows the variation of the critical Reynolds number Re_{c1}, with the width to radius ratio W/R for three values of H/R. It is seen that the critical Reynolds number increases with H/R (i.e. with decreasing relative radius of curvature). It was previously seen, and is apparent again, that Re_{c1} also increases with increasing W/R. It is also seen that the dependence on H/R becomes exceedingly weak for W/R less than about 0.2.

Fig. 8 is a replot of the data of Fig. 7, this time plotting Re_{c1} vs. the aspect ratio H/W for different value of W/R.

Some data was taken using a lengthened entrance channel. This data is presented in Figs. 9 and 10, where the shorter channel data is also presented for comparison. It is seen that increasing the inlet length increases the critical Reynolds number. One plausibly expects a maximum critical Reynolds number for fully developed flow.

Hysteresis

As previously pointed out, if $W/R < 0.30$ and if the Reynolds number is decreased from a value greater than Re_{c1}, it must be reduced to a value $Re_{c2} < Re_{c1}$ before a return to a configuration with only a laminar separation occurs. The

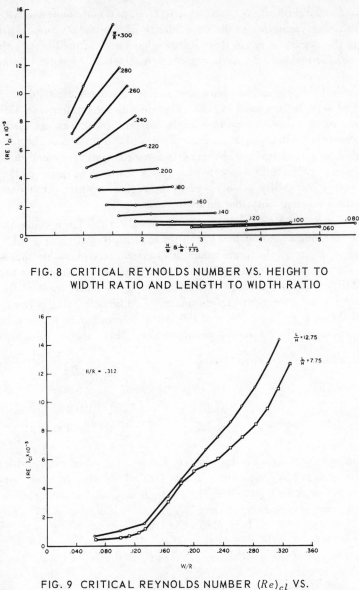

FIG. 8 CRITICAL REYNOLDS NUMBER VS. HEIGHT TO
WIDTH RATIO AND LENGTH TO WIDTH RATIO

FIG. 9 CRITICAL REYNOLDS NUMBER $(Re)_{cl}$ VS.
WIDTH TO RADIUS RATIO

hysteresis phenomenon is conveniently described by a per cent hysteresis defined as:

$$\% \text{ Hysteresis} = \frac{Re_{c1} - Re_{c2}}{Re_{c1}} \cdot 100$$

The variation of per cent hysteresis with W/R for different values of H/R is
shown in Fig. 11.

24

Note that for height to radius ratios of 0.225 and 0.300, the per cent hysteresis goes to zero before the jet becomes unstable in the vicinity of the critical Reynolds number. This means that for these values of H/R these is a discontinuity in departure angle without hysteresis. For a height to radius ratio of 0.450, instability occurs before the hysteresis disappears. For $H/R = 0.450$, there is a peak in the curve of per cent hysteresis vs. W/R. The reason for this is unknown.

Velocity Profile at Channel Exit

The initial jet in all of these experiments was considerably far from fully developed. This is conveniently seen from the velocity profile as shown in Fig. 12.

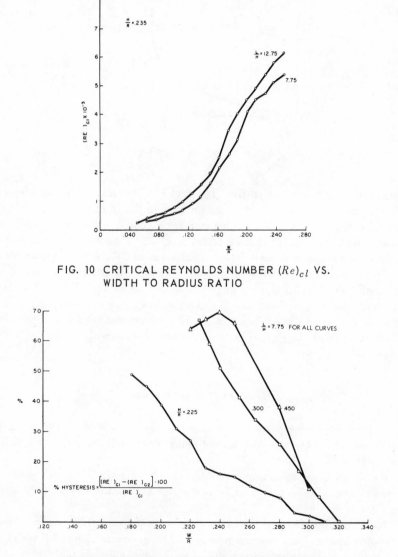

FIG. 10   CRITICAL REYNOLDS NUMBER $(Re)_{cl}$ VS.
WIDTH TO RADIUS RATIO

FIG. 11   PER CENT HYSTERESIS VS. WIDTH TO
RADIUS RATIO

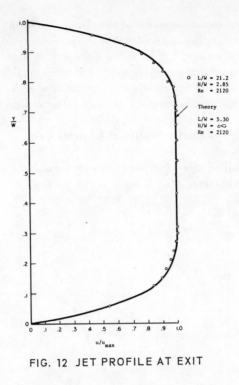

FIG. 12 JET PROFILE AT EXIT

The points are for a measured profile. The line is a theoretical profile chosen
from Schlictings [7] solution for the laminar flow in the inlet region of a channel.
The particular theoretical curve was chosen for a good qualitative fit with the experimental points. Note that the theoretical profile is for a length of run equal to
5.3 W, and the experimental profile for a length run of 21.2 W. The slower development of the experimental profiles is probably attributable to the low aspect ratios.

The length to width ratios used in the experiments are well below those required for fully developed flow, and the experiments show that the profiles develop more slowly than the predictions of two-dimensional theory. Consequently,
the velocity profile at the channel exit is closer to uniform flow than fully developed flow.

Effects of Heating the Wall

Some experiments were performed to examine the effects of wall heating on the
behavior of the jet. The wall was heated using a resistive ribbon attached to the
test model. (See Fig. 13).

One of the two clamps holding the ribbon was provided with a jack screw to
stretch the ribbon when it was cool so that it did not buckle due to thermal expansion when it was heated.

Fig. 14 shows the effect of wall temperature on the departure angle variation
with Reynolds number for constant geometry. The geometry is one for which no
hysteresis occurs. The temperature shown is that measured at the center of the
straight portion of the heating ribbon, midway between the cover plates. Spot

26

checks showed that this temperature did not vary much with location on the heated portion of the wall. These results show that:

1) For Reynolds numbers below the critical value Re_{c1}, departure angle decreases with increasing wall temperature

2) The critical Reynolds number increases with increasing wall temperature.

3) The value of the laminar departure angle θ_{c1}, at the critical Reynolds number, decreases slightly with increasing wall temperature.

4) The asymptotic value of the turbulent departure angle θ_f is virtually independent of wall temperature.

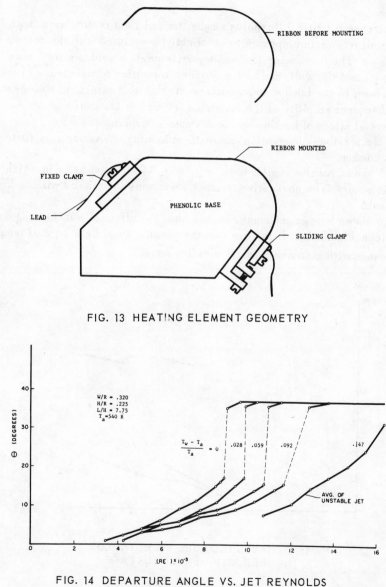

FIG. 13 HEATING ELEMENT GEOMETRY

FIG. 14 DEPARTURE ANGLE VS. JET REYNOLDS
NUMBER WITH HEATED SURFACE

27

The decrease in departure angle with wall temperature is apparently associated with the increase (for a gas) of kinematic viscosity with temperature. The effect of heating is somewhat equivalent to reducing the effective Reynolds number of the jet, and hence results in a decreased departure angle. Note that this analogy should not be stretched too far. It is known, for example, that wall heating makes a laminar gas boundary layer less stable, that is, it becomes turbulent at a lower Reynolds number. So for stability considerations of a boundary layer, heating has a result similar to increasing the effective Reynolds number, despite the increased kinematic viscosity. This simply means that detail changes in the velocity profiles must be considered before one can give a sound explanation of the phenomena.

The increase in critical Reynolds number for turbulent reattachment with increasing wall temperature appears to be directly associated with the decrease in laminar angle. The decreasing laminar departure angle provides more "room" between the jet and the wall, and hence requires transition to turbulence in the jet to occur closer to the laminar separation point. Possible effects of wall heating on the subsequent stability of the separated jet are not yet known.

The lack of effect of heating on the asymptotic departure angle θ_f is consistent with the previous observation that without heating, θ_f varies very little with Reynolds number.

Fig. 15 shows results similar to those of Fig. 14 for a geometry in which hysteresis occurs. The qualitative remarks concerning the results with no hysteresis still hold.

Fig. 16 shows how geometrical changes alter the effect of wall heating on the critical Reynolds number. It is seen that the sensitivity of Re_{c1} to wall temperature increases with increasing width to radius ratio.

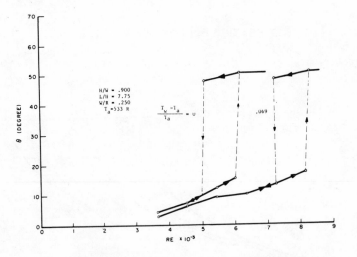

FIG. 15 DEPARTURE ANGLE VS. REYNOLDS
NUMBER WITH HEATED SURFACE

28

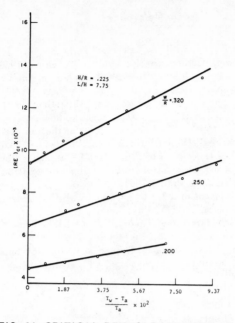

FIG. 16   CRITICAL REYNOLDS NUMBER VS.
WALL TEMPERATURE RATIO

Conclusion

The experiments show that depending on geometry and Reynolds number an initially laminar jet flowing on a curved wall may separate as a laminar jet, separate as a turbulent jet, or separate as a laminar jet and reattach farther downstream as a turbulent jet with subsequent turbulent separation. The separation-reattachment configuration may sometimes be associated with hysteresis in the variation of departure angle with Reynolds number and may also be associated with unstable oscillation of the jet.

The experiments show that wall heating tends, for gas flow, to delay all effects to higher Reynolds numbers.

The detailed behavior is extremely important in fluid amplifier design. The hysteresis is sometimes undesirable and sometimes can be made use of. The effects of heating can obviously be utilized. Some of the design implications have been discussed by one of the authors (D. McGlaughlin) in Reference [8]. The instabilities may be at the root of some observed oscillations of fluid amplifiers under presumably steady external conditions. This is being investigated by one of the authors (I. Greber).

Acknowledgments

The research described in this paper was performed with partial support from "The Fluid Element Research Industrial Group Support Program" as Case Institute of Technology, Cleveland, Ohio; Dr. C. K. Taft, Principal Investigator.

29

References

[1] J. A. Giles, A. P. Hays, and R. A. Sawyer, "Turbulent Wall Jets on Logarithmic Spiral Surfaces," The Aeronautical Quarterly, Vol. XVII, August, 1966.

[2] D. P. Margolis and J. L. Lumley, "Curved Turbulent Mixing Layer," Physics of Fluids, Vol. 8, No. 10, October, 1965.

[3] A. B. Bailey, "Use of The Coanda Effect for the Deflection of Jet Sheets Over Smoothly Curved Surfaces" (Part I) UTIA TN49, August, 1961

[4] W. E. B. Roderick, "Use of The Coanda Effect for the Deflection of Jet Sheets Over Smoothly Curved Surfaces" (Part II) UTIA TN51, September, 1961.

[5] B. G. Newman, "The Deflection of Plane Jets by Adjacent Boundaries Coanda Effect," Boundary Layer and Flow Control its Principles and Application, edited by G. V. Lachman, Vol. I., Pergamon Press, 1961.

[6] M. Kadosch, "Attachment of a Jet to a Curved Wall," Proceedings of the 2nd Fluid Amplification Symposium, Vol. IV, May, 1964.

[7] H. Schlichting, "Boundary Layer Theory," (4th ed.), McGraw-Hill, New York, 1960.

[8] D. W. McGlaughlin, "Development of Curved Wall Fluidic Control Elements," Ph.D Thesis, 1966, Case Institute of Technology, Cleveland, Ohio.

Transversely Impinging, Two-Dimensional Jet Flows

William J. Sheeran

Cornell Aeronautical Laboratory
Box 235, Buffalo, New York

Darshan S. Dosanjh

Syracuse University
Syracuse, New York

Abstract

Shadowgraphic and interferometric investigations of the transverse impingement of a two-dimensional side jet flow onto a two-dimensional underexpanded
main jet flow issuing from a sonic nozzle resulted in much more detailed information of the behavior of the main jet shock structure and the nature of the
flow in the interaction region of the jet flows than has been available from previous studies. On the basis of this new information, structure which was identified as a slipstream in an earlier model proposed by the authors for the interaction of two such jets is shown to be actually a shock wave. The interaction
region is shown to be a zone of nonuniform, higher than ambient pressure.

Introduction

With the recent advances in pneumatic control and logic systems and with the
possibility of the design of supersonic momentum exchange amplifiers, increasing emphasis has been placed on the need to understand the basic flow phenomena and the behavior of the shock structure in the case of interacting two-
dimensional jet flows where one or more of such interacting jets are operated
in an underexpanded mode. Mutually impinging, two-dimensional, underexpanded
jet flows have also been employed in chemical and textile processing equipment.
As an extension of the initial work reported by the authors in the Proceedings of
the First and Second Fluid Amplification Symposia held at Washington, D.C. in
1962 and 1964, respectively [1, 2] and elsewhere [3, 4], the transverse impingement of a two-dimensional side jet flow onto a two-dimensional underexpanded
main jet flow issuing from a sonic nozzle has been further investigated [5]. The
present paper will be concerned primarily with the observed changes in the main
jet shock structure as a result of the side jet impingement and also with the
region of interaction of the jet flows. Other experimentally determined details,
such as the density distributions in the main and side jet flows, sidewall
boundary layer effects, etc., of the flow field resulting from the interaction of

31

the two-dimensional jets, along with a brief discussion of possible analytical approaches to the interacting two-dimensional underexpanded jet flows, are presented elsewhere [5], [6].

Experimental Arrangement and Procedure

The details of the experimental facility may be found in a previous report by the authors [5]. Only those aspects of the experimental facility which are of immediate concern to the present discussion are briefly discussed here. A schematic of the nozzle arrangement is shown in Fig. 1 where the jet width, w, is 1/4 in. which is much larger than the $w = 1/32$ in. used in the previous investigations [2]. The nozzle exit aspect ratio (i.e. ratio of the exit length, or distance between sidewalls, to the width, w) was equal to 8. In the previous investigations with the $w = 1/32$ in. jets, an aspect ratio of 12 was employed. Since side walls were used, the aspect ratio could be considered to be infinite if the influence of the boundary layer is neglected. The stagnation pressure and temperature of the air supplied to the jets were measured in the individual jet

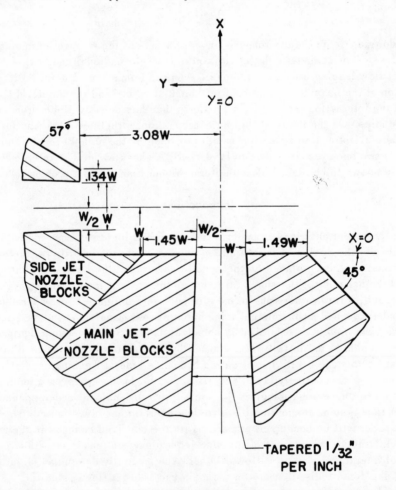

FIG. 1 DETAILS OF THE ARRANGEMENT OF THE NOZZLES

supply chambers. The flow fields of the jets were investigated by shadow-graphic, schlieren and interferometric techniques. The advantage of these optical techniques is that they allow quantitative measurement of flow properties without introducing any disturbance into the phenomena to be investigated. The interferometric technique provides quantitative information on the local flow density which coupled with assumptions on the flow processes can be used to deduce distributions of pressure, Mach number, etc. Pitot pressure distributions in such interacting flows were previously reported by the authors [1-4] and therefore were not recorded during the present investigations. To facilitate the optical studies, interferometric quality glass was used for the test section side walls, and thus static wall taps were not employed.

The main jet was operated in a choked condition (i.e. $M = 1$ at the nozzle exit since converging nozzles were used, see Fig. 1) and in the operating pressure range in which the Riemann wave (i.e. the strong, apparently normal shock structure) was present. For such two-dimensional jet flows, the Riemann wave is present if the operating pressure ratios (i.e. ratio of the nozzle exit static pressure to the ambient pressure) is greater than 5.15 approximately [5]. The side jet was operated in both the subsonic and choked flow regimes. Based on conditions at the nozzle exit, the Reynolds number of the main jet flow was on the order of 6.8×10^7 per foot for these investigations.

Results and Discussion

The larger size of the flow field from the $w = 1/4$ in. nozzle resulted in many more details of the flow being discernible in the optical records than was the case in the previous investigations. A shadowgraph of a typical main jet flow alone is presented as Fig. 2 where the operating conditions such as P_t (main jet supply pressure), P_{ts} (side jet supply pressure), P_n (main jet nozzle exit static pressure), P_a (ambient pressure), T_t (main and side jet supply temperature) and T_a (ambient temperature), are listed.

The interaction between the side jet flow and the main jet flow results in flow pressure P_i in the region of interaction which is higher than the ambient pressure. For a fixed main jet operating pressure (i.e., fixed P_n/P_a), P_i increases with increasing side jet supply pressure. This behavior is evident from the P_i/P_a vs P_{ts}/P_t plot shown in Fig. 3. The P_i values were determined from interferograms, as well as from the orientations of the expansion fan structure as measured from shadowgraphs. The actual flow in the region of interaction is nonuniform, as will be discussed later in the text, and the values of P_i used in Fig. 3 were chosen as representative of those in this region.

The higher pressure in the interaction region alters the position of the effective main jet flow boundary nearest to the side jet nozzle (i.e., near-side boundary). This near-side boundary may, over the initial upstream portion, be considered as a slipstream between the main and side jet flows; the side jet flow having been deflected such that it flows nearly parallel to the main jet nozzle centerplane (i.e., the plane halfway between the main jet nozzle blocks and perpendicular to the test section side walls). Thus, when the side jet flow is impinged, one may think of the near-side boundary condition on the main jet flow

33

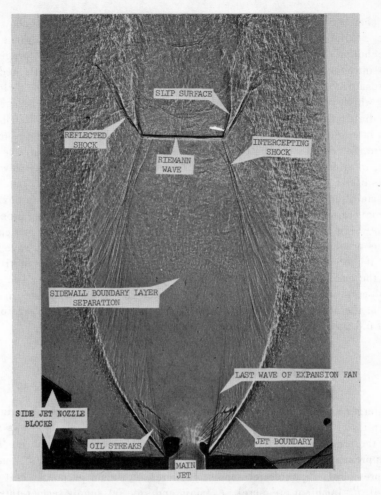

FIG. 2 TYPICAL SHADOWGRAPH OF AN UNDEREXPANDED,
TWO-DIMENSIONAL JET FLOW FROM A SONIC NOZZLE.

P_t = 217.1 psia P_a = 14.53 psia P_n/P_a = 7.89

T_t = 79 F T_a = 75 F P_{ts} = 14.53 psia
                                            (no Side-jet Flow)

changing from one of constant pressure all along the boundary to one of specific
local flow direction which is related to the varying pressure along the slipstream.
In this sense, the upstream portion of the near-side boundary is like a nozzle wall
in its effect on the main jet flow. Any change in the position of this near-side
boundary naturally affects the orientation of the main jet flow compression waves
which result from the reflection of the far-side nozzle lip expansion from this
boundary. This change in orientation in turn affects the coalescence of these
reflected compression waves and thus also the position of the near-side intercepting shock.

A representative sequence of shadowgraphs showing the effects of the impingement of flows from the side jet when it is operated at various supply pressures is presented as Figs. 4a-e. The main jet flow alone corresponding to the

34

operating conditions used during the recording of these shadowgraphs is similar to that shown in Fig. 2. With increasing side jet supply pressure (i.e, increasing P_{ts}/P_t), the near-side intercepting shock in the main jet flow is initiated closer and closer to the main jet nozzle exit. At the same time it also relocates progressively inward towards the main jet nozzle centerplane and makes successively larger shock-angles to the main jet flow streamlines. This near-side intercepting shock is referred to here as the "relocated intercepting shock" (see Fig. 4a). The successive positions of the relocated intercepting shock as a function of P_{ts}/P_t are sketched in Fig. 5. The shock locations were taken from the shadowgraphs presented as Figs. 4a-e. For $P_{ts}/P_t < .10$ the far side intercepting shock is unaffected by the side jet impingement. At $P_{ts}/P_t \approx .10$, the relocated intercepting shock is orientated such that it intersects the far-side intercepting shock. For increasing values of P_{ts}/P_t, the relocated intercepting shock adjusts at greater and greater shock-angles to the main jet flow and thus crosses the far-side intercepting shock closer and closer to the main jet nozzle exit (see Figs. 4c-e and 5).

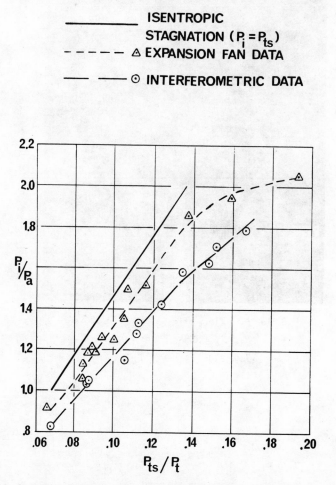

FIG. 3 INTERACTION REGION PRESSURE AS A FUNCTION OF SIDE JET SUPPLY PRESSURES ($P_n/P_a = 7.76$)

FIG. 4 SEQUENCE OF SHADOWGRAPHS OF TRANSVERSELY
IMPINGING, TWO-DIMENSIONAL JET FLOWS $(P_n/P_a = 7.89)$

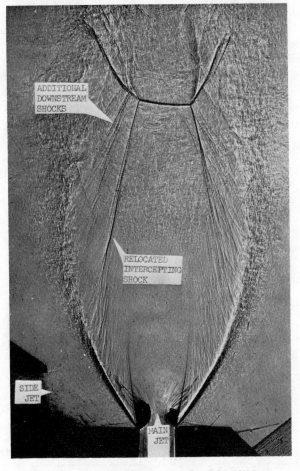

FIG. 4a $P_t = 216.8$ psia $P_a = 14.52$ psia

$P_{ts}/P_t = .079$

$T_t = 81$ F $T_a = 77$ F

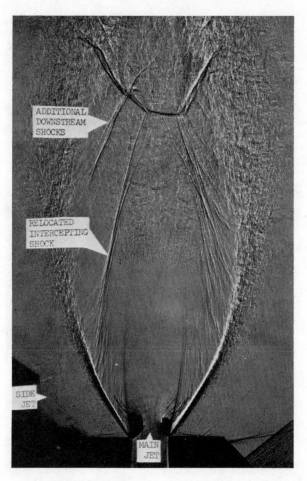

FIG. 4b P_t = 217.0 psia P_a = 14.53 psia

P_{ts}/P_t = .088

T_t = 81 F T_a = 74 F

37

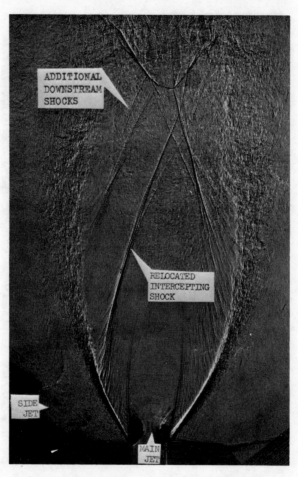

FIG. 4c $P_t = 217.0$ psia $P_a = 14.53$ psia

$P_{ts}/P_t = .105$

$T_t = 80$ F $T_a = 73$ F

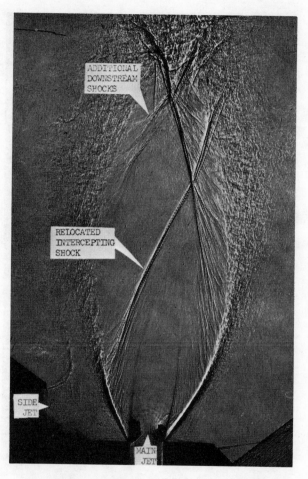

FIG. 4d $P_t = 217.0$ psia $P_a = 14.53$ psia

$P_{ts}/P_t = .137$

$T_t = 79$ F $T_a = 76$ F

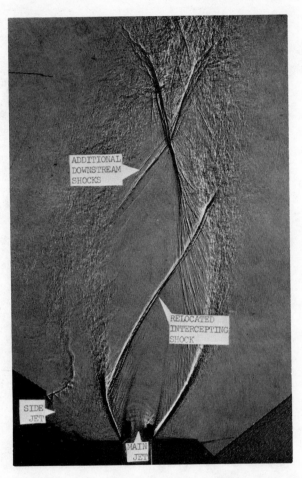

FIG. 4e $P_t = 217.0$ psia $P_a = 14.53$ psia

$P_{ts}/P_t = .193$

$T_t = 78$ F $T_a = 76$ F

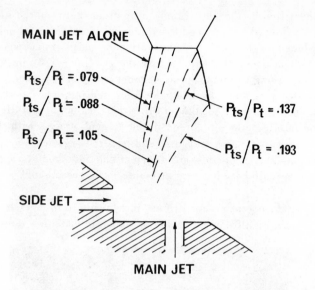

MAIN JET ALONE

$P_{ts}/P_t = .079$

$P_{ts}/P_t = .088$

$P_{ts}/P_t = .105$

$P_{ts}/P_t = .137$

$P_{ts}/P_t = .193$

SIDE JET →

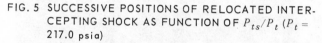

MAIN JET

FIG. 5 SUCCESSIVE POSITIONS OF RELOCATED INTER-
CEPTING SHOCK AS FUNCTION OF P_{ts}/P_t ($P_t =$
217.0 psia)

Additional shock structure is observed in the main jet flow downstream of the relocated intercepting shock. The expansion waves associated with the down-stream portions of the expansion fan at the far-side nozzle lip of the main jet cross the relocated intercepting shock and are reflected from the sonic line in the mixing region of the two jet flows as compression waves which coalesce to form a second oblique shock. This shock lies downstream of and roughly parallel to, the relocated intercepting shock (Figs. 4a and 4b). The expansion waves associated with the upstream portions of the far-side expansion fan reflect as compression waves from the upstream portion of this interface between the jet flows and coalesce to form the relocated intercepting shock. The formation of these two pieces of shock structure due to the reflection of the single far-side expansion fan indicates that the boundary conditions on the main jet flow as provided by the interface between the two jet flows vary along this interface. This is in contrast to the constant pressure condition along the boundary of a single jet flow which gives rise to the formation of the single oblique intercepting shock on each side. For values of $P_{ts}/P_t > .105$ (see Figs. 4d and 4e), the resulting shock structure has an appearance similar to the repetitive diamond type shocks which occur in single jet flows operated at lower pressure ratios. Indeed, as was noted during the earlier investigations [2,4], when the entire Riemann wave is replaced by the oblique relocated intercepting shock, a repetitive cellular shock pattern does occur in the resultant jet flow. Only the initial shock cell is present when the Riemann wave dominates the shock structure. As established by pitot pressure distributions [2], all the main shock structure discussed above occurred in two-dimensional flow and was not the result of any three-dimensional effects such as boundary layer separation. The effects of the shock structure changes on the pitot pressure distribution have been presented previously by the authors [1-4]. On the basis of earlier studies [3], the second oblique shock discussed above was

41

erroneously identified by the authors as a slipstream between the side jet flow
and the main jet flow which crossed the relocated intercepting shock. This earlier
model was deduced on the basis of relatively poor quality shadowgraphs (compared to the present ones) of jet flows from the small $w = 1/32$ in., two-
dimensional converging nozzles. In subsequent work [2,4] it was surmised that
the additional structure downstream of the relocated intercepting shock was more
likely to be a shock wave rather than a slipstream. From the detailed shadowgraphs and the interferograms recorded in the present studies with the much
larger $w = 1/4$ in. two-dimensional jets, and from the arguments proposed previously on the basis of pitot pressure distributions and shadowgraphs [2,4], it
has been firmly established that this structure is indeed a shock wave and not a
slipstream.

At higher P_{ts}/P_t operating conditions, in addition to the shock structure
changes a discrete, high frequency, intense acoustic emission was observed.

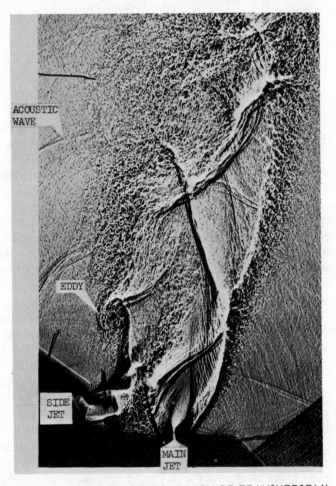

FIG. 6 NON-FOCUSED SHADOWGRAPH OF TRANSVERSELY
IMPINGING, TWO-DIMENSIONAL JET FLOWS.

$P_t = 162.4$ psia	$P_a = 14.52$ psia	$P_n/P_a = 5.91$
$P_{ts}/P_t = .370$	$T_t = 81$ F	$T_a = 78$ F

42

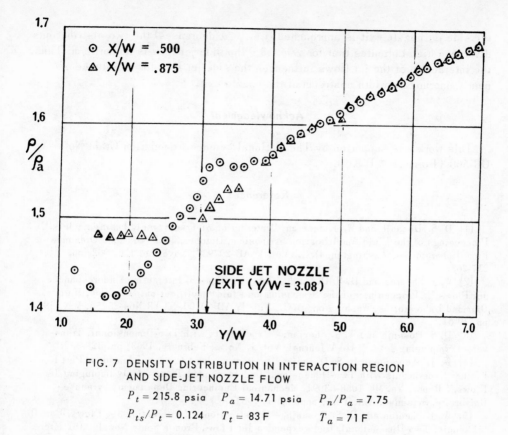

FIG. 7 DENSITY DISTRIBUTION IN INTERACTION REGION
AND SIDE-JET NOZZLE FLOW

$$P_t = 215.8 \text{ psia} \quad P_a = 14.71 \text{ psia} \quad P_n/P_a = 7.75$$
$$P_{ts}/P_t = 0.124 \quad T_t = 83 \text{ F} \quad T_a = 71 \text{ F}$$

The shadowgraph presented as Fig. 6 shows several of the acoustic waves (in the shadowgraphs covering a larger portion of the flow field, more are seen) as well as an eddy which appears to have been shed from the interaction region. It is surmised that the interactions of such eddies with the resultant jet flow shock structure are responsible for production of the discrete component of the acoustic emission.

Relative to the ambient pressure, the side jet supply pressure may be such that the flow should choke. However, due to the higher than ambient pressure in the interaction region the effective pressure ratio may be subcritical and the actual side jet flow may remain subsonic (see Fig. 4d) or supersonic conditions may occur only locally within the side jet flow. Such localized regions of supersonic flow, such as evidenced in Fig. 4e by the shock structure along the boundary near the upper nozzle lip of the side jet (i.e., near the side jet nozzle lip located at the greater x/w, x being measured downstream from the main jet nozzle exit) clearly indicate the nonuniform flow conditions in the interaction region. The interferometrically determined density distributions presented in Fig. 7 clearly show that conditions are nonuniform in the interaction region as well as within the side jet nozzle itself near the nozzle exit. In Fig. 7 the side jet nozzle exit is located at $y/w = 3.08$ (y being measured normal to the main jet nozzle center-plane) and thus the density values at $y/w < 3.08$ correspond to those within the interaction region and at $y/w > 3.08$ correspond to those within the side jet nozzle itself. For $y/w > 3.9$ the flow within the side jet nozzle is uniform. As

43

the side jet nozzle exit is approached (i.e., y/w decreases) the two distributions diverge, which indicates that for $y/w < 3.9$ the side jet flow is nonuniform. Thus, the interaction of the jet flows influences the side jet flow for a distance of nearly one nozzle width upstream of the nozzle exit.

Acknowledgment

This work was supported by The National Science Foundation Grant No. GR-568 (Formerly GP-839).

References

[1] D. S. Dosanjh and W. J. Sheeran, "Interaction of Transversely Impinging Jets," Proceedings of the Fluid Amplification Symposium, October, 1962, Diamond Ordnance Fuze Laboratories, Washington, D.C., Vol. 1, AD-297937, November 15, 1962, pp. 217-265.

[2] W. J. Sheeran and D. S. Dosanjh, "Investigations of Interacting Underexpanded Jet Flows," Proceedings of the Symposium on Fluid Amplification, May 1964, Harry Diamond Laboratories, Washington, D.C., Vol. 1, AD-60200, STAR N64-25256, May, 1964, pp. 39-61.

[3] D. S. Dosanjh and W. J. Sheeran, "Experiments with Two-Dimensional, Transversely Impinging Jets," AIAA Journal, Vol. 1, No. 2, February, 1963, pp. 329-333.

[4] W. J. Sheeran and D. S. Dosanjh, "Interacting Jet Flow Investigations, Part I. Further Experiments with Two-Dimensional Underexpanded Transversely Impinging Jet Flows," Report No. ME 1058-63091, Mechanical Engineering Department, Syracuse University, Syracuse, New York, September, 1963.

[5] W. J. Sheeran and D. S. Dosanjh, "Investigations of Interacting Jet Flows, Part II. (a) Single, Two-Dimensional, Underexpanded Jet Flows From a Sonic Nozzle. (b) Interaction of Transversely Impinging, Two-Dimensional Jet Flows," Final Report submitted to NSF: Report No. ME 1058-6608F, Department of Mechanical and Aerospace Engineering, Syracuse University, Syracuse, New York, August, 1966. STAR N66-37599.

[6] W. J. Sheeran and D. S. Dosanjh, "Noise from Impinging, Two-Dimensional, Underexpanded Jet Flows," The Journal of the Acoustical Society of America, Vol. 38, No. 3, September, 1965, pp. 482-484.

Flow Characteristics of the Defined Region Geometry for High-Gain Proportional Amplifiers

J. F. Foss

Michigan State University

East Lansing, Michigan

Abstract

The defined region geometry, wherein the control jets are separated from the power jet by setback and standoff walls, offers significant possibilities as a design configuration for high gain proportional fluid jet amplifiers. The increased static pressure in the near pocket (i.e., the region bounded by the active control and power jets and the setback and standoff walls) provides a surface force which acts, in addition to the momentum flux of the control jet, to deflect the power jet. An analytical model to predict the deflection angle of the resultant jet and the pocket static pressures has been formulated. Experimental data were obtained for three representative geometric configurations of the defined region. The observed results are compared with the present analysis and the earlier analysis of Manion and Goto. Recommendations for future efforts are included.

Nomenclature

a = nozzle width

C_p = static pressure coefficient, $\dfrac{p - p_{\text{atmospheric}}}{1/2\,\rho\,u_0^2}$

mfr = momentum flux ratio, q_2/q_1

P = intersection point of the control and power jet center lines

p = static pressure

q = momentum flux per unit depth

R = radius of the deflected jet

u = x-component, mean velocity vector

v = y-component, mean velocity vector

$\overline{uv}$ = turbulence correlation, negative of a kinematic Reynolds stress

45

x = longitudinal coordinate, measured from the plane of the power jet nozzle opening

x_{app} = x location of the apparent pivot point, the intersection of the resultant jet's center line with the x axis

X = length of standoff wall

y = transverse coordinate

Y = length of setback wall

$\Delta y_{\cancel{C}}$ = transverse displacement of the resultant jet's center line

z = coordinate normal to the x-y plane (x-y-z form a right hand system)

α = deflection angle of the resultant jet

β = angle used in the analytical study

γ = angle used in the analytical study

ρ = fluid density

Subscripts

F = refers to the far pocket, i.e., the pocket between the power jet and the inactive control jet nozzle

N = refers to the near pocket, i.e., the pocket between the power jet and the active control jet nozzle

0 = quantity at the power jet nozzle exit

1 = refers to the power jet

2 = refers to the control jet

3 = refers to the resultant jet

Introduction

The defined-region configuration initially investigated by Manion and Goto [1] offers a significant design geometry for high-gain proportional fluid amplifiers. The defined region is shown in Fig. 1. Since the gain of an amplifier is the slope of the curve describing the differential output as a function of the differential input, and since the differential output is related to the total deflection (and the velocity profile) of the resultant jet, the term "high-gain" implies an increased deflection of the resultant jet for a given input.

The deflection angle α is governed by momentum considerations; therefore, in order to describe physically why the defined region is suitable for the design of high-gain amplifiers, consider a momentum analysis applied to control volume 1 (see Fig. 1). The momentum fluxes of the power and control jets are inputs to the control volume. If there were a zero net pressure force on the control volume, the equation $\tan \alpha = $ mfr would describe the deflection angle of the resultant jet. The condition of zero net static pressure is closely approximated in the typical pro-

46

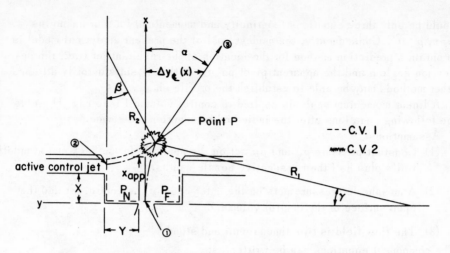

FIG. 1 DEFINITION OF TERMS USED IN THE ANALYSIS

portional amplifier design wherein $X = 0$. For positive X and Y values a greater than ambient pressure is developed in the near pocket. This pressure provides a net transverse surface force which, acting with the control jet momentum flux, results in an increased deflection angle (i.e., tan α > mfr). If one relates this analysis to the proportional amplifier, it can be seen that the differential output (pressure or mass rate of flow) can be increased by adding the setback and stand-off walls without changing the control jet pressure. (Note that the momentum flux of the control jet will be a function of the control jet supply pressure.)

The objectives of the investigation reported herein were (i) to establish an analytical model for α, (ii) to compare the analytical predictions with experimental results, and (iii) to compare the present results with those of Manion and Goto in order to infer, from the similarities and differences, the character of this flow field. This paper presents and reinterprets some of the items previously investigated by the writer [2]. Because of the detailed presentation in reference 2 of the analysis, the description of the equipment, and the method of testing, their description in this communication will be quite concise.

Although it is not directly applicable to the present study, the analytical study by Simson [3] should be mentioned herein since it deals with the same application, namely, high-gain proportional fluid jet amplifiers. The analytical model for the jet deflection process in reference (3) is rather different from that of either Manion and Goto or the present study. Simson deals with pressure effects only in establishing the magnitude of the deflection. Simson's model deals with the entire geometry of the amplifier; design curves are provided which would allow a complete amplifier design to be established (within the confines of the assumptions which were made concerning the flow model).

Analysis

As in all three-dimensional turbulent shear flows, there are four governing equations with ten unknowns for this problem. Even if the assumptions of two-dimensional flow and negligible normal Reynolds stresses were made, there

47

would be only three equations (continuity and momentum) for four unknowns $(u, v, p, \overline{uv})$. Consequently, the modest goal of the present analytical model is to obtain a prediction method for the location of the resultant jet (i.e., the deflection angle α and the apparent pivot point). If this is satisfactorily attained, other methods may be able to establish the profile shape.

A linear momentum analysis applied to control volume 1 (see Fig. 1) yields the following equations after the indicated assumptions are made.

Assumptions:

(1) Constant pressure p_N and p_F act on the near and far setback and standoff walls plus half their respective nozzle widths.

(2) Atmospheric pressure acts on the outer edge of the control jet and the open surface of the control volume.

(3) The flow field is two dimensional and steady.[1]

The component equations can be written as:

y-direction

$$(p_N - p_F)(X + a_2/2) = q_3 \sin \alpha - q_2$$

x-direction

$$(p_N + p_F)(Y + a_1/2) = q_3 \cos \alpha - q_1 \quad .$$

Combining these relations yields

$$\tan \alpha = \frac{q_2 + (p_N - p_F)(X + a_2/2)}{q_1 + (p_N + p_F)(Y + a_1/2)} \quad . \tag{1}$$

The Euler equation written along the normal to a streamline, viz., $\partial p/\partial n = \rho V^2/R$ where n is the coordinate normal to the streamline and R is the radius of curvature at the point under investigation, can be used in conjunction with the following assumptions to yield equations (2) and (3).

Assumptions:

(1) There is no jet spreading before point P.

(2) Atmospheric pressure acts on the outside of the control jet.

(3) The pressures p_N and p_F are constant to approximately point P.

(4) The pressure variation across the jet is linear.

For these assumptions, the following expressions may be written:

for the control jet

$$\frac{\partial p}{\partial n} = \frac{p_N}{a_2} = \frac{(q_2/a_2)}{R_2}$$

for the power jet

$$\frac{\partial p}{\partial n} = \frac{p_N - p_F}{a_1} = \frac{(q_1/a_1)}{R_1}$$

---

[1] This assumption is common to all portions of the analysis and will not be repeated for these other portions.

and solving for the pressures

$$p_N = q_2/R_2 \tag{2}$$

$$p_F = q_2/R_2 - q_1/R_1 \quad . \tag{3}$$

Static pressure measurements made in the present study show that the assumption of constant pressure on the standoff and setback walls is quite reasonable and that the assumption of atmospheric pressure on the open surface is satisfactory (see Fig. 5). However, the assumption of constant values of p_N and p_F to develop equations (2) and (3) is probably in serious error near the point P. To compensate for this, control volume 2 can be analyzed as if the net pressure forces are zero. This assumption allows for the momentum flux components to be added (vectorially) yielding a second equation for $\tan \alpha$.

The y component of the momentum equation yields

$$q_3 \sin \alpha = q_1 \sin \gamma + q_2 \cos \beta \quad .$$

For the x component we obtain

$$q_3 \cos \alpha = q_1 \cos \gamma + q_2 \sin \beta \quad .$$

Combining these gives

$$\tan \alpha = \frac{q_1 \sin \gamma + q_2 \cos \beta}{q_1 \cos \gamma + q_2 \sin \beta} \tag{4}$$

Two more equations may be obtained from purely geometric conditions

$$R_1 + Y + a_1/2 = R_1 \cos \gamma + R_2 \sin \beta$$

or

$$1 + (Y + a_1/2) \, R_1 = \cos \gamma + (R_2/R_1) \sin \beta \tag{5}$$

and

$$R_2 + X + a_2/2 = R_1 \sin \gamma + R_2 \cos \beta$$

or

$$1 + (X + a_2)/R = (R_1/R_2) \sin \gamma + \cos \beta \tag{6}$$

At this point, 6 independent equations for 7 variables are available. One new variable, the apparent pivot point, will be introduced which will provide an additional geometric equation and which will necessitate the introduction of an empirical relationship. This, of course, sacrifices the purely analytical character

49

of the analysis. Referring to Figure 1, consider a line of length "m" drawn from point P to the apparent pivot point. The following geometric equations may be written.

$$m \sin \alpha = R_1 (1 - \cos \gamma)$$

$$m \cos \alpha + x_{app} = R_1 \sin \gamma$$

and

$$\tan \alpha = \frac{R_1 (1 - \cos \gamma)}{R_1 \sin \gamma - x_{app}} \qquad (7)$$

The empirically determined equation, which is a good approximation for the experimental data for the geometries tested,

$$\frac{x_{app}}{(X + a_2/2)} = (0.25) \frac{Y}{X} \frac{Y}{(Y + a_1/2)} + 0.875 \frac{X}{(X + a_2/2)} \qquad (8)$$

has been determined from the data of the present study. It completes the system of equations; that is, there are eight equations for the eight unknowns R_1, R_2, p_N, p_F, α, β, γ, x_{app}. Appendix A presents the computing equations and the computational technique used to produce the numerical answers resulting from the analysis.

There are overall similarities and some basic differences between the analysis of Manion and Goto and that of the present study. These will be briefly noted.

Manion and Goto first solved for the (assumed constant) radius of curvature for the power jet. Using a control volume bounded by the near pocket walls and the far side of the power jet, they developed an equation[2] similar to equation (1) except for the presence of the radius of curvature because of the placement of the control volume boundary. A fundamental difference between the two analyses was next introduced by Manion and Goto. They considered that the interaction between the control and power jet could be modeled such that the normal components of the control jet would behave as though it struck a solid boundary, i.e., this flow would divide evenly in the upstream and downstream directions parallel to the deflected power jet. Then, by implicity using a control volume analysis similar to that used for control volume 2 of the present study (i.e., the vectorial addition of momentum vectors) and noting that the momenta fluxes directed upstream were the causal factors for the greater than atmospheric p_N, they were able to develop an expression for p_N in terms of the angle α, q_1, and q_2. Although an analysis was developed to predict p_F, Manion and Goto used an empirically observed value for p_F for the analytical computations because of the lack of agreement between the predicted and measured values for this pressure.

---

[2] Appendix B presents a summary of the Manion and Goto paper including a presentation of the equations developed by their analysis.

The analysis of the present study was undertaken to find a modeling procedure which was not dependent on the development of an expression for p_N based on the (at best) difficult to describe interaction process. Considering both analyses, it is clear that avoiding the prediction of p_N has led to a more complicated, and not an obviously improved, analysis. A discussion of the validity and utility of the two analysis is given in the "Discussion of Results" section of this paper.

Flow System and Experimental Method

Two centrifugal blower-plenum chamber units were used to supply the 6 x 1 in. power and control jet nozzles. The flow field, which was bounded by 2 x 8 ft Formica faced plates, was open to the atmosphere in the lateral and downstream directions. The control jet nozzle was fitted with seven static taps at $z = 0$.

The traverse device used to determine the centerline of the resultant jet (hence α) had three degrees of freedom, x, y, and the yaw angle. The experimental value of α was determined by two independent methods: (1) A null probe (two hypodermic total pressure tubes spaced at $0.25a_1$) was used to determine the displacement of the centerline of the resultant jet ($\Delta y_\mathcal{L}$); the slope of the $\Delta y_\mathcal{L}$ vs x curve is $\tan \alpha$. (2) Once the position of maximum velocity was determined by the null probe, the yaw probe was used to measure α directly. The results of the two measurements techniques were in excellent agreement for all tests.

A second traverse device was available which had three translational degrees of freedom, (x, y, z). This was used to investigate the z variation of the $\Delta y_\mathcal{L}$. All of the data reported for $\Delta y_\mathcal{L}$ were taken at $z = 0$ because the y displacement of the resultant jet's centerline did not change with respect to z.

Results

The analytical[3] and experimental results for the deflection angle (α) as a function of the mfr are given by Figs. 2, 3, and 4; these figures clearly indicate the significant effect of the defined region geometry. The solid line, with a slope of one, would be obtained if there were no pressure effect. Table 1 is included to emphasize the magnitude of the near pocket static pressure effects on the deflection angle; note that if the static pressure effect were zero, the values of $\tan \alpha / mfr$ would be unity. The interpretation of the accuracy of both analyses with respect to the experimental data is considered in the next section.

Table 2 indicates the values of the predicted and measured pocket pressures. The far pocket pressure must be empirically determined for the analysis of Manion and Goto and is therefore not included in the table. (It should also be noted that the Manion and Goto analysis did not involve the appapent pivot point.) The results of a static pressure survey made in the interaction region with a plate static probe are shown in Fig. 5. Since this probe is highly susceptible to pitch induced errors, several of the readings near the active portions of the jet are marked as uncertain. This probe was traversed in the ± z direction; no appreciable variation was found in the static pressure values.

---

[3] The computer solutions of the Manion and Goto computing equations were supplied by the Harry Diamond Laboratories using the necessary inputs from the present study.

The Manion and Goto report [1] provides the only direct comparison for the experimental results of the present study. The major features of their work are: (1) a compressible power jet flow, power jet plenum pressures of 5, 10, and 20 psig, (2) an aspect ratio of 8, (3) a dual pitot probe of spacing $2.88a_1$ was used for the determination of the location of the maximum velocity point. Manion and Goto did not use the specific geometry $X = Y = 2a$; they did, however, determine tan α versus mfr for $X = Y = 3a$ and $X = Y = 1a$. Two trends are apparent in these data; (1) a higher plenum pressure yields a higher tan α for the same mfr and (2) the larger pocket ($X = Y = 3a$) gave overall higher values of tan α for a given mfr. These data, along with the data of the present study for $X = Y = 2a$ are shown on Figs. 6 and 7. The deflection angles of the present study are seen to be of the order of the maximum deflection angles obtained in reference 1.

Additional results, which deal with the character of the flow field, are presented in reference 2; they are (1) mean velocity profiles $u(y)$ at $z/a = \pm 2\frac{1}{2}$, $\pm 2, \pm 1$, and 0 for $x/a = 5, 15, 30$, (2) isobaric contours at $x/a = 5, 15, 30$, and (3) computed values of the mass momentum and energy flux values for these stations. These results are for $X = Y = 2a$ and a mfr of 0.1. Additional studies were made to establish the effects of the mfr and the nozzle geometry on the velocity and static pressure distributions.

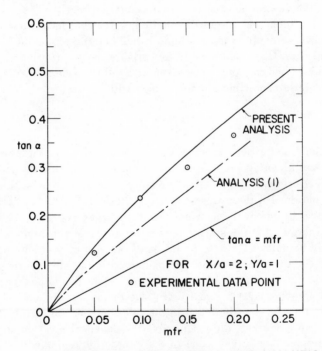

FIG. 2 Tan α versus mfr, EXPERIMENTAL AND ANALYTICAL
VALUES, $Y/X = 0.5$

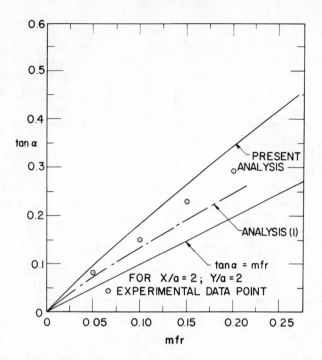

FIG. 3 Tan α versus mfr, EXPERIMENTAL AND ANALYTICAL
VALUES, $Y/X = 1.0$

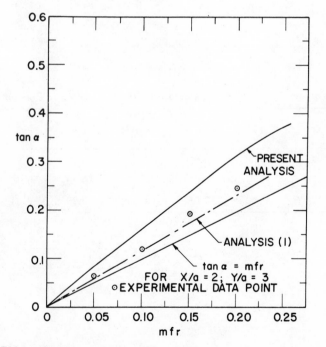

FIG. 4 Tan α versus mfr, EXPERIMENTAL AND ANALYTICAL
VALUES, $Y/X = 1.5$

53

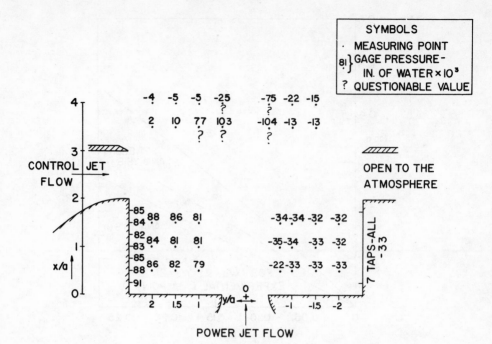

FIG. 5 STATIC PRESSURE DISTRIBUTION FOR mfr = 0.1,
$X = Y = 2a$ $1/2 \rho u_0^2 = 2.15$ INCHES OF WATER

TABLE 1

Values of tan α/mfr to Indicate the Effect of the Static Pressure

X/a	Y/a	mfr	$\dfrac{\tan \alpha}{\text{mfr}}$	mfr	$\dfrac{\tan \alpha}{\text{mfr}}$
2	1	0.05	2.40	0.20	1.80
2	2	0.05	1.60	0.20	1.45
2	3	0.05	1.25	0.20	1.24

54

TABLE 2

Experimental and Analytical Static Pressure Coefficients
for the Near and Far Pockets

Y/X	mfr	C_{P_N}			C_{P_F}	
		Experimental	Analytical	Analytical (reference 1)	Experimental	Analytical
0.5	0.05	0.015	0.041	0.005	−0.018	0.001
0.5	1.10	0.041	0.073	0.011	−0.021	0.005
0.5	0.15	0.057	0.100	0.017	−0.024	0.010
0.5	0.20	0.075	0.123	0.023	−0.030	0.014
1.0	0.05	0.008	0.022	0.002	−0.008	−0.001
1.0	0.10	0.023	0.041	0.005	−0.008	−0.005
1.0	0.15	0.038	0.058	0.008	−0.008	−0.004
1.0	0.20	0.050	0.072	0.011	−0.008	−0.002
1.5	0.05	0.008	0.015	0.002	−0.004	−0.001
1.5	0.10	0.016	0.028	0.004	−0.004	−0.001
1.5	0.15	0.027	0.040	0.005	−0.005	−0.003
1.5	0.20	0.037	0.050	0.007	−0.006	−0.004

Discussion

Sufficient information is available from the present study and the Manion and Goto investigation to establish several important aspects of the flow field associated with the defined region geometry. In addition to delineating the present knowledge about this flow field, these items can be used as a guide for future investigations.

The results of both investigations indicate that an optimum choice of X and Y exists (for given values of a_1, a_2, aspect ratio, the power jet plenum pressure, and the angle of incidence of the control jet). The present study shows that tan α increases as Y/X decreases (for $X = 2a$ = constant) and the data of (1) indicates that tan α increases with increasing X (for $Y = X$). If these trends are generalized, the optimum should occur for a "large" X and "small" Y; the proper magnitudes are, at present, unknown.

The implications of the comparison of the available data as shown in Figs. 6 and 7 may be logically described by three statements. Without further experimental or more refined analytical investigations it cannot be ascertained which statement, or combination of statements provides the most accurate description of the physical occurrence. The statements are:

(1) Assuming that the trend, in reference (1), of increasing α for an increasing power jet plenum pressure at a given mfr may be extrapolated to the incompressible regime, then the large angles (α) of the present study are attributable to the strong effect of the aspect ratio. That is, the gain of the proportional amplifier is higher for smaller aspects ratios.

(2) Assuming that the aspect ratio effect between 6 and 8 is of negligible importance, the incompressible regime is seen to yield better amplifier performance than the compressible regime.

(3) The comparison with reference 1 is predicated on the assumption that the performance of $X = Y = 2a$ should lie between $X = Y = 1a$ and $X = Y = 3a$, all the other factors being equal. The physical phenomena involved may not be amenable to such a simple analysis.

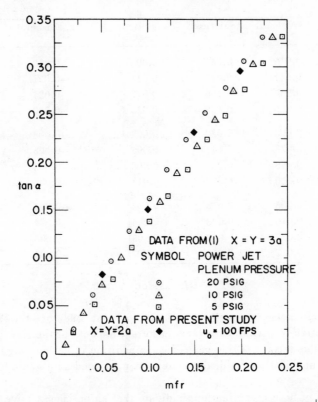

FIG. 6 COMPARISON OF tan α FROM MANION AND GOTO [1]
AND THE PRESENT STUDY

Discussion of the two analyses has purposely been deferred until the interpretation of the available experimental data could be established. The interpretation of the two existing analyses in the light of the experimental data and an examination of the factors which will serve as guiding elements for future efforts will be considered; however, certain objective items should first be considered which describe the accuracy of the analyses.

For the optimum geometry tested, viz., $X = 2Y = 2a$, the present analysis predicted tan α to within 10 per cent up to a mfr value of 0.2 (see Fig. 2). The Manion and Goto analysis was not as successful for this geometry; however, it was much more accurate than the present one for $X = 2a$, $Y = 3a$ (see Fig. 4). Neither analysis was successful in predicting the near pocket static pressure (see Table 2); the present analysis was quite unsuccessful in predicting the far pocket pressure and the analysis of Manion and Goto required the far pocket pressure as input information (which places a serious handicap on its utility as an a priori prediction method).

For any approach which is less than an attempt to solve the field equations, continuity and Reynolds (momentum), the two analyses are both similar and rather

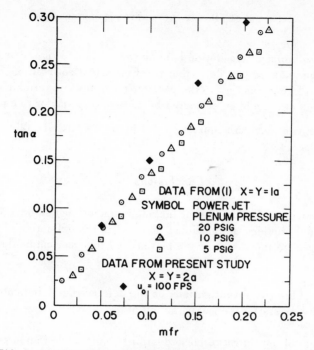

FIG. 7 COMPARISON OF tan α FROM MANION AND GOTO [1]
AND THE PRESENT STUDY

logical applications of the pertinent fluid flow equations. However, neither analysis considers the effects of compressibility or aspect ratio; two effects which have been proposed as possible explanations for the observed trends regarding the combined data of Manion and Goto and the present study (see Figs. 6 and 7).

A summary of the information established to date for this problem is: (1) the defined region geometry is feasible for high-gain proportional fluid amplifiers, (2) it appears that at least one set of geometric parameters exist which will provide a maximum deflection angle (α) for a given mfr, (3) the extant analyses do not provide a fully accurate modeling process for $\alpha = \alpha$ (mfr).

These considerations suggest that future efforts be directed toward finding the optimum geometry (with cognizance of machinability, size, and other limitations). This investigation can profit from the two investigations to date. Specifically:

(1) The combined experimental data indicates that "large" X and "small" Y values should be employed.

(2) The analysis of the present study can be used as an approximate guide in that a large number of different configurations could be investigated via numerical computer solutions and/or optimization techniques could be applied to the implicit equations for $\alpha = \alpha$ (mfr).

(3) The modeling procedure for p_N of Manion and Goto's analysis would indicate that p_N should be a strong function of the orientation of the jets (geometric) centerlines, this would suggest "pointing" the control jet at

57

the power jet instead of placing the control jet perpendicular to the power jet.

(4) The control volume formulation leading to equation (1) provides a means of correlating experimental data; that is, if empirical correlations could be found to relate p_N and p_F to the geometric and the mfr variables, the desired value of α could be computed by an equation similar to equation (1).

Finally, the entire program could be guided by the fractional analysis technique described by Kline [4].

Conclusions

1. The geometric configuration that includes standoff and setback walls (i.e., the defined region) provides a significant increase in the deflection of the resultant jet with respect to that which would be realized from momentum flux interactions alone.

2. The data of the two investigations on the defined region indicate that an optimum geometry exists for the maximization of α.

3. The effects of aspect ratio, compressibility and nozzle region geometry for this geometry have not been fully established by the investigations to date.

Appendix A

The analysis of the jet deflection problem resulted in eight equations for eight unknowns; these are given in the "Analysis" section. The terms in these equations were nondimensionalized as shown below and algebraically combined into the two equations (A-1) and (A-2). Because of the complicated nature of these equations no further algebraic reduction was attempted; instead, a numerical procedure was used in which R_1' was first evaluated for a wide range of γ values $(1 \le \gamma \le 42$ degrees) from equation (A-1) and this value of R_1 was used in equation (A-2) (with the same γ). The correct solution was chosen as that γ which resulted in positive, real values for R_1, R_2, β and α. A more detailed account of this computational procedure is given in Appendix C of reference 1. The nondimensionalization procedure and the equations are:

$$X' = X + a_2/2 \qquad Y' = Y + a_1/2$$

$$Y/X = k \qquad x/X' = \delta$$

$$R_1/X' = R_1' \qquad R_2/X' = R_2'$$

$$R_1'^{\,4}\{2(1 - \cos \gamma)[\,mfr\,(\sin \gamma) - (1 - \cos \gamma)]\}$$

$$+ R_1'^{\,3}\{4 \sin \gamma\,(1 - \cos \gamma) - 2\,mfr\,\delta\,(1 - \cos \gamma)$$

$$- 2\,mfr\,(\sin \gamma - k(1 - \cos \gamma)\sin \gamma\}$$

$$+ R_1'^{\,2}\{2\,\delta[\,mfr \sin \gamma - k(1 - \cos \gamma)\,mfr - (1 - \cos \gamma)\}$$

$$+ R_1'\,\{[\,2\,k\,(1 - \cos \gamma) - 2 \sin \gamma]\,\delta$$

$$+ [\sin \gamma - mfr\,\delta + k\,(1 - \cos \gamma)]\,(k^2 + 1)\}$$

$$+ (k^2 + 1)\,(- 8) = 0 \qquad\qquad\qquad\qquad \text{(A-1)}$$

$$(mfr)^2\,k\,8\,(1 - R_1' \sin \gamma)^3$$

$$+ \{(mfr + \sin \gamma)\,(1 - k/R_1') - \cos \gamma(1/R_1' + mfr)\}$$

$$\{[R_1'(1 - \cos \gamma) + k]^2 + (1 - R_1' \sin \gamma)^2\}^2$$

$$- 2\,mfr\,(1 - R_1' \sin \gamma)\,\{2k\,(mfr + \sin \gamma) + (1 - R_1' \sin\gamma)\,(1 - 1/R_1')$$

$$- (1/R_1' - mfr)\,[k + R_1'\,(1 - \cos \gamma)]\}$$

$$\{[R_1'\,(1 - \cos \gamma) + k]^2 + [1 - R_1' \sin \gamma]^2\} = 0 \qquad\qquad \text{(A-2)}$$

Appendix B

The work reported in this paper was performed after, and was guided by, the study by Manion and Goto [1]. Since their paper is not available to the general reader and since several of the major conclusions presented in this paper depend on the content of their report, their work will be summarized in this appendix. This summary cannot do full justice to their complete report; however, an attempt has been made to include items which are necessary for an understanding of the relation between their work and that of the present paper. These items are presented in either this appendix or with the appropriate discussion in the text.

A summary of their analysis will first be presented. Using a control volume bounded by the setback and standoff walls of the near pocket and the far side of the power jet, and by assuming that the average pressure of $p_F/2$ acted on the latter surface, the following equation was developed using a constant value for the pressure p_N.

$$\tan \alpha = \frac{q_2 + X \, p_N}{q_1 + Y \, p_N + r \, p_F/2} \tag{B-1}$$

where r is the radius of curvature for the power jet. An expression for r was developed by assuming that a constant pressure difference $(p_N - p_F)$ exists across the (uniform width) power jet. The relation for r is given by:

$$r = \frac{q_1}{p_N - p_F} \tag{B-2}$$

Combining this equation with (B-1) and expressing the result as a quadratic equation for p_N provides one of their two computing equations, viz.,

$$(Y \tan \alpha - X) \, p_N^2 + [q_1 \tan \alpha - q_2 - (Y \tan \alpha - X) \, p_F] \, p_N$$

$$+ (q_2 - q_1/2 \tan \alpha) \, p_N = 0 \tag{B-3}$$

The model for the interaction process which was adopted by Manion and Goto can be described as the impingement of a jet onto an inclined surface (the power jet). For this flow configuration, the component of the control jet which is normal to the power jet is assumed to divide equally in the up and downstream directions. To quote the authors (page 16 of reference 1)... "Since the pocket walls exert forces to balance the two components of the returning momentum flux, the pressure along each wall (setback and standoff walls) can be written...". This approach does not consider the momentum efflux from the region defined by the near pocket walls and the power and control jets, neglecting this effect results in too low a value for p_N. (This would be a difficult effect to accurately include in the analysis since the details of the velocity profile would have to be known). The equation resulting from this portion of the analysis provides the second computing equation for $\alpha = \alpha \, (q_1, q_2, X, Y)$. It is also given as a quadratic expression for p_N and has the form:

$$\left[\frac{16(1 + mfr^2)}{\frac{f_1}{f_2}(\frac{1}{Y} + \frac{2}{X})^2} + \frac{8 \, f_1}{\frac{f_1}{f_2}(\frac{1}{Y} + \frac{2}{X})} + Y \right] \, p_N^2$$

$$\tag{B-4}$$

$$- 2 \, q_2 \left[\frac{4(1 + mfr^2)}{\frac{f_1}{f_2}(\frac{1}{Y} + \frac{2}{X})} + Y \, f_1 \right] \, p_N + q_2^2 \left[1 - \frac{f_2^2}{1 + mfr^2} \right] = 0$$

60

where $f_1 = \cos \alpha + (\text{mfr}) \sin \alpha$, and

$f_2 = \sin \alpha - (\text{mfr}) \cos \alpha$.

The required value of p_F was taken from experimental data.

The experimental configurations and test conditions used by Manion and Goto and some of their results for tan as a function of the mfr are presented in the results section and Figs. 6 and 7 of the present paper. For their experimental procedure they placed the flow model on a rotating table and rotated the nozzles and plate assembly past a stationary dual probe. The control jet was continuously adjusted such that a null reading was obtained from the dual probe for a fixed power jet plenum pressure. The result was a direct readout of tan α versus mfr.

Two additional results which are pertinent to the present study are: (1) the apparent pivot point was located at, or near, the geometric intersection of the nozzle centerlines, and (2) data (at an unspecified downstream location) for tan α versus mfr show only a slight three-dimensional effect; the displacement angle is greater near the upper plate and decreases monotonically as the lower plate is approached. (This effect is approximately ±5 per cent about the mean value of tan α at $z = 0$ for a mfr of 0.15.) This could be caused by a nonvertical alignment of their nozzle blocks. These small model sizes (nozzle width = 0.32 in., height = 0.25 in.) would be rather susceptible to possible misalignments resulting from the fabricating process.

References

[1] F. M. Manion and J. Goto, "Jet Interaction in a Defined Region" Harry Diamond Laboratories Rept. No. R-RCA-6323, 30 August 1963. (This is an internal report and is not available for general circulation.) This report is summarized in Appendix B.

[2] J. F. Foss, and J. B. Jones, "A Study of Incompressible Turbulent Bounded Jets." A report prepared for the Harry Diamond Laboratories under contract DA-83(D) AMXDO-CSA 40 (A).

J. F. Foss, "A study of Incompressible Turbulent Bounded Jets" A Ph.D. thesis, Purdue University, January 1965.

[3] A. K. Simson, "Gain Characteristics of Subsonic Pressure Controlled, Proportional, Fluid-Jet Amplifiers," ASME Paper No. 64-WA Aut-2.

[4] S. J. Kline, "Similitude and Approximation Theory," McGraw-Hill, New York, 1965, particularly Chapter 4.

Acknowledgments

I gratefully acknowledge the guidance provided by Dr. J. B. Jones during the original investigation and in the preparation of this paper.

The original study was a portion of an investigation conducted under the sponsorship of the Harry Diamond Laboratories, Contract DA-83(D) AMXDO-CSA 40 (A).

Proportional
Amplifier Simulation

Francis M. Manion

Harry Diamond Laboratories
Washington, D.C.

Abstract

Proportional amplification techniques are reexamined. Designs most commonly used are limited by gain and noise and are difficult to interconnect; thus, their usefulness is restricted. In this paper the concepts and designs of the momentum beam deflection amplifier are reviewed and its operation is analyzed by a control synthesis. The study leads to two amplifier designs, and also suggests a way to isolate the load from the active part of the amplifier.

Nomenclature

A = area $x\sqrt{\dfrac{2}{\rho}}, \dfrac{m^7}{kg}$

C = capacitance, $\dfrac{m^5}{kN}$

K = scaling constant

k = spread constant

L = inductance, $kN - \sec^2 / m^5$

P = pressure, kN / m^2

Q = volume flow, $m^3 / \sec$

R = resistance, $kN \sec / m^5$

s = length of potential core, m

U = velocity, $m/\sec$

W = nozzle exit width of supply jet, m

x = downstream displacement, m

y = cross stream, m

Z = impedance, $kN \sec / m^5$

$f(\eta)$ = jet flow function, dimensionless

$g(\eta)$ = average jet pressure across receiver aperture, kN/m^2

η = similarity parameter, $\sigma y / x$, dimensionless

ρ = density, kg/m^3

σ = Goertler spread parameter, dimensionless

Subscripts

D = dynamic (pertaining to pressure)

d = demand characteristic

e = entrainment

i = input or control

j = jet

m = momentum

o = output

r = collector or receiver

s = spilled, flow outside outboard collector edge

v = vent

l = one side of two-sided system

$+$ = pertaining to the power or supply jet

Introduction

The proportional or analog amplifier is a basic component in control or analog simulation systems. The first flueric proportional amplifier was a momentum interaction jet deflection device. The deflected jet was partitioned about a stream divider and the variation in the collected quantities of momentum, flow, and pressure exceeded the input signal so that amplification was achieved.

Jet deflection amplifiers have been studied and developed by several investigators while others have refined the momentum interaction approach. The background for the design discussions of the jet deflection amplifier is given in references [1], [2], and [3].

After seven years of development, the jet deflection amplifier is still not a really useful and reliable element. Its pressure gain is low; it is difficult to interconnect; it is sensitive to control level; and it is noisy. In spite of the shortcomings it has been used in systems where it is represented as a time delay and a simple lag. This representation is limited to low frequencies and is somewhat inaccurate.

63

The purpose of this paper is to point out the difficulties in present amplifier design and to suggest solutions that will enable the full potential of proportional jet deflection amplifiers to be realized.

The momentum jet deflection amplifier was synthesized on an analog computer. This simulation is used to aid in the understanding of the physical model of the actual amplifier. The simulation model included the effect of nonlinear receiver impedance on the flow balance in the interaction region. Therefore, pressure fields, vent flows, and jet flow entrainment were all considered. However, it is not possible to simulate the noise, but it is hoped that the improved amplifier design will decrease the amplifier noise. The results of the simulation suggest that continuity considerations are very important to avoid adverse pressure gradients across the jets that reduce the gain of the element.

Based on the simulation model, a mathematical model was prepared and, by the use of demand flow characteristics, the adverse pressure field effect is clearly shown. The mathematical model used was greatly simplified by the use of a receiver impedance which was defined by the width of the receiver aperture only. In the analog simulation receiver, impedance has a strong influence on the flow balance, but the mathematical model for simplicity was limited to the impedance where all flow intersected by the receiver aperature passes through the receiver. In addition, the mathematical model assumes constant input impedance for the control nozzles, but the simulated model does not make this assumption. Two solutions of the mathematical model are suggested so that the amplifier can be designed to operate without a pressure field. These approaches result in a fixed relationship between the receiver aperture and the center vent or a fixed receiver aperture for a device that has no center vent. The use of control nozzles of the same widths as that of the receiver aperture is still considered correct for maximum power transfer, even though it was based on a linear assumption. One typical amplifier was experimentally tested and the vent pressure difference influence on the amplifier gain was verified.

Simulation of a Proportional Amplifier

Model Description. Simulation of the proportional amplifier was undertaken to provide further understanding of the proportional flueric element as presently designed and to assist in refinement of the model used. The design of a proportional amplifier involves many interdependent parameters. Although the amplifier is conceptionally simple, the interdependencies are quite complex. The amplifier problem is not amenable to direct mathematical treatment; yet a good amplifier design is based on the understanding of such relationships. To develop this insight and to facilitate parametric changes, the proportional jet interaction amplifier was simulated on the analog computer.

The simulation of the fluid amplifier on the analog computer is limited, but it did allow the effect of receiver impedance on the flow balance in the jet interaction region to be studied. The limitation on the simulation results from the use of Goertler's jet velocity profile. Goertler's profile for the turbulent jet assumes a constant pressure on each side of the jet stream; whereas, in this simulation, static pressure differences up to 2 per cent of the source pressure were encountered. Although the use of the Goertler profile is inexact, it greatly simplified the simulation because a function generator was used to provide the jet's flow profile and average pressure integral. If the function generated were to be changed for each static pressure variation, the degree of problem complexity greatly increases. For this reason, the inexact Goertler profile was used, and since the pressure field was small — 1 to 2 per cent of source — the results are useful.

The proportional amplifier simulated is based on a two-dimensional jet stream. The Goertler expression for the jet stream is used. This expression is

$$U = U_+ \left(\frac{s}{x}\right)^{\frac{1}{2}} \sec h^2 \left(\frac{\sigma y}{x}\right)$$

where

U_+ = velocity at supply nozzle exit

s = length of potential core

σ = spread parameter

x, y = downstream and cross-stream dimensions

The similarity variable $\eta = \sigma y / x$ is used. The spread parameter is considered constant and the receiver apertures are located at a fixed x, downstream position, so η is proportional to y.

The block diagram for the simulation is shown in Fig. 1. In this figure there are two functions of η, $f(\eta)$ and $g(\eta)$. These are jet functions and are obtained by integration of the jet stream profile; $f(\eta)$ is the flow on one side of the stream divider; $g(\eta)$ is the average pressure across the stream receiver aperture. The functional expressions can be written

$$f(\eta) = Q_+ (0.866) \left(\frac{x}{\sigma}\right)^{\frac{1}{2}} (1 \pm \tan h \, \Delta \eta)$$

$$g(\eta) = \frac{P_+}{4 \eta_r} (3 \tan h \, \eta - \tan h^3 \eta) \Big|_{\pm \Delta \eta}^{\eta_r \, \pm \Delta \eta}$$

where $\Delta \eta$ is the lateral deflection of the jet P_+ and Q_+ are the supply jet's pressure level and volume flow. To simplify, x was made equal to σ. This is a good estimate, since the receivers are usually at 10 W and σ is about 10 [4].

There are two impedance terms, Z_r and Z_v. These are lumped representations of the receiver impedance and the vent impedance and are approximated for low frequency by the analogous schematics shown in Fig. 2.

The simulation model is merely a statement of continuity, momentum vector summation, and accelerations due to the action of a pressure field. Fig. 1 shows a simulation model of a typical push-pull amplifier; η is the similarity variable and indicates a lateral jet stream deflection. The way the limits are taken for $f(\eta)$ and $g(\eta)$ defines — $\Delta \eta$ as the jet being deflected toward the particular side. In Fig. 1, the flow that exhausts out the receiver, $g(\eta) / Z_r$, is subtracted from the total flow on this side of the amplifier defined as $f(\eta)$. The jet entrainment Q_e and the control or input flow must also be summed to determine the vent flow. The input flow is determined by the difference between input control pressure and vent pressure. The entrained flow is subtracted from the input flow. The difference

65

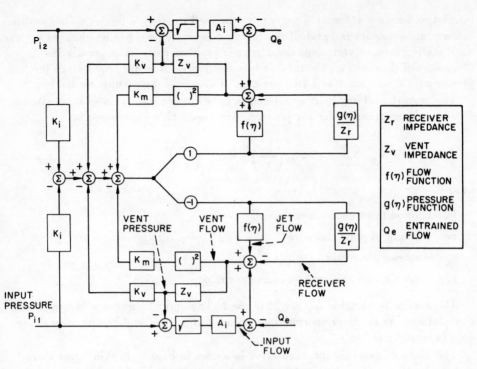

FIG. 1 SIMULATION MODEL

between the entrained flow and the control flow is added to the difference between the total flow and the flow passing through the receiver. This sum determines the vent flow. The vent flow times the vent impedance defines the vent pressure. The vent flow squared times a scaling factor defines the internal feedback momentum flux. The control input, vent pressure, and feedback momentum flux are scaled to by K_i, K_v, and K_m. On one side of the amplifier all these act to oppose the deflection and are summed negatively. These scaling constants are defined as

$$K_i = x\, \eta_i\, \frac{1}{P_+},\quad K_v = \frac{x^2}{4\,P_+},\quad \text{and } K_m = \frac{1}{k\,w\,U_+^2}$$

where k is an area factor taken as 2.5. This accounts for the spreading of the vent momentum flux. Although several approximations were made, this model is considered close to the physical model.

Model Testing. The model was tested dynamically and statically. In the dynamic testing, the jet transport time was about 0.05 msec and was neglected. Fig. 3 presents the dynamic results on a Bode diagram. The jet deflection, $\Delta \eta$, and the output pressure signal are compared with their d-c values. $\Delta \eta$ reaches a minimum at about 4340 cps; this is about the resonant frequency of the vent tank circuits. This resonance (high negative feedback) falls at higher frequencies and the jet assumes a larger angular deflection.

The second variable shown in the figure is output pressure. This pressure is shown beyond 1000 cps, although above this value the data are inaccurate because the circuit equivalent is not accurate. These data show that the expected

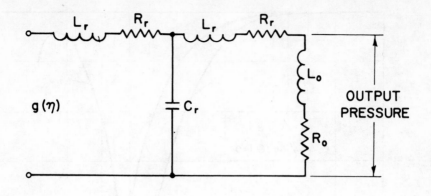

RECEIVER ELECTRICAL ANALOG

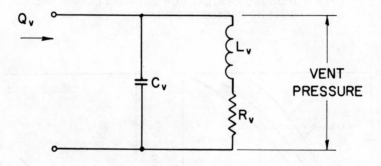

VENT ELECTRICAL ANALOG

FIG. 2 RECEIVER AND VENT ELECTRICAL ANALOGS

characteristics in amplitude fall off with increasing frequency. It should be mentioned that the collector line network resonance frequency is considerably higher than would be expected if a tube connection were used between the two amplifiers.

The dynamic test data indicate the effect of the vent circuit, but these data are not accurate because some small scaling errors were found. These were corrected so that the static tests would be accurate. The errors do not appreciably change the character of the dynamic results.

The static tests consisted in deflecting the jet by an input differential pressure, ΔP_i, for various control pressure levels P_i. The output pressure signal

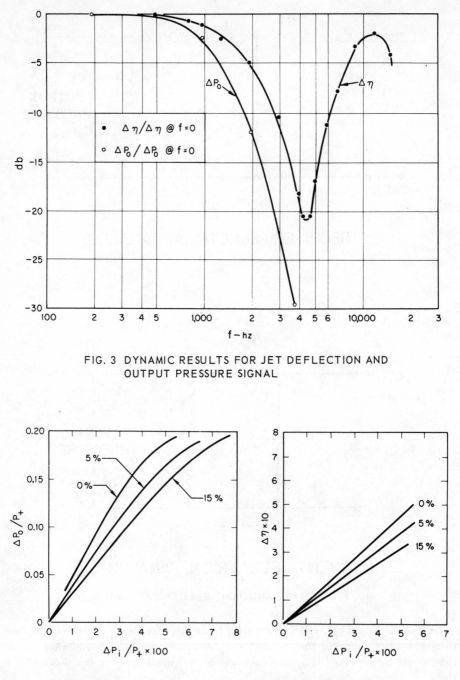

FIG. 3 DYNAMIC RESULTS FOR JET DEFLECTION AND
OUTPUT PRESSURE SIGNAL

FIG. 4 STATIC RESULTS OF JET DEFLECTION AND OUTPUT
PRESSURE SIGNAL FOR CONTROL LEVELS OF 0, 5 AND
15 PER CENT P_+

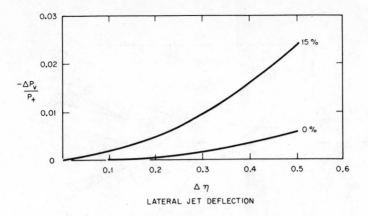

FIG. 5 VENT PRESSURE DIFFERENCE FOR CONTROL LEVELS
OF 0 AND 15 PER CENT P_+.

and jet deflection $\Delta\eta$ are plotted against the input pressure signal in Fig. 4. Fig. 5 presents the difference between the two vent chamber pressures. These differences are negative (opposing the control signal) for the full range of deflection except for the zero input level case below $\Delta\eta = 0.10$. A $\Delta\eta = 0.5$ for this model has a lateral jet deflection of 0.5 W at 10 W downstream.

The test data presented in Figs. 3, 4, and 5 give a great deal of understanding about the actual model. The degradation of gain, as shown, has been partly attributed to a change in the velocity profile, but this model does not have profile changes; therefore, it must be assumed the vent flow field is very important for it acts as negative feedback to decrease the net gain. The resonance in the vent chamber certainly limits the frequency response of the element and it certainly affects the input control signal. The vent problem is compounded by the dependency of spilled flow on receiver impedance and jet deflection angle. This simulation is further confirmed by the data of Roffman and Katz [5] on some high frequency values of gain greater than 1 at 5 kc. This can be explained as the effect of the vent acting in conjunction with the collector line. Suppose both were operating at a phase shift of 90 degrees; the total of 180 degrees would occur at the sum point and this negative feedback would become positive and account for the sharp increase in gain.

The simulation indicates the need for a careful evaluation of the flow field in order to improve the proportional amplifier.

Amplifier Design Discussion

Problem Analysis. The reduction in jet deflection, shown in Fig. 4, and the adverse pressure field developed, shown in Fig. 5, indicate proper flow summation was not achieved. This indicates that an adverse pressure field reduced the lateral deflection of the jet. This reduction in deflection causes a reduction in amplifier gain.

To analyze the continuity requirements of a proportional amplifier, the control volumes shown in Fig. 6 were drawn. There are four flows that enter or leave this volume – the entrained flow Q_e, the spilled flow Q_s, the vent flow Q_v, and the

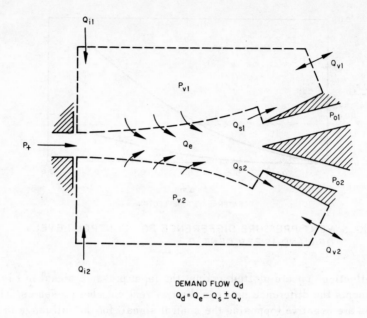

DEMAND FLOW Q_d

$$Q_d = Q_e - Q_s \pm Q_v$$

FIG. 6 CONTROL VOLUME

input control flow Q_i. The vent flow is the adjustment between the others. The sum $Q_e - Q_s - Q_i$ determines the vent flow. If this sum is greater than zero, the vent flow enters the control volume. If this sum is less than zero, the vent flow must leave the volume. The vent flow can change direction during a jet deflection because Q_s and Q_i will change.

The entrained flow is assumed constant because of the fixed downstream distance and the constant spread parameter. This flow is total flow on one side of the jet minus one-half the original jet flow.

$$Q_e = Q_+ \left[0.866 \left(\frac{x}{\sigma} \right)^{\frac{1}{2}} - 0.5 \right]$$

or

$$Q_e = 0.366 \, Q_+$$

$$\text{for } x/\sigma = 1$$

The spilled flow can be determined for the case where the receiver has zero impedance. Zero impedance implies that all the jet flow intercepted by the receiver passes through the receiver. The spilled flow in this case is the flow in the jet profile from the far edge of the collector outward. This flow is defined as

$$Q_s = Q_+ \, (0.866) \, [1 - \tanh (\eta_r \pm \Delta \eta)]$$

The spilled flow depends on the width of the receiver and, of course, on the lateral deflection of the jet. If η_r, the receiver aperture, were made zero, this would approximate an infinite impedance without cross-coupling effects.

70

The vent flow can be defined in terms of vent chamber pressure as

$$Q_v = A_v \sqrt{P_v}$$

To facilitate analysis, the sum of the entrained, spilled, and vent flows is defined as demand flow [6]:

$$Q_d = Q_e - Q_s \pm Q_v$$

For stable operation, the demand flow must be zero. This can be emphasized by the dependency of the vent pressure time derivative on the demand flow. This dependency is given by the equation

$$Q_d = -C \frac{dP_v}{dt}$$

where C is the capacitance of the volume. A positive demand flow indicates a shortage of flow and therefore a decreasing P_v. For equilibrium

$$\frac{dP_v}{dt} = 0 \text{ and thus } Q_d = 0$$

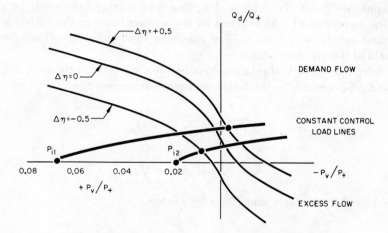

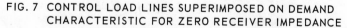

FIG. 7 CONTROL LOAD LINES SUPERIMPOSED ON DEMAND
CHARACTERISTIC FOR ZERO RECEIVER IMPEDANCE

The demand flow is plotted in Fig. 7 for zero jet deflection and for deflection of $\Delta \eta = \pm 0.5$. The demand flow normalized by the supply flow is the ordinate and the abscissa is the vent pressure. A positive vent pressure increases the demand flow because vent flow leaves the control volume. Without input control flow, the equilibrium vent pressure for $\Delta \eta = 0$ is negative.

The positive vent pressure is plotted to the left to permit the input control load lines to be placed on the figure in the familiar orientation. The P_{i_1} load line intersects the $\Delta \eta = +0.5$ demand characteristics and the P_{i_2} load line intersects the $\Delta \eta = -0.5$ demand characteristic. This results in $P_{v_2} > P_{v_1}$ which is an ad-

71

verse pressure field that decreases the jet deflection. This adverse pressure field was found in the simulation and is presented in Fig. 5.

Design Approaches. The problem is to design an amplifier that does not have an adverse pressure field. A solution might be to enlarge the vents sufficiently to make the influence of the generated pressure field negligible, but this would expose the stream, partitioned by the stream divider, to external influences. Environmental and acoustic noise would be amplified by the very sensitive partitioning process about the stream divider, and the amplifier would be very noisy.

Maximum stream deflection can be achieved only by eliminating the pressure field influence for momentum interaction designs. For a zero pressure difference between the vent chambers, the input flow difference must match the difference in flow between the $+0.5\,\Delta\eta$ and $-0.5\,\Delta\eta$ demand curves. There are two ways to accomplish this matching of flows. These approaches are shown in Fig. 8 for a zero pressure difference between the two vent chambers. Although it is possible to operate with a favorable pressure difference, this leads to a pressure field design rather than a momentum interaction device. The two approaches are for zero offside control flow and for finite offside control flow.

Fig. 8 shows the demand characteristics for $\Delta\eta = \pm 0.5$; Fig. 8a shows the design approach for $P_{v1} = P_{v2} = P_{i2}$, i.e., offside control flow equal to zero; Fig. 8b presents the design approach for $P_{v1} = P_{v2}$ but allowing control flow. In the case of Fig. 8a, the $\Delta\eta = -0.5$ demand characteristic must be in the excess flow regime at $P_v = 0$. To achieve this, flow from another source may be necessary. The method of Fig. 8a requires an in-line vent between the collector and the control nozzle so that the no-flow condition on the offside will not disrupt the flow field of the previous stage.

To determine the actual relationships between control nozzle area, collector area, and pressure levels, the following equations are written:

$$\sqrt{P_{i1}} \cdot A_i \cdot \eta_i = Q_{d1} \tag{1}$$

$$\sqrt{P_{i2}} \cdot A_i \cdot \eta_i = Q_{d2} \tag{2}$$

For $\Delta\eta = 0.5$, the input signal can be written

$$(P_{i1} - P_{i2})\,\eta_i = 0.05 \tag{3}$$

when x is taken as 10 W and P_+ as unity and equation (1) becomes

$$\sqrt{P_{i2} + \frac{0.05}{\eta_i}}\,(A_i\,\eta_i) = Q_{d1} \tag{4}$$

If equation (2) is squared and subtracted from equation (4) squared, the following expression results:

$$(0.05)\,A_i^2\,\eta_i^{\cdot} = Q_{d1}^2 - Q_{d2}^2 \tag{5}$$

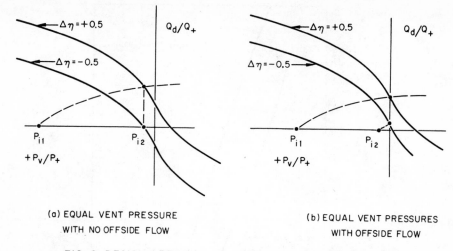

(a) EQUAL VENT PRESSURE
WITH NO OFFSIDE FLOW

(b) EQUAL VENT PRESSURES
WITH OFFSIDE FLOW

FIG. 8 DESIGN APPROACHES FOR EQUAL VENT PRESSURES

A_i is the area of supply power nozzle times $\sqrt{2/\rho}$. Q_{d1} and Q_{d2} are functions of η and can be written

$$Q_{d1} = Q_e - Q_+ \, (0.866) \, [1 - \tanh (\eta_r + 0.5)] \qquad (6)$$

$$Q_{d2} = Q_e - Q_+ \, (0.866) \, [1 - \tanh (\eta_r - 0.5)] \qquad (7)$$

Equation (5) is defined only for $Q_{d2} > 0$. This equation is based on the concept that the collector width should equal the control width to obtain maximum inter-stage power transfer. Equation (5) is for the approach given in Fig. 8b; Fig. 8a is another approach with no offside control flow and, in this case, the left side of equation (2) becomes zero. The flow supplied by P_{i1} must equal the demand flow Q_{d1} at the particular vent pressure. Since the flow difference between $\Delta\eta = +.5$ and $\Delta\eta = -.5$ is constant, the demand flow can be written as $Q_{d1} - Q_{d2}$. This results in equation (8) for the case of equal vent pressures with no offside control flow.

$$(0.05)^2 \, A_i \, \eta_i = (Q_{d1} - Q_{d2})^2 \qquad (8)$$

It may be seen that the left sides of equations (5) and (8) are the same, but the right sides are quite different. These equations were solved and the correct η_i for the two cases plotted in Fig. 9. The solutions can be extended by the use of a center vent. The center vent adds a term in the argument of the hyperbolic tangent function of equations (6) and (7). The arguments can be written as $\eta_r + \eta_v/2 \pm \Delta\eta$ instead of $\eta_r \pm \Delta\eta$. Again the condition of solution is that the input nozzle width equals the receiver width.

The relationships between η_r and η_v given in Fig. 9 are the solutions to operate with no vent pressure difference. For $\eta_v = 0$ the no offside flow approach Fig. (8a) requires $\eta_i = \eta_r = 1.28\,W$. The Fig. 8b approach without a center vent requires $\eta_i = \eta_r = 1.6\,W$. The use of a center vent allows the use of smaller input

73

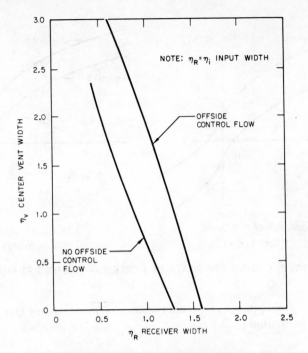

FIG. 9 SOLUTION RELATIONSHIP BETWEEN η_r AND η_v, FOR
INPUT WIDTH EQUAL RECEIVER WIDTH

and receiver widths. This follows directly from the flow in the jet velocity profile. The larger the argument of the hyperbolic tangent, the smaller the differ-
ence flow for a deflection. The $\partial Q / \partial \eta$ is proportional to $\sec h^2 \eta$ and as η becomes large $\partial Q / \partial \eta$ decreases.

Operation at $\eta_r = \eta_i$ when larger than required results in a favorable pressure
difference between vent chambers. Operation at smaller widths results in an adverse pressure difference. In this case, more control difference is needed to deflect the jet a given amount.

The most familiar design is the amplifier that has offside control flow. If this
design is used without a center vent, the control nozzles and receiver apertures
should be 1.6 times the supply or power nozzle width. The use of widths larger
than 1.6 W results in a favorable pressure difference, whereas smaller widths result in adverse pressure difference between vents. A center vent of 1.1 W results
in receiver and input widths of 1.3 W. The center vent designs are not recommended because the position of the receivers is further out on the jet velocity
profile and, as a result, a great deal of the jet power is lost.

To stage amplifiers assumed identical in dimension, the output and input pressure signal must be considered. For example, if $\eta_i = \eta_r = 1.6$ W, the average pressure on the receiver is 0.115 P_+ for the $+\Delta \eta$ side and 0.522 P_+ for the $-\Delta \eta$ side.
When $\Delta \eta = 0$, both sides see 0.328 P_+. Computing the required input pressure
levels for an amplifier of this design, the $+\Delta \eta$ side should be 0.0113 P_+, the
$-\Delta \eta$ side should be 0.0423 P_+, and the $\Delta \eta = 0$ pressure level should be
0.0345 P_+. These pressures are required to supply the flow for a zero pressure
difference between vents. This amplifier cannot be perfectly matched because
for $\Delta \eta = \pm 0.5$ and $\Delta \eta = 0$, there are different ratios between pressure available

74

and pressure required. If a match at $\Delta \eta = 0$ is made, a supply pressure staging of 9.5 is required between stages. However, the $\Delta \eta \neq 0$ terms are not quite matched. The required ΔP_i is only 0.03 P_+ because the nozzles are 1.6 W wide. The available signal is too much. However, line attenuation will tend to reduce the signal at both zero and full deflection. If the pressure levels are all reduced to 50 per cent by losses, the staging progression is 4.75 or 5. Experience has shown that the difference signal tends to be reduced more than the level; therefore, the use of $\Delta \eta = 0$ level to match is a good estimate. This is not exact, but it is close and it results in a very little pressure field influence for small vents that sufficiently isolate the jet divider partitioning.

The second approach requires an in-line vent between receiver aperture and the following control input. This vent is necessary so that the zero offside control flow condition does not drastically change the flow balance of the preceding stage. Actually, the in-line vent is recommended to isolate the jet partitioning process from downstream load as well as to maintain a designed flow balance.

The use of the inline vent in the zero offside control flow (case 8a) results in a simplified matching problem. Only the ΔP signal must be matched into the next stage; the level can be adjusted by the design of the vent area. To operate with zero offside control flow, the demand flow characteristic for the $-\Delta \eta$ deflection must be in the excess flow region at $P_v = 0$, as shown in Fig. 8a. This requires supplementary flow to the control volume of Fig. 6. This additional flow results in an outflow through the vent area and a positive vent pressure. The area of vent determines the pressure for a given excess flow and permits the vent chamber to be matched with the low pressure of the input signal. Supplementary flow can be drawn from the supply through orifice-type restrictions. This flow also increases the input impedance because less flow is drawn at the input and decreases the noise-producing pressure field caused by unsatisfied entrainment. The supply pressure varies continually and therefore its entrainment requirement also varies in some random way. The jet obtains entrainment by the generation of a pressure field. These fields become strong during transient jet pressure variations because the new entrainment flow cannot immediately respond to the jet level changes. These entrainment pressure fields are considered a significant contributor to the low frequency noise of proportional amplifiers. The supplementary flow reduces the field strength greatly because it is supplied by power pressure and immediately satisfies most of the entrainment requirements. Thus, entrainment pressure fields do not develop to nearly their former strength.

The design for no offside control flow is shown in Fig. 9. For a design without a center vent $\eta_i = \eta_r = 1.2\ W$. Another design with a center vent of 0.7 W has $\eta_i = \eta_r = 1.0\ W$. Both of these designs are considered reasonable. However, both will require supplementary flow which must be greater than 14 per cent Q_+ for the $\eta_r = 1.28$ design. This supplementary flow must be greater than 16 per cent Q_+ for the center vent ($\eta_r = 1.0$) design.

In summary, the design with offside control flow appears easier but in practice it is more difficult. Both the input pressure signal and the signal level must be carefully matched to each stage. The zero offside control flow design requires an in-line vent and supplementary flow, but both of these seem to be worthwhile additions in that they increase the amplifier input impedance and reduce its noise. The zero offside control case has the advantage of smaller receivers and thus the $\Delta P_o / \Delta \eta$ is expected to be larger for this design. Estimates of $\Delta P_o / \Delta P_i$ for these

75

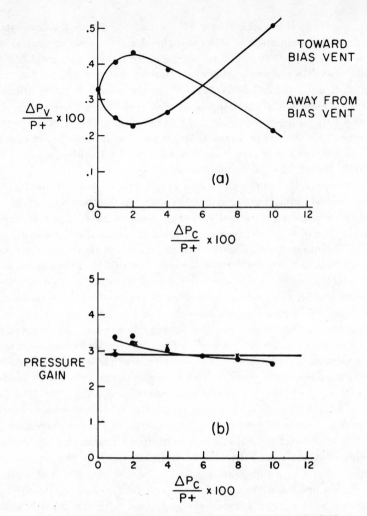

FIG. 10 VENT PRESSURE AND PRESSURE GAIN VERSUS
CONTROL SIGNAL

designs are 9 to 11 for a 10-W separation between the supply nozzle and the receiver (ΔP_o is the change in average output pressure across the receiving aperture). The value of 11 is for zero offside control flow and 9 is for the design with offside control flow.

Experimental Tests

The amplifier model tested was an HDL design with a special vent size. A 1.5 mm vent diameter was used. The amplifier had a supply nozzle of 0.5 mm; control nozzles of 0.75 mm, and receivers of 0.62 mm. The amplifier's aspect ratio was 2.5. Static pressure taps were placed in the vent chamber.

Vent pressure data versus difference control signal is shown in Fig. 10a. The figure shows the element to be structurally biased, since a vent pressure difference of 0.33 per cent P_+ existed without control signal. The side with the highest vent pressure had the lowest output pressure. This amplifier was connected into nozzles that had an area 40 per cent larger than the receiver. No attempt was made to obtain high impedance for higher gain. The vent pressure difference increases the deflection of the jet.

Fig. 10a contains two curves, the vent pressure difference when the stream is directed away from the bias and when the stream is deflected toward the bias. The vent pressure initially changes to create a favorable vent pressure gradient; then finally, the adverse pressure gradient results. This particular element has receiver widths and control nozzles such that an adverse pressure gradient between the vents should result. The favorable pressure that initially occurs is due to the receiver impedance. The jet spills more flow on the vent side which has the higher pressure. When the jet is deflected toward the higher vent pressure, the jet's average pressure (measured before the receiver) increases faster than its flow so that less flow vents and the vent pressure decreases. The opposite occurs when the stream is deflected away from the bias vent. To confirm the effect of receiver impedance, the control pressure on both sides was set equal. The vent pressure difference was measured. When the outputs of the amplifier were disconnected from the nozzle loads, the vent pressure difference was reversed and reduced. Thus, the effect of receiver impedance on vent pressure was demonstrated.

Fig. 10b shows the pressure gain of the amplifier. The amplifier gain, without influence of a vent field, does not vary with control signal. Corrected gain is presented by influence of the pressure field. The gain of this curve is higher initially and then decreases to a lower value, as the vent field becomes adverse. Data of the measured gain is presented. The x's indicate jet deflection away from the bias vent and o's indicate deflection toward the vent. Agreement is good and seems to confirm the vent field's influence. The experimental tests indicate the receiver impedance is very important in amplifier design. However, a better arrangement would be a receiver that does not influence the pressure field of the interaction chamber. This can be accomplished by inline venting between stages as discussed earlier in the paper.

Conclusion

The analysis and simulation indicate that pressure fields strongly influence the gain of a momentum interaction device and can result in considerable pressure gain reduction. Two design approaches are outlined to avoid pressure field influence and result in pressure gains of 9 to 11. These are considered the best achievable with a single-stage momentum interaction amplifier for the jet spread parameter equal to 10.

Acknowledgment

The author wishes to express his appreciation to Paul G. Hershall for his assistance in the analog computer simulation.

References

[1] S. J. Peperone, S. Katz, and J. M. Goto, "Gain Analysis of the Proportional Fluid Amplifier," DOFL TR-1073, October, 1962, pp. 1-43.

[2] E. M. Dexter, "An Analog Pure Fluid Amplifier," ASME Fluid Jet Control Devices, November, 1962. Edited by Forbes T. Brown.

[3] R. J. Reilly and F. A. Moynihan, "Notes on a Proportional Amplifier," ASME Fluid Jet Control Devices, November, 1962. Edited by Forbes T. Brown.

[4] R. D. Trapani, "An Experimental Study of Bounded and Confined Turbulent Jet," HDL Report on Fluerics, No. 22, November 1966, pp. 1-56.

[5] G. L. Roffman and S. Katz, "Predicting Closed Loop Stability of Fluid Amplifiers from Frequency Response Measurements," HDL Fluid Amplification Symposium Proceedings, October, 1965, Vol. I, pp. 297-314.

[6] F. T. Brown, "A Combined Analytical and Experimental Approach to the Development of Fluid-Jet Amplifiers," ASME Paper No. 62-WA-154, ASME Transactions, June, 1964, Journal of Basic Engineering, Vol. 86, pp. 175-184.

Effects of Transverse Secondary Flow on the Laminar-Turbulent Transition of a Free Axisymmetric Jet

M. A. Boyd and A. R. Barbin
Auburn University
Auburn, Alabama

Abstract

This paper reports measurements of mean velocities and turbulence intensities in the transition region of a free axisymmetric jet with and without transverse secondary flow. The data were taken downstream of a 1/16-in. i.d. tube (primary jet) with a hot-wire anemometer and analyzed in light of Wille's model of laminar-turbulent jet flow. Secondary flow injection near the exit plane effects premature transition through its influence on the structure of annular vortices within the laminar portion of the jet. There exists a lower or threshold limit to the secondary flow, below which laminar-turbulent transition is virtually unaffected; in the present investigation, this threshold limit occurred near a supply pressure ratio (secondary to primary jet) of 0.02. At secondary flows less than the threshold, the velocity profiles become asymmetric with the profile peak displaced toward the secondary flow. At secondary flows above the threshold the velocity profile peak is displaced away from the secondary flow.

Nomenclature

D = diameter of jet aperture

P_p = primary jet supply pressure (gage)

P_s = secondary jet supply pressure (gage)

R = radial coordinate of flow field

U = instantaneous component of velocity in the axial direction

U_{cl} = jet centerline velocity

U_o = jet centerline velocity at the exit plane

$\sqrt{\overline{U'^2}}$ = root-mean-square of axial velocity fluctuation

X = axial coordinate of flow field

Introduction

Turbulence amplifiers operate by effecting premature laminar-turbulent transition of a free axisymmetric jet by means of transverse flow from a second jet [1]. This note is a summary of an experimental study of the flow field within such a device.

Apparatus

In the apparatus, a laminar (primary) jet was projected horizontally from a 1/16-in. i.d. tube connected to a constant pressure air supply. A secondary jet was projected vertically upward from a similar tube having a variable supply pressure. The centerlines of the primary and secondary jets intersected at a point 1.75 jet-tube diameters downstream of their exit planes. The relative positions and intersection angles of the two jets remained fixed. The jets were not isolated from background noise within the laboratory. The primary noise sources were the supply blower and its motor.

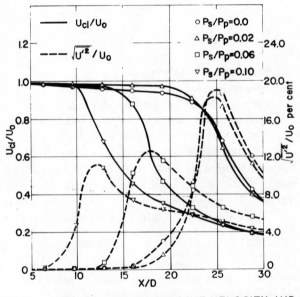

FIG. 1 VARIATION IN CENTERLINE VELOCITY AND TURBULENCE INTENSITY

Results

Data were taken with a constant temperature hot-wire anemometer for various secondary to primary jet supply pressure ratios. The resulting distributions of velocity and percentage turbulence intensity are shown in Figs. 1 through 5. In Figs. 2 through 5 the data points for the turbulence intensity are indicated by small circles. For clarity, the mean velocity profile data points are not shown but are represented by a solid line closely fitted to the actual data points.

The exit plane Reynolds number was 3900, well within the Reynolds number range for which transition occurs slowly with the growth of large vortices [2].

Thus, the plots were interpreted in the light of the laminar-turbulent jet flow model proposed by Wille, et al [3, 4]. Briefly, this model is as follows. When a jet exits from a nozzle or tube, the laminar boundary layer existing at the wall of the nozzle or tube is projected as a free laminar "boundary layer" surrounding the jet. Disturbances downstream of the exit plane cause this layer to roll up, thereby forming a system of laminar annular vortices. Farther downstream the vortices become unstable and begin to decay. They eventually do slipping motions one through another, coalesce, and finally collapse resulting in the onset of turbulence. With this model in mind, the following observations were made with respect to Figs. 1 through 5.

Fig. 1 clearly shows that with the present combination of background noise and jet tube geometry, the primary jet is insensitive to low secondary flow, i.e., $P_s/P_p = 0.02$. Secondary flow became the dominant factor affecting transition somewhere between $P_s/P_p = 0.02$ and $P_s/P_p = 0.06$.

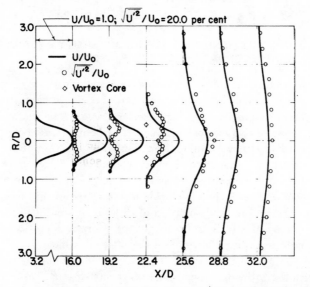

FIG. 2 VELOCITY AND TURBULENCE INTENSITY PROFILES
IN UNDISTURBED JET $(P_s/P_p = 0.00)$

The evolution of a laminar jet with no flow disturbance and no secondary jet tube present is depicted in Fig. 2. Upstream of 16.0 diameters both the jet and the ring vortices were laminar. Measurable velocity fluctuations first appeared at 16.0 diameters. Downstream of this point the shape of the turbulence intensity profile is indicative of the presence of instability within the vortices. The location of the vortex cores, as revealed by the anemometer, corresponds to the single peak to either side of the jet centerline. This peak has approximately the same radial location as the point of inflection of its corresponding velocity profile. This has also been observed in the two-dimensional jet [5]. At 22.4 diameters the jet was well into transition. The velocity profile exhibits distortion and the turbulence intensity profile has two peaks to either side of the centerline. In this region the location of the vortex core was indistinct and there were indications of the presence of two cores, implying that two vortices were performing slipping motions one through another. Finally, true turbulence begins to develop at 25.6

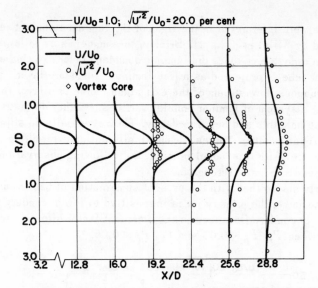

FIG. 3 VELOCITY AND TURBULENCE INTENSITY PROFILES,
LOW SECONDARY FLOW ($P_s / P_p = 0.02$)

diameters as revealed by the sudden increase in jet width, the recovery of velocity profile symmetry, and the rapid emergence of a single centerline peak in
the turbulence intensity profile. These phenomena result from the sudden coalescence and collapse of two or more vortices. The peaks in centerline turbulence
intensity shown in Fig. 1 can be taken as the average location of coalesence of
vortices. The intermittent character of vortex coalescence makes it very difficult
to accurately measure velocities in the outer portion of the jet at stations close
to the peaks shown in Fig. 1. The evolution of the shape of the turbulence intensity profiles exhibited in the transition of this jet is similar to that observed
by Corrsin in the case of a fully turbulent jet [6]. Corrsin's profiles, however,
reveal only a single peak to either side of the jet centerline.

The addition of flow from the secondary jet yielded results similar to those
stated above with the following important exceptions. For $P_s / P_p = 0.02$ the
velocity profiles between the exit plane and 12.8 diameters were asymmetric with
the profile peak displaced below the jet centerline. The amount of displacement
increased with distance downstream and reached its maximum value at 12.8
diameters (only the profile at 12.8 diameters is shown in Fig. 3.) Downstream
of this point the peak once again occurred at the centerline. This distortion was
evidently due to the fact that while the low secondary flow had no effect on the
transition of the jet, it was strong enough to distort the lower half of the laminar
vortices. As a result, the superposition of vortex circumferential and longitudinal
velocities was no longer symmetric with respect to the centerline and the point of
maximum velocity was thus shifted below the centerline. The vortices regained
their symmetry previous to the onset of instability as revealed by the symmetric
velocity profiles and vortex core locations shown in Fig. 3.

Figs. 4 and 5 reveal that $P_s / P_p = 0.06$ and $P_s / P_p = 0.10$ not only effect premature jet transition but also effectively retard the flow in the lower half of the
laminar portion of the jet thus producing distorted velocity profiles. The turbulence intensity profiles are also distorted due to the more rapid development of

82

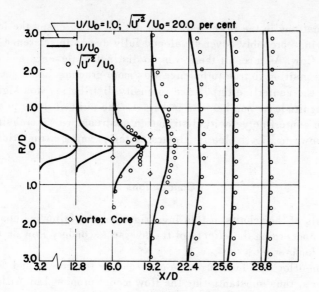

FIG. 4 VELOCITY AND TURBULENCE INTENSITY PROFILES
$P_s/P_p = 0.06$

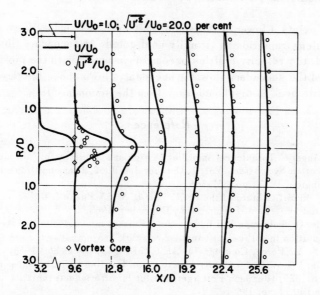

FIG. 5 VELOCITY AND TURBULENCE INTENSITY PROFILES
$P_s/P_p = 0.10$

velocity fluctuations in the lower half of the jet. In these cases the lower halves of the vortex rings probably never developed fully due to interference from the secondary jet flow. As a result there was no distinct coalesence and collapse of vortices and transition to true turbulence was more gradual. Consequently, the sharp peak in the centerline turbulence intensity distribution was significantly reduced in magnitude as can be seen in Fig. 1. The shift of these peaks and the "knee" of the centerline velocity distribution upstream with increasing secondary jet flow as shown in Fig. 1 clearly illustrates the premature transition of the jet.

Conclusions

On the basis of the results of this investigation, the following conclusions can be drawn concerning the effects of transverse secondary flow on the transition of a free laminar jet.

1) The transition of a laminar jet is governed by the growth and decay of annular vortices, thus substantiating the flow model proposed by Wille, et al [3, 4].

2) The lateral distributions of turbulence intensity in the transition region of a laminar-turbulent jet exhibit local minima at, and away from, the jet centerline.

3) There exists a lower or threshold limit to the secondary flow, below which laminar-turbulent transition is virtually unaffected. At secondary flows less than the threshold, the velocity profiles become asymmetric with the profile peak displaced toward the secondary flow. At secondary flows above the threshold the velocity profile peak is displaced away from the secondary flow.

References

[1] R. N. Auger, "Turbulence Amplifier Design and Application," *Proceedings of the Fluid Amplification Symposium*, Vol. 1, October 2-4, 1962, Diamond Ordnance Fuze Laboratory, Washington, D. C., pp. 357-366.

[2] "Fluid Amplifier State of the Art," Vol. 1, NASA Phase I, Report Contract NAS 8-5408, Prepared by General Electric Co., December, 1963.

[3] R. Wille, O. Wehrmann and H. Fabian, "Further Investigations of the Laminar-Turbulent Transition in a Free Jet (Annular Nozzle)," Air Research and Development Command, U. S. Air Force, Contract No. AF 61(514)-915, December, 1956.

[4] R. Wille, "Growth of Velocity Fluctuations Leading to Turbulence in Free Shear Flow," AFOSR 5325, (Hermann Fottinger-Institut fur Stromungstechnik an der Technischen Universitat Berlin), June, 1963.

[5] R. C. Chanaud, and Alan Powell, "Experiments Concerning the Sound-Sensitive Jet," *Journal of the Accoustical Society of America*, Vol. 34, No. 7, July, 1962, pp. 907-915.

[6] S. Corrsin, "Investigation of Flow in an Axially Symmetrical Heated Jet of Air," NACA WTR W-94, December, 1943.

Laminar Versus Turbulent Separation of a Jet from a Curved Wall

M. Kadosch and A. Kirszenblat

Société Bertin & Cie
Plaisir, France

The attachment of a jet to a curved wall differs from the attachment to a straight wall in that there is no separation bubble. The curved wall effect has been calculated as an effect of the separation of the boundary layer along the wall, at least when the ratio $r/h < 10$ (r, radius of the curved wall; h, width of the nozzle) so that there exists a potential core. In ref [1] and [2], formulae are given both for laminar and turbulent boundary layers. The theory indicates an influence of the Reynolds number on the angle through which the jet is attached, and predicts that the curved wall effect should disappear in the laminar case. When the curved wall effect does not occur, the jet is attached through a small angle of about 20 degrees. The curved wall effect largely increases the angle beyond the treshold 20 degrees.

Fig. 1 and 2 are given in order to illustrate the influence of Reynolds Number. The boundary layer is laminar in Fig. 1 and turbulent in Fig. 2. The nature of the boundary layer is determined by numerous factors, among which the scale is perhaps the most important.

FIG. 1 SUBMERGED JET OF
WATER WITH LAMINAR
BOUNDARY LAYER
$h/r = 0.15$ $vh/\nu = 360$

FIG. 2 SUBMERGED JET OF
WATER WITH TURBU-
LENT BOUNDARY LAYER
$h/r = 0.15$ $vh/\nu = 1000$

References

[1] M. Kadosch, "Calculation of the separation of a jet attached to a convex wall" Proceedings of the Fluid Amplification Symposium, Vol. 1, October, 1965

[2] "The curved wall effect." Proceedings of the 2nd Cranfield Fluidics Conference, Cambridge, 2nd January, 1967.

Analytical Procedure for Predicting Performance of Single-Stage Momentum Exchange Proportional Amplifiers

F. J. Camarata

United Aircraft Research Laboratories
East Hartford, Connecticut

Abstract

An outline of an analytical procedure is presented for predicting the static operating characteristics of vented single-stage momentum exchange proportional amplifiers, the procedure being applicable for compressible as well as incompressible flow regimes. It is shown, by comparision of calculated and measured operating characteristics, that the performance of this type of amplifier can be predicted to a reasonable degree of accuracy.

Nomenclature

A	=	Area of surface having unit depth
D	=	Dump width
h	=	Receiver entrance width
h_{ex}	=	Receiver exit width
L	=	Distance between power jet nozzle exit and receiver entrance
M	=	Mach number
P	=	Static pressure
P_G	=	Pressure gain — slope of input-output pressure characteristic
P_T	=	Total pressure
S	=	Setback
U	=	Velocity
W	=	Nozzle width
$\mathring{w}$	=	Weight flow
X	=	Distance from power jet nozzle exit measured along axis of symmetry

87

X_C = Inviscid core length

X_D = Displacement of effective jet impingement point

y = Distance measured perpendicular to axis of symmetry

y^* = Distance from centerline of jet to point where velocity is half of the centerline velocity

y_C^* = Value of y^* at end of inviscid core

θ_C = Jet deflection angle calculated

θ_m = Measured jet deflection angle

Subscripts

0 = Conditions in vent region or no control flow

1 = Conditions pertaining to lower control nozzle or upper receiver

2 = Conditions pertaining to upper control or lower receiver

3, 4, 5 = Conditions at the boundary of the jet interaction region control volume (see Fig. 2)

ex = Conditions to which receiver is exhausting

FJ = Free jet

J = Power jet

R = Receiver

Superscript

$-$ = Stream thrust average

Introduction

The momentum-exchange type proportional amplifier was one of the first practical fluidic devices developed; yet to date, the design of an amplifier of this type to meet specific performance requirements generally entails a trial-and-error process. Such a design technique is neither efficient nor conducive to the attainment of optimum performance, and consequently, analytical design techniques which can be readily programmed for rapid machine computation are needed. It is the purpose of this note to present an outline of an analytical procedure which enables the static operating characteristics of a vented single-stage amplifier to be readily calculated for a wide range of flow conditions in the subsonic regime and variations in the basic geometry. A detailed description of this analysis is presented in [1].

Description of Procedure

The procedure, which is semiempirical in nature, is divided into two parts: (1) the treatment of the free jet flow including consideration of the interaction region and subsequent development of the resulting jet and (2) analysis of the receiver flow including the effect of the load impressed across the output of the amplifier. Nomenclature, as well as a general description of the amplifier geometry being treated, are illustrated in Figs. 1 and 2.

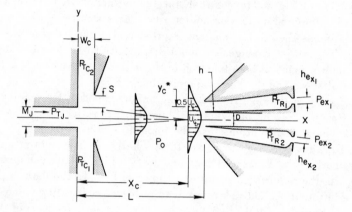

FIG. 1 – AMPLIFIER GEOMETRY AND NOMENCLATURE

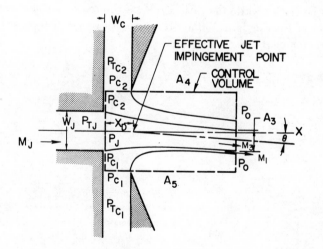

FIG. 2 – JET INTERACTION REGION FLOW MODEL

Free Jet Flow

The flow model used for the jet interaction region is presented in Fig. 2. The region considered is that in the immediate vicinity of the nozzle exits where viscous effects are relatively small and mixing of the three streams can be considered negligible. The jet deflection angle, θ, is determined by applying the principles of conservation of mass and momentum to the control volume shown in a manner similar to that suggested by Moynihan and Reilly [2] for incompressible flow. In employing the resulting relations it is assumed that the pressures $P_{T_{c_1}}$, $P_{T_{c_2}}$, P_{T_J}, and P_O are known a priori. The static pressures P_{C_1}, P_{C_2}, and P_J, as well as the pressure distribution along the surfaces A_4 and A_5 are evaluated from correlations of experimental data. The good correlation obtained between measured deflection angles and those calculated in this manner is illustrated in the upper portion of Fig. 3. In contrast, the lack of correlation between the measured and calculated deflection angles when the static pressure in the inter-action region is assumed to be constant is presented in the lower portion of the figure. The effective jet impingement point displacement, X_D, is also determined empirically and is found to be a function of the difference in momentum between the two control flows and the control port setback, S.

Characteristics of the resulting jet in the neighborhood of the receivers are determined from the free jet analysis of [3] modified to reflect the influence of the control jets. These modifications take the form of correction factors for altering the length of the inviscid core, X_C, and the jet half-velocity width at the end of the inviscid core, y_C^*. Values for these correction factors have been experimentally determined with the resulting correlations shown in Fig. 4. The data in this figure show the variation of X_C and y_C^* referenced to the corresponding values for no control flow (where $X_{C_0} \approx 0.9 X_{C_{FJ}}$, $y^*_{C_0} \approx 1.2 y^*_{FJ}$) as a function of the corre-

lation parameter $W_J/A_3 (1 - M_1/M_3)$. The term W_J/A_3 in this parameter reflects the throttling of the power jet while the ratio M_1/M_3 is related to the mixing rate be-- tween the control and power jets. Values for these ratios are determined from the jet interaction region analysis.

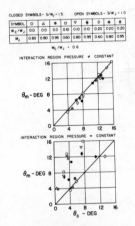

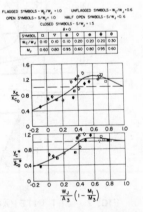

FIG. 3 – COMPARISON OF MEASURED
AND CALCULATED
JET DEFLECTION ANGLES

FIG. 4 – EFFECT OF CONTROL FLOW
ON INVISCID CORE
LENGTH AND JET
HALF-VELOCITY WIDTH

Receiver Flow

Receiver operating conditions are determined through an iterative procedure employing a diffuser source characteristic similar to that shown in Fig. 5. Such a characteristic is generated for both receivers at each jet deflection being considered. These characteristics are determined by (1) calculating the blocked load condition as described in [4], (2) determining the design point conditions (see Fig. 5) and the slope through the design point using stream thrust averaging and perturbation techniques detailed in [1], (3) fitting a parabola between the blocked load and design points, and (4) extending this curve linearly for weight flows greater than design. As shown by the data of Fig. 5, a very satisfactory representation of the desired characteristic can be obtained. The iterative procedure for evaluating the actual diffuser operating point is initiated by assuming a total pressure at the end of the receiver, $\bar{P}_{T_R}$ just upstream of the load impedance.

This pressure and the receiver source characteristic determine a receiver weight flow. This weight flow is compared with a corresponding value determined from the known receiver load impedance characteristic. The process is repeated until the two weight flows agree within acceptable limits.

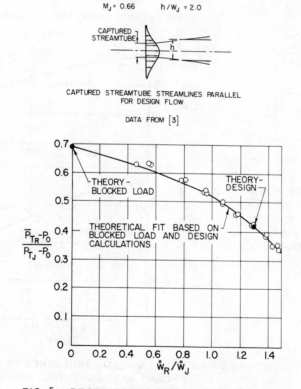

FIG. 5 – RECEIVER SOURCE CHARACTERISTIC

Typical Results and Comparison with Experiment

The data and curves of Fig. 6 show typical comparisons between calculated and measured amplifier performance characteristics for a fixed output load. A similar comparison between calculated and measured pressure gains and maximum output pressure differences over a wide range of output loads is presented in Fig. 7. From these and similar comparisons not presented herein, it has been shown that the procedure predicts performance of single-stage vented proportional amplifiers to a reasonable degree of accuracy. The procedure can also be used to synthesize fluidic systems using these amplifiers.

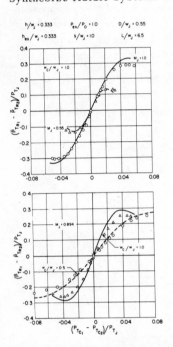

FIG. 6 – EFFECT OF POWER
JET MACH NUMBER AND
CONTROL PORT WIDTH
ON AMPLIFIER
PERFORMANCE

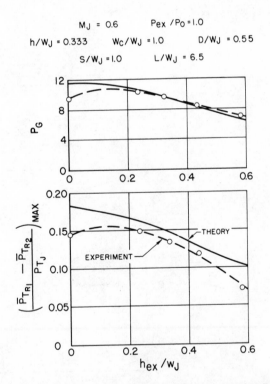

FIG. 7 – EFFECT OF LOAD IMPEDANCE ON PRESSURE
GAIN AND MAXIMUM OUTPUT PRESSURE
DIFFERENCE

References

[1] F. J. Camarata, "Analytical Procedure for Predicting Performance of Single-Stage Momentum Exchange Proportional Amplifiers." UARL Report F110117-1, January 1967.

[2] F. A. Moynihan and R. J. Reilly, "Deflection and Relative Flow of Three Interacting Jets." Proceedings of Harry Diamond Laboratories Fluid Amplification Symposium, Washington, D.C. May, 1964.

[3] R. E. Olson and D. P. Miller, "Aerodynamic Studies of Free and Attached Jets." UARL Report A-1771-24, December 1963.

[4] R. E. Olson and F. J. Camarata, "Pressure Recovery Characteristics of Compressible Two-Dimensional Free Jet Flows." Proceedings of Harry Diamond Laboratories Fluid Amplification Symposium, Washington, D.C., October 1965.

Effect of Aspect Ratio on Noise in Proportional Fluid Amplifiers

Sanford D. Weinger

Harry Diamond Laboratories
Washington, D.C.

Introduction

As the field of fluerics has progressed, it has become increasingly obvious that noise, in the form of turbulence, limits the use of no-moving-parts analog fluid devices. This brief describes an experimental investigation of noise in jet-deflection-type proportional fluid amplifiers as a function of the aspect ratio (height divided by width) of the power jet. Aspect ratios from ½ to 7 were tested for noise properties at power jet pressures of 1.7 to 34.5 kilo-newtons/meter^2 (¼ to 5 psig).

Experiment

The experiment was conducted on an HDL proportional fluid amplifier shown in Fig. 1. The aspect ratio was changed by installing cut-out plates of various heights between the cover plates. A constant-temperature hot-wire anemometer measured the mean velocity U and root-mean-square velocity $\sqrt{\overline{u^2}}$ at the output of the amplifier. The anemometer output was connected to a spectrum analyzer. The hot-wire probe was located in the center of the right channel by means of a micrometer movement. From these measurements, the turbulence intensity I can be calculated by

$$I = \frac{\sqrt{\overline{u^2}}}{U}.$$

The turbulence intensity was measured for eleven power-jet pressures and six aspect ratios. All turbulence measurements were made with the amplifier unloaded.

The turbulence intensity measurements are shown in Fig. 2. Plotted is the percentage of turbulence (100 I) versus the power-jet pressure for the various aspect ratios (AR). Three general trends can be observed. First, the smaller aspect ratios show a much greater percentage variation in percentage of turbulence with low

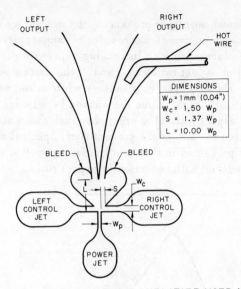

FIG. 1 – PROPORTIONAL AMPLIFIER USED IN
ASPECT RATIO STUDIES

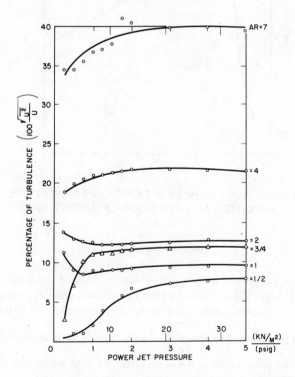

FIG. 2 – PERCENTAGE OF TURBULENCE AS A FUNCTION
OF POWER JET PRESSURE FOR ASPECT RATIOS
FROM ½ TO 7

95

power-jet pressures. Second, at higher pressures, the percentage of turbulence is approximately constant with pressure changes, for all aspect ratios. Third, the peak percentage of turbulence increases with increasing aspect ratio. The curves exhibit some inconsistencies. For aspect ratios of 1 and 2, the percentage of turbulence initially decreases with rising power jet pressures while it increases for the other aspect ratios. These initially high values are caused by jet-edge oscillations. Also, the values for an aspect ratio of ¾ are higher than those at an aspect ratio of 1. There is no explanation for this at the present time. Spectral data of the turbulence in the output (not presented in this brief) have shown that the high-frequency noise components are reduced with reduction in aspect ratio.

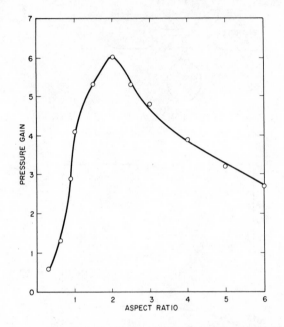

FIG. 3 – PRESSURE GAIN OF A TYPICAL PROPORTIONAL
AMPLIFIER AS A FUNCTION OF ASPECT RATIO

Discussion

The data may be expressed as a signal-to-noise ratio. A convenient definition is given in Refs. [1] and [2] where it is found that, to a good approximation, the pressure-amplitude signal-to-noise ratio at the entrance of a point (infinitely small) receiver is $\dfrac{1}{2I}$. The turbulence intensity can be easily measured with a hot wire anemomenter. Let us then define a noise coefficient N to be measured at the output of a fluid amplifier as,

$$N = 2I.$$

Such a coefficient would be a meaningful indication of the noise in fluid amplifiers. It is obviously desirable to lower the noise of proportional fluid amplifiers.

However, an improved signal-to-noise ratio is not obtained without paying a price; in this case, a reduction in gain. Fig. 3 (Ref. [3]) is a typical curve of the variation of pressure gain with aspect ratio. Experimental data, taken on a proportional amplifier loaded by an identical amplifier, show that the pressure gain is almost insensitive to the power jet pressure but varies with aspect ratio. In particular, the gain falls off rapidly below an aspect ratio of 2. This, as was noted in the previous section, is also the range in which the turbulence intensity becomes a function of power-jet pressure and assumes very small values at low pressures. For these reasons, it is necessary to define a figure of merit to enable determination of the gain that can be traded for a reduction in noise. One possible definition is

$$f_{gn} = \frac{G_p}{N}$$

where

$$f_{gn} = \text{gain-noise figure of merit}$$

$$N = \text{noise coefficient}$$

$$G_p = \text{pressure gain}$$

An important design goal is the modification of the geometry of the proportional amplifier to obtain reasonable gains at low aspect ratios and power-jet pressures while yielding a low noise coefficient. This could lead to a very substantial improvement in performance.

References

[1] R. N. Gottron, and S. D. Weinger, "Parameters Affecting the Noise in No-Moving-Parts Fluid Devices," HDL TR-1283, April 1965.

[2] D. W. Prosser, and M. J. Fisher, "Some Influences of Turbulence On the Noise of Proportional Fluid Amplifiers," Fluid Amplification Symposium, Vol. 2, October 1965.

[3] R. W. Von Tilburg, and W. L. Cochron, "Development of a Proportional Fluid Amplifier for Multi-Stage Operation," Fluid Amplification Symposium, Vol. 2, May 1964.

The Impact of Opposing Axially Symmetric Jets

Kenneth W. Misevich

Johnson Service Company
507 East Michigan Street
Milwaukee, Wisconsin

Abstract

A variety of techniques are employed to both qualitatively and quantitatively characterize the mechanisms involved in the impact of small axisymmetric jets. Precision small diameter nozzles are used initially to formulate an empirical flow coefficient which can be used to predict the subsonic mass flow in the whole class of uniform throat, circular nozzles. Then the impact situation is considered for broad ranges of geometry and pressure to ultimately yield a composite of the impact effects and to form a basis for a simple impact position model.

Nomenclature

a = speed of sound, in./min (8.2×10^5 in./min at 75 F)

C = flow coefficient

D = nozzle diameter, in.

D_o = plenum chamber diameter, in.

D_s = stagnation core diameter, in.

k = ratio of specific heats

L_f = free jet potential flow core length, in.

L_i = impacting jet core length, in.

p = pressure, psig

P = ratio of absolute nozzle exit pressure to plenum chamber pressure

Q = volume flow, in.^{3}/min

U = mainstream velocity, in./min

z = axial coordinate, in.

δ = boundary layer thickness, in.

δ^* = displacement thickness, in.

ρ = mass density, lb-f min^2/in.^{4}

ρ_a = 31.2 x 10^{-12} lb-f min^2/in.^{4}

ϕ = half angle expansion for pressure degradation model

Subscripts

a = atmospheric condition at 75 F

o = plenum chamber condition

Introduction

Nozzle flow and jet impingement have been studied for years, with the consequent evolution of elegant theories [1, 2, 3]. But while a myriad of the phenomena have been handled very nicely, the typical compressible flow problem quickly develops into an untractable mathematical exercise often with undetermined boundary conditions. Thus experiment is the recourse with the adaption to theory following the synthesis of simplified models which eventually become well understood. Such is the case of the impacting air jets.

In this paper the work is restricted to subsonic turbulent flow of axially symmetric nozzles under the conditions of free flow and under direct impact with an identical stream in an unbounded medium. The experimental investigation is then taken in the spirit of determining the essential effects, correlation of mechanisms, and, finally prediction of the impact characteristics.

Using three sizes of small axially symmetric nozzles (.007 in., .016 in., and .025 in. diameter) as test objects, the initial goal is the accurate determination of their free mass flow. To this end the empirical flow coefficient of the adiabatic flow equation is formulated as an analytical function of pressure and geometry. But since the test geometry is specific, other designs are inspected in their generalized form to extend the usefulness to the whole class of circular nozzles with a uniform throat.

Next the impact situation is investigated over broad ranges of the independent variables in several ways: hot wire anemometry, the pitot tube, water simulation, and smoke visualization. Selection of the significant information of the experiments of each method allows the formation of a composite phenomenon which is, indeed, beautifully complex.

With the qualitative features of the impacting streams in mind, the concept of an impact core length is introduced and verified by the measurement of the axial pressure degradation of the impacting jet. Finally, a simple impact model based on total pressure balance at the impact position is shown to be in good agreement with experiment.

Nozzle Flow and the Free Jet

Nozzle Flow. The accurate prediction of the mass flow of a small nozzle has always been an annoying problem when a real viscous fluid such as air is involved. While the adiabatic flow equation [4, 5] does a good job for inviscid potential flow, boundary layer formation can reduce the flow significantly from the ideal. Thus the mass flow, which can be written in the following convenient form

$$\rho_a Q = \frac{k}{a_o} \left(\frac{2}{k-1}\right)^{\frac{1}{2}} \left(\frac{\pi D^2}{4}\right) P_o \left[P^{\frac{2}{k}} - P^{\frac{k+1}{k}} \middle/ 1 - P^{\frac{2}{k}} \left(\frac{D}{D_o}\right)^4 \right]^{\frac{1}{2}}$$

(1)

must be reduced by a factor commonly called the flow coefficient, C. This flow coefficient must be found experimentally for a given nozzle geometry and operating pressure.

Now when the flow coefficient is viewed as an effective reduction of the nozzle area due to the existence of an annular boundary layer, further insight can be gained. Using Schlicting's approximation of the boundary layer thickness, δ, and the displacement thickness, δ^*, one can speak of equivalent flow [6]. That is, the annular ring of zero equivalent flow is about $\delta/3$ thick and is called the displacement thickness. Noting that the effective flow by definition passes through an area of diameter $C^{\frac{1}{2}}D$, one can relate C to δ^* by

$$C = \left(1 - \frac{2\delta^*}{D}\right)^2$$

(2)

Since δ^* is roughly proportional to $U^{-\frac{1}{2}}$, it is clear that C should increase with both the nozzle diameter and pressure differential. But to find the exact functional dependence from theory is unnecessarily complex as compared to simply measuring the flow of some standard test nozzles of well known geometry.

For this purpose, then, a set of precision, geometrically similar, nozzles were constructed from brass with diameters of 0.007 in., 0.016 in., and 0.025 in. The design, as shown in Fig. 1, is based on the same reasoning used by Williams and Smetana [7]. That is, an entrance contraction of a $2D$ radius provides a $5D$ plenum chamber diameter for negligible approach velocities, and it compromises the boundary layer and centrifugal effects. The throat length was limited to $2D$ for no other reason than satisfactory fabrication of the 0.007 in. diameter nozzles.

In determining the flow coefficients, the diameters of the three best nozzles of each size were measured to within 0.00005 in. optically, and then their flows to atmospheric pressure were found. Equation 1 was employed to tabulate C as a function of pressure ratio as shown in Fig. 2. Also shown are the linear graphical approximations empirically given by:

$$C = 1.0 - (0.29 - 6.3\ D)P$$

(3)

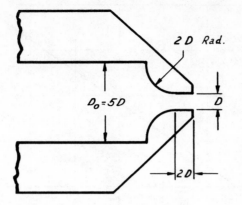

FIG. 1 TEST NOZZLE DESIGN

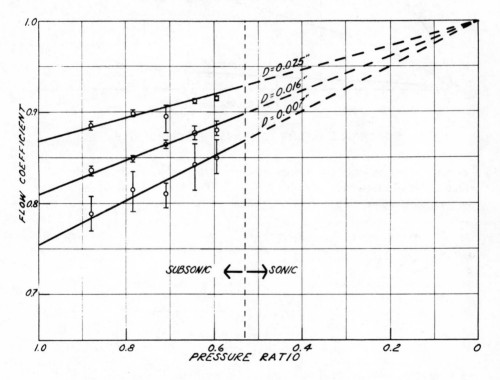

FIG. 2 NOZZLE FLOW COEFFICIENTS

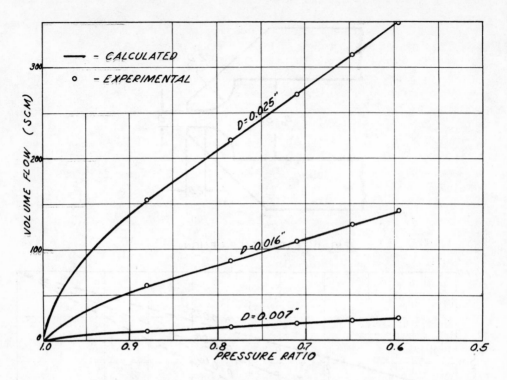

FIG. 3 NOZZLE FLOW TO ATMOSPHERIC PRESSURE

For clarity, examples of the agreement of the experimental and calculated standard volume flows are provided in Fig. 3. The completed flow equation in the form of standard volume flow to atmospheric pressure is

$$Q = \left[\frac{k}{a_o \rho_a} \left(\frac{2}{k-1}\right)^{\frac{1}{2}}\right] \left[1.0 - (0.29 - 6.3D)P\right] \frac{\pi D^2}{4}$$

$$X \quad P_o \left[\frac{P^{\frac{2}{k}} - P^{\frac{k+1}{k}}}{1 - P^{\frac{2}{k}} \left(\frac{D}{D_o}\right)^4}\right]^{\frac{1}{2}} \tag{4}$$

This equation has predicted to within 2% the test nozzle flows for $0.6 \leq P \leq 0.95$ and, also, for downstream pressures from atmospheric to 10 psig. In addition, the absolute error for $0.95 \leq P \leq 1.0$ will be very small. On the other hand, the empirical flow coefficient diverges from observations in the sonic flow range, but still provides an upper bound to the flow with a maximum error of 10 per cent.

The accuracy has also been verified for a wide selection of nozzle geometries. No correction is required if the throat length is one to three diameters, but thereafter, a reduction in flow very close to 1 per cent per diameter increase occurs at least up to seven diameters total length. Errors arising in any reasonably contoured contraction will not exceed one per cent, and with even a sharp edged entrance, a flow reduction of not more than 5-7 per cent has been observed. From

102

comparison to molded plastic nozzles it has been proven that the combination of channel roughness and exit geometry will not cause errors in excess of one or two per cent. Finally, the equation can reasonably be extended to nozzles greater than 0.025 in. in diameter with very little deviation. Then Equation 4 is, in fact, capable of accurately predicting the subsonic flow for the whole class of axially symmetric nozzles. While not rigorously developed, it is nonetheless a practical equation which does not require further experimental determination of the flow coefficient.

The Free Jet. Attention now can be turned to the jet which issues from such nozzles, in particular, to a turbulent stream exiting with a potential flow core and a thin annular boundary layer. As is well known, the centerline velocity of the jet will be maintained for a certain distance — the core length — before it begins to degrade. The stream then proceeds through a transitional mixing region until the velocity profile is fully developed.

While the literature is filled with the theory of jet development through the velocity profile, one is always confronted with constants which must be found empirically. The two primary ones are the core length and the expansion angle. Unfortunately the former is not constant and indeed is a rather strong function of the nozzle pressure for subsonic flow. As will be seen later, the core length is basic to the consideration of impacting jets; thus it demands some analytical approximation.

The hot film anemometer becomes an efficient tool in this endeavor, since axial profiles (see Appendix) of the stream along the centerline indicate the onset of degradation in most cases. But to avoid ambiguity additional profiles were taken at 0.001 in. radial intervals out to the nozzle diameter. The surface of the core is very nearly conical, so these additional profiles always allowed the interpolation of doubtful points. Fig. 4 shows the results of the core length measurements for the three nozzle sizes along with the graphical approximation given empirically by:

$$L_f = \left[30(P - .528)^{2.4} + 2.25\right] D \tag{5}$$

The second constant, the expansion angle, does not appear in the literature with sufficient accuracy to avoid its measurement, particularly for jets of such small sizes. Since absolute velocity measurements become nearly impossible with a hot film for flows which are non-uniform over the sensitive length of the sensor, meaningful velocity profiles cannot be acquired. But an alternative method has yielded a lucid picture of the expansion characteristics of the free jet. Radial profiles of the r.m.s. turbulence intensity at successive axial stations effectively outlines a 0.025 in. diameter stream and shows a nearly constant expansion half angle of nearly 6 degrees out to an axial length of at least seven nozzle diameters (Fig. 5).

The important results here are that a sharp turbulence profile is generated on the circumference of the nozzle and that the peak intensity propagates along the expansion cone. While the amplitudes of the turbulence intensities were measured only relatively, it is clear that the turbulence amplitude significantly increases with both the exit velocity of the stream, and its progression downstream. Further, the turbulence intensity distribution spreads symmetrically about the expansion cone. Finally, it should be noted that the turbulence intensity is related to the core length and the mixing region of the free jet. Qualitatively one can say that the centerline flow does not experience macroscopic turbulence until the turbulence profile spreads to the axis, and then the well known mixing region constitutes the development of this annular turbulence distribution to the point where the velocity profiles enter the region of self-sustaining similarity.

However scant, this experimental picture of the free jet will later be seen to be consistent with the impact phenomena. To pursue this matter further extensive literature is available [8-9].

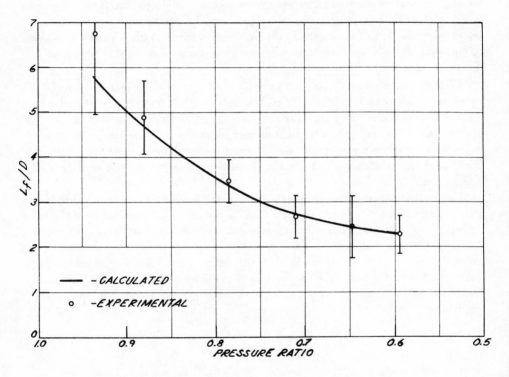

FIG. 4 FREE JET POTENTIAL FLOW CORE LENGTH

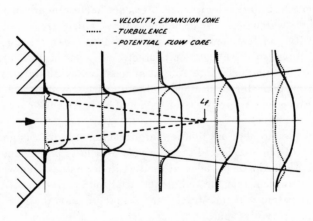

FIG. 5 SCHEMATIC OF A FREE JET

With the broad aspects of the free jet in mind, consider now the situation where the stream impinges normally on a flat surface or an identical opposing stream. If the stream were of an incompressible fluid, it is obvious that at the first instant of impact the stream would like to stagnate completely. But the jet is unbounded so the flow redistributes itself to satisfy the energy, momentum, and mass conservation laws. The stagnation effects in a compressible viscous fluid represent some of the most complex mechanisms in fluid dynamics and are, consequently, not well known. At the outset, therefore, one must be satisfied with simply putting the problems into perspective and estimate the magnitude of the observable phenomena.

The Stagnation Core. Suppose a flat circular plate of about stream diameter is placed normal and concentric to the stream axis at a very large distance from the nozzle face. What will happen as the impact distance is decreased? At what point will the emerging jet experience some change due to the presence of the impact? The first measurable change near the nozzle, as determined by radial velocity profiles with a 0.0001 in. hot wire anemometer, occurs at an impact distance of about seven to ten diameters from the nozzle face. Here the annular boundary layer begins to narrow, but with a steeper velocity gradient, and the velocity of the entrained air consequently increases. The rate of these changes can generally be described as monotonically increasing with further reduction in the impact distance.

It is usually assumed that stagnation effects are not transmitted upstream to any extent. The supporting argument is that there is no variation in the total nozzle flow until the impact is very near the nozzle, one half to one quarter of a nozzle diameter, and until the continuity law demands a flow reduction. However, upstream stagnation has been observed at much greater impact distances repeatedly throughout this investigation.

There is really only one way that stagnation and flow maintenance can be reconciled, but it does not become apparent until the stagnation region near the impact is considered in more detail. First note that the "stagnation region" is roughly conical in shape, extending back upstream from the impact, and is not completely stagnated until the impact is moved to within a characteristic length from the nozzle. Here the flow begins to stagnate in a small axisymmetric area whose diameter, at the nozzle, has a definite limit until the impact position is actually moved close enough to cause a reduction in total flow. The limiting area has been shown to be just equal to the annular displacement thickness area mentioned before. Thus the limiting diameter, D_s, of this stagnation core can be written as a function of the flow coefficient:

$$D_s = D \sqrt{1-C} \qquad (6)$$

This relationship has been shown through experiment to be valid for the subsonic flow range of interest here, and for all three nozzle sizes.

In other words, as the impact position is moved toward the nozzle, the displacement thickness of the circumferential boundary layer decreases, and an inner annular boundary layer forms. As the impact approaches the limiting distance

105

where flow reduction must occur, the entire nozzle flow is annular about the stagnation core and has two very sharp boundary layers.

When the case of impacting jets is considered, there is further evidence compelling the acknowledgment of a core of at least partial stagnation at the nozzle for greater impact distances. It has been found that any physical penetration of one of the impacting streams near its nozzle, does not affect the axial balance position of the radial impact jet until this core is touched. Thus it appears that the balance of the jets is not upset until the stagnation core is disrupted at its boundary.

Fig. 6 schematically summarizes this core structure in the stream. Note also that the peak of the turbulence intensity is definitely deflected as it approaches the impact position.

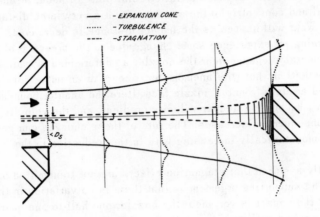

FIG. 6 SCHEMATIC OF AN IMPACTING JET

The Radial Jet. It would now be appropriate to look at the gross characteristics of the impacting jets. The radial impact jet can be visualized satisfactorily by impinging a 0.025 in. diameter smoke jet on an identical air jet at about a 6 psig upstream stagnation pressure, and a six diameter gap between nozzles. A sequence of photographs as the impact is moved toward the air nozzle (Fig. 7) shows that it becomes progressively less defined. The reason is found in the impact interface. As the stagnation core builds up in the air jet, the effect of the annular flow is seen as an apparent penetration of the smoke into the air stream. This flow is decisive in disrupting the radial jet and actually cupping it away from the nozzle.

To get to the interesting and, as of now, unexplained characteristics of the impacting streams, we must turn to another visualization method. Impacting water jets dramatically exaggerate the hypersensitivity of low pressure impact and the standing undulations which have been observed a number of times with hot wire and pitot tube probing of the equivalent air streams. Overall, the radial jet, which is extremely sharp and well-defined at low pressures, tends to become increasingly turbulent as the nozzle pressure increases. However, at low pressures in the laminar flow range, the position of the impact is hypersensitive to pressure fluctuations; therefore, it oscillates between nozzles. Fig. 8 vividly portrays this for water at about 0.5 psig pressure issuing from 0.007 in. nozzles. To stabilize

Δp = 0.0 psig

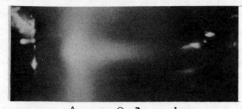

Δp = 0.1 psig

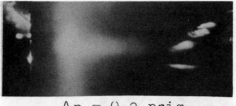

Δp = 0.2 psig

Δp = 0.3 psig

Δp = 0.4 psig

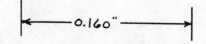

FIG. 7 SEQUENCE OF SMOKE VISUALIZED RADIAL JET

the impact position the pressure differential between nozzles can be increased until the radial jet is pinned to one of the nozzles as shown in Fig. 9. As the gap or pressure level is increased, however, a stable position away from the nozzle, even to the center of the gap, is realizable.

Thus the radial jet is actually well defined only in the flow range where the sensitivity to pressure fluctuation is small and the pressure level of the jets is still not so great as to begin turbulent disruptions. This sharp radial jet prevails in the 4 to 8 psig pressure range for air.

The most fascinating of the impact phenomena, however, is the standing undulation present in the impacting stream. To illustrate, Fig. 10 depicts a case where a low pressure water stream completely overcomes the other. Note that the undulations exhibit a characteristic length and the amplitude is damped from a pronounced contraction near the impact to a negligible ripple upstream. As the pressure increases both the amplitude and characteristic length decrease. (Refer back to Fig. 9). At higher pressure levels, the undulations are compressed and made visible if the radial jet is moved near one of the nozzles as shown in Figs. 11 and 12.

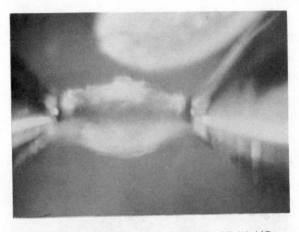

FIG. 8 UNSTABLE WATER JET IMPACT IN AIR

FIG. 9 STABLE WATER JET IMPACT IN AIR

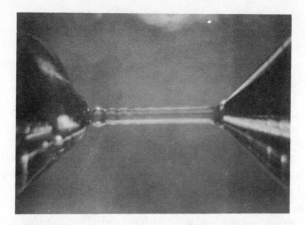

FIG. 10 LOW PRESSURE STANDING UNDULATIONS

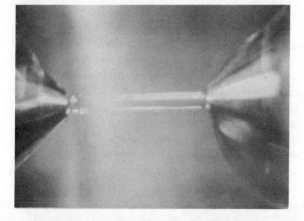

FIG. 11 RADIAL WATER JET IN AIR

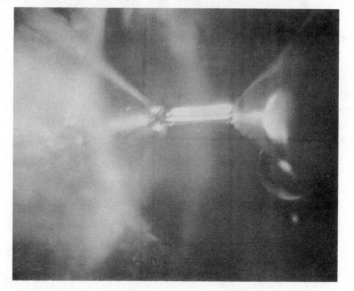

FIG. 12 OBLIQUE VIEW OF RADIAL WATER JET IN AIR

109

For air, this effect has been observed both as static pressure peaks with pitot tubes and as velocity undulations with the hot film anemometer. It is evidenced at higher pressure levels as step changes in impact position when the radial jet is moved near a nozzle and, also, as an axial undulation in the collected dynamic pressure of a single stream. That it has not been observed in larger nozzles may be an indication that it is related to the annular flow due to the stagnation core. But there has not yet been sufficient study to postulate the mechanism.

The Impact Position. As with many experimental investigations, initial observations of the impact phenomena led to several misinterpretations of the data. Because of the very high sensitivity of the impact position to pressure differential of the jets, the only way the impact position could be found as a function of pressure was to hold a hot film probe at a known axial position, sufficiently far from the stream centerline so as not to interact with the jet, and then sweep the radial jet past it while recording the pressure differential. The pressure differential at the peak anemometer output determines a single point on the pressure-position curve, for a single geometry, and for a single pressure level of the nozzles. An extensive test series finally showed only that the impact position pressure sensitivity was a very strong non-linear function of pressure level and nozzle gap. The sensitivity increases markedly with a decrease in either. It was not known for some time thereafter that there were two distinct impact situations.

Smoke visualization first provided an indication that for some conditions of pressure and geometry the impact position was unstable in the central portion of the gap. Efforts to balance the jets at the exact center led to axial oscillation. However, as the pressure level or gap was increased the amplitude of oscillation was reduced to zero and the radial jet could be placed anywhere.

Since the existence of a potential flow core in a free jet was known, it was thought to be reasonable that the high sensitivity region on the axis was due to an effective overlap of core lengths, and, in addition, that the impact movement past the end of the "impact core length" should be related to the degradation of the axial velocity or total stream pressure in a hypothetical stream cylinder. A determination of the extent of the high sensitivity and bounding low sensitivity regions as a function of pressure and geometry was then required.

Development of the Impact Model

By using the hot film anemometer as an indicator of the position of the radial jet, the pressure differential between nozzles (up to 0.25 psi) was found for the impact position at small intervals for every stable position within the gap. The experiment was performed for all nozzle sizes, at 2,4,6,8, and 10 psig to atmospheric flow, and for gaps of 4,5, and 6 diameters. The high sensitivity region was immediately discernible and its axial range, indeed, seemed to suggest an overlap of some core length. Some of the values of the high sensitivities were tabulated but will not be discussed here. Attention is focused on the range itself and on the low sensitivity regions at its ends.

From the shape of the pressure-position curves of some of the initial data it was fairly obvious that the pressure differential for change in impact position was given by something like

$$\Delta p \; \alpha \; \Delta z^2 \qquad\qquad (7)$$

110

in the low sensitivity region. Though the proportionality constants were fitted, they were erratic and only hinted at possible pressure and geometry dependences.

Going on the assumption that the impact position is indeed a condition of total pressure balance of the two streams, the investigation turned to the measurement of the axial dynamic pressure or total momentum flux.

Pressure Degradation of the Impacting Streams. If it is noted that the diameter of the face of each test nozzle is always twice as large as its orifice diameter (Fig. 1) then it is clear that collecting a test jet with a like, or smaller, nozzle simulates an impact condition. This method is satisfactory because the radial gradients of the axial velocity within a hypothetical cylinder of the initial stream diameter are small and relatively free of turbulence. As it turns out, collecting a 0.025 in. diameter stream with any of the three nozzle sizes results in practically the same axial pressure profile. The total pressure collected by a like nozzle is less than that collected by the smaller diameter nozzles.

In this investigation the jet of each test nozzle was impacted on the smallest .007 in. diameter nozzle. Thus the stream saw an effective .014 in. diameter flat plate with a concentric .007 in. diameter collector orifice. The axial profiles of the collected total pressure are very similar for the .016 in. and .025 in. streams when the axial coordinate, z, is normalized to the respective stream diameter. The collected pressure of the 0.007 in. jet appears to degrade more rapidly, but it was collected by a nozzle identical to itself. Also, the alignment tolerances are more severe for such a small stream and collector combination.

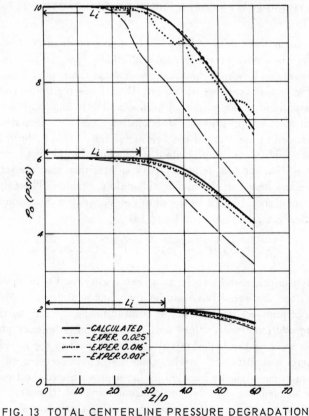

FIG. 13 TOTAL CENTERLINE PRESSURE DEGRADATION
IN AN IMPACTING JET

111

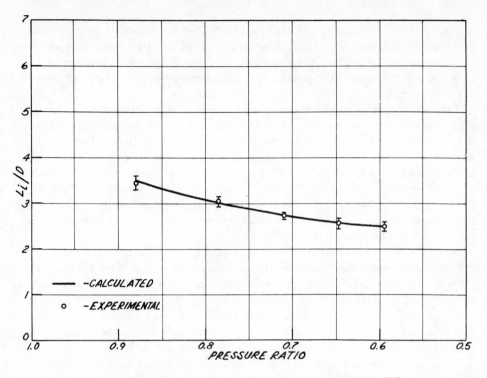

FIG. 14 EFFECTIVE CORE LENGTH OF AN IMPACTING JET

Consider the normalized data of Fig. 13. In a poor analogue to the core length of a free jet, there is a characteristic impact distance from the nozzle face, at each pressure level, up to which the total pressure at the impact is only negligibly less than the supply pressure of the jet. By exhaustive inspection of these profiles and comparison to the ranges of high sensitivity impact, it was verified that the onset of stream total pressure degradation under the simulated conditions closely corresponded to the start of the low sensitivity impact. Here, this axial distance for the condition of negligible degradation of total pressure at the impact is called the "impact core length". It is shorter than the free jet core length at low pressures and longer at the higher subsonic pressures. The empirical equation resulting from a graphical fit to the data can be written in a form similar to Equation 5 for the free jet. (See Fig. 4 and 14)

$$L_i = \left[8.0(P - 0.528)^2 + 2.47\right]D \qquad (8)$$

This equation is presented merely as a practicality, and without comment, so that the onset of the low sensitivity can be specified analytically. More important here is the rate of pressure degradation as related to the impact position.

Pressure Degradation Model. Since both viscous and turbulence stresses appear to be rather weak in the hypothetical stream cylinder of the nozzle diameter for impact distances significantly greater than the impact core length, it was presumed that the problem might be handled as incompressible to the first approximation. An *ad hoc* assumption then defined a stream cross section area of the initial jet diameter, and at the impact core length, expanding thereafter so as to con-

112

serve the total stagnation force. A mechanism need not be specified. The total pressure is simply viewed as degrading with a corresponding increase in area. If the small degradation out to the impact core length is neglected, then the total axial pressure, p, within this area can be related to supply pressure of the jet, p_o, by

$$p_o \frac{\pi D^2}{4}\Big|_{z = L_i} = p \frac{\pi}{4}(D + 2(z - L_i)\tan \varphi)^2 \qquad z \geq L_i$$

(9)

where the area on the right is the expanding cross section.

Using the data of Fig. 13, the $\tan \phi$ was calculated for every half diameter along the axis for every case. It fits remarkably well to

$$\tan \varphi = 0.009(z - L_i) / D \qquad (10)$$

Offering no explanation, Equation (10) can be substituted into Equation (9) to arrive at

$$p = p_o \left[1.0 + 0.018 \frac{(z-L_i)^2}{D^2}\right]^{-2} \qquad (11)$$

which is also graphed in Fig. 13 for comparison to the data. Note that for small $(z-L_i)$ Equation (11) can be put into the form of Equation (7).

Impact Position Model. Now assume that the turbulent boundary layer of the impacting jet, and its state of stagnation are superfluous to the problem. Consider that the impact position for identical opposing streams is predominately determined by a total pressure balance in a cylinder of the nozzle diameters, D.

The impact position can be calculated by applying Equation (11) to both streams when the impact core lengths do not overlap. For small gaps where the cores do overlap, giving rise to a high sensitivity region, the stream pressure of the nozzle nearest the impact is constant, of course. Since the pressure differential between nozzles is less than 0.25 psi for the experimental conditions, the impact core lengths, as given by Equation (8), are taken as constant and equal for each operating pressure level.

Upon computation, good correlation to the experimental data was achieved. While there were a few small discrepancies in the starting points of the low sensitivity regions, the hypothesis of an effective impact core length is essentially proven. The predictions of the low sensitivity impact positions also show that they are definitely determined by a total pressure balance.

In particular, the 0.016 in. and 0.025 in. stream impacts are in very good agreement with the model, where the 0.007 in. data has a trend of divergence with increasing impact pressures. To illustrate, consider Fig. 15 for which the data of the smallest gap, four nozzle diameters, will serve as examples of the perform-

113

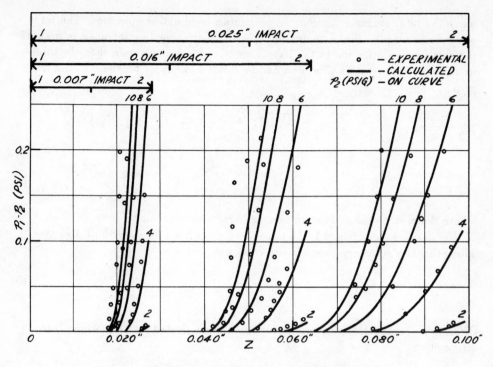

FIG. 15 COMPARISON OF IMPACT POSITION MODEL
TO EXPERIMENT

ances of each nozzle size. The only changes in the impact characteristics for the larger gaps are a slight reduction in the position pressure sensitivity and the obvious diminution of the high sensitivity range as the overlap of cores is decreased.

This graph presents only half of the impact position curve because of symmetry. Thus the high sensitivity range at each pressure is given by twice the distance from the center of each nozzle gap to the onset of the low sensitivity.

Note that the 0.007 in. stream impact clearly shows divergence of the model and experiment. Though the lower observed sensitivity is in accord with the axial pressure profiles of Fig. 13, there is a violation of the assumptions in the model. Namely, it was assumed that the radial velocity gradients are negligible within the original stream diameter, and this does not appear to be strictly valid for the smaller stream diameters.

On the whole, however, one can see that the model is satisfactory.

Concluding Remarks

The impact phenomenon has been carried through from the basic free jet flow to a final impact position model which correlates to the experimental observations. Along the way, an empirical equation was determined for the flow coefficient and when related to the displacement thickness of the exiting jet, it describes the limiting area of stream stagnation at the nozzle for impacting conditions.

The intimacies of the impact structure and the nozzle geometry clearly indicate new boundary conditions for compressible flow problems. Similarly, the ex-

114

istence of the condition of an effective impact core length may offer new insight into stagnation and degradation mechanisms, especially in light of the observed turbulence intensities. Since detail is sacrificed here for a composite presentation, it is hoped that the description of the gross impact characteristics justifies the approach. This is certainly just another case of a complex fluid flow problem being specified empirically and then approximated by simple models, but it does provide sufficient information to form an adequate base for further theoretical study.

References

[1] A. H. Shapiro, *Compressible Fluid Flow*, (Vol. I; New York: The Ronald Press Co., 1953).

[2] Pai Shih-I, *Fluid Dynamics of Jets*, (New York: D. Van Nostrand Co., Inc., 1954).

[3] Victor L. Streeter, (ed.), *Handbook of Fluid Dynamics*, (New York: McGraw-Hill Book Co., Inc., 1961).

[4] G. V. Kreinin, "Determining the Air Flow in a Complex Pneumatic System," *Automation and Remote Control*, XXV (July, 1964), pp. 1010-15.

[5] Victor L. Streeter, *Fluid Mechanics*, (New York: McGraw-Hill Book Co., Inc., 1950), p. 101.

[6] H. Schlicting, *Boundary Layer Theory*, (New York: McGraw-Hill Book Co., Inc., 1960).

[7] J. C. Williams, III, and F. O. Smetana, "Theoretical Study of a Convergent Nozzle and Free Jet Flow," *Proceedings of the Fluid Amplification Symposium*, (Vol. 1; Washington, D.C.: Harry Diamond Laboratories, October, 1965).

[8] J. O. Hinze, *Turbulence*, (New York: McGraw-Hill Book Co., Inc., 1959).

[9] P. Bradshaw, "The Effect of Initial Conditions on the Development of a Free Shear Layer," *J. Fl. Mech.*, XXVI, Part 2, (October, 1966).

Appendix

Experimental Apparatus and Procedure. The fundamental tool of this investigation was the hot film anemometer, a 0.001 in. diameter sensor with a sensitive length of about 0.010 in. and an overall support length of 0.050 in. The non-linear output of a Thermo-Systems, Model 1000A, anemometer was employed to observe only the peak velocities of the radial jets, the relative stream velocities, and relative r.m.s. turbulence. Quantitative velocity measurements of flows which are non-linear over the sensor length are meaningless.

All geometries were measured optically and all coordinate positions determined by employing a versatile support fixture. The nozzles, set with a fixed geometry, were mounted on a two-dimensional micrometer table and then the probe was introduced externally with a third degree of freedom. Since all three coordinate positions could be measured continuously with linear variable differential transformers, accurate position specification was achieved by measuring only relative distances from optically determined reference points. Because of the precision (±0.0001 in. tolerances) nozzle holder and the described technique, cumulative errors in nozzle alignment and relative coordinate measurement did not exceed ±0.0005 in.

Pressures were measured with validated Magnehelic gauges and Statham pressure transducers.

The prime flow measuring instruments were Brook's Vol-U-Meter Flow Rate Calibrators (Models 1052 and 1057) and a validated Meriam Model 30EB25 Mercury Manometer.

Pressure Gain Analysis of an Impacting Jet Amplifier Stage

Silas Katz

Harry Diamond Laboratories
Washington, D. C.

Abstract

The impact stage of impacting jet amplifiers is analyzed. The amplifiers are treated as the flueric counterpart of the flapper valve. The analysis is based on a model in which a disk is interposed between the two opposing coaxial jets. A force balance on the disk determines its equilibrium position as a function of the jet pressures. Using this balance position, a relation between output pressure and control pressure is determined.

Experiments made on impacting circular jets for several different spacings between jets are described. The experimental results are compared with the theory. The pressure gain in both cases decreases with increasing spacing. However, the magnitude of the experimental pressure gain is only about 50 per cent of the predicted value. The discrepancy is attributed to the extreme sensitivity of the gain mechanism in impacting jet amplifiers. The assumed model would require only very small modifications to improve the agreement significantly.

Noise and erratic behavior were observed in the experimental test setup. The reason for this is believed to be a combination of feedback instability and turbulent fluctuations.

Nomenclature

A = cross-sectional area of jet, m^2

C_d = discharge coefficient

D = diameter of jet, m

F = force, kN

G_p = pressure gain

L = jet spacing, m

p = pressure, kN/m^2

x = distance from supply nozzle, m

116

Subscripts

c = control

o = output

s = supply

a = atmosphere

1. Introduction

It is always possible to represent an amplifier as a variable resistance. This representation facilitates circuit design and often provides valuable insight into the gain mechanism. In fluid circuits, a variable resistance is a valve. Thus, a valve is an especially appropriate component to use in the description of a fluid amplifier. In this way some of the analysis performed on conventional fluid valves can be applied to their flueric counterparts. To accomplish this, it is necessary to relate a particular type of proportional fluid amplifier to a conventional type valve.

As an example, the similarity between a jet deflection proportional fluid amplifier and a conventional jet pipe valve is well known. In the jet pipe valve [1] a power jet nozzle is moved mechanically, thereby redistributing fluid between two collecting passages. In the jet deflection amplifier, the power jet is vectored by the thrust of control jets rather than by mechanical means. Here again, the fluid is collected in passages positioned downstream of the power nozzle.

The purpose of this paper is to present a simplified analysis of the impacting stage of impacting jet fluid amplifiers. This impacting stage is considered to be the flueric counterpart of the conventional flapper valve. In the conventional flapper valve [1], the discharge from an orifice is controlled by the motion of a mechanical plate in close proximity to the exit of the orifice. In impacting jet amplifiers, the flow is restricted by an axially opposed jet of fluid rather than by a mechanical plate. The available exit area depends on the position and shape of the mean streamline that separates one impacting jet from the other. This, in turn, is a function of the force the jets exert on each other and the spacing between them.

The postulated mean flow streamline pattern for two axially opposed jets is shown in Fig. 1. The flow from the power jet at supply pressure, p_s, is restricted by an axial opposing control jet at pressure, p_c. The output pressure p_o is the static pressure measured near the nozzle exit. The flow from the supply nozzle must pass through a restriction bounded on one side by the fixed wall of the supply nozzle and on the other side by the dividing streamline. Changing the control pressure changes the position and shape of the dividing streamline. When the flow from the supply side is completely blocked, the dividing streamline lies along the fixed wall on the outside of the supply nozzle. In this case the output pressure equals the supply pressure. Fig. 1b shows the conditions when there is a slight amount of flow leaving the supply nozzle. If the control pressure is now sufficiently lowered, the dividing streamline will move far enough from the fixed wall so that the flow from the supply nozzle depends only on the size of the circular supply orifice (Fig. 1a). Now the output pressure is approximately atmospheric. Between the two extreme positions for the dividing streamline it is sometimes possible for the output

117

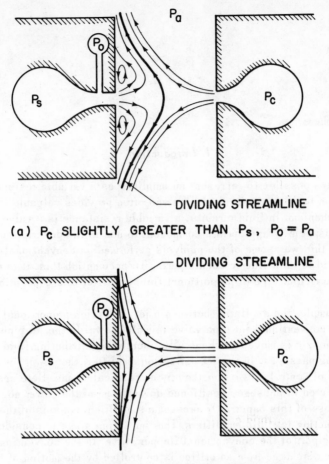

(a) P_C SLIGHTLY GREATER THAN P_S, $P_O = P_a$

(b) P_C INCREASED, P_O ALMOST EQUAL TO P_S

FIG. 1 STREAMLINE PATTERNS OF IMPACTING JETS

pressure to fall below atmospheric. This occurs when the flow from the power
supply nozzle is forced, by the shape of the restriction formed, to spread slightly before it reaches the atmosphere.

Impact modulators [2] also operate on the motion balance principle. In Fig. 2a,
only the impacting stage of the impact modulator is shown. An annular ring surrounding the power jet serves several purposes. It is primarily a circular static
pressure tap to measure the output pressure p_o, but it also provides the fixed wall
for the flow restriction. It is also possible to use other shapes for the supply-output configuration. Some of these are shown in Fig. 2b.

The complete impact modulator is really a two-stage device. The control jet
of the second or impacting stage (Fig. 2a) is the output jet of the first stage. It
is controlled by first stage control jets (not shown) which may provide deflection
or axial thrust augmentation. In this paper the analysis is confined to the impacting stage.

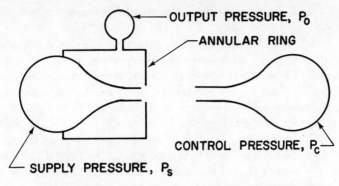

(a) IMPACTING STAGE OF IMPACT MODULATOR

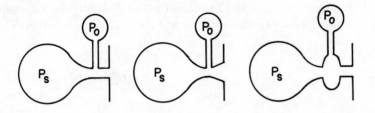

(b) OTHER POSSIBLE SUPPLY-OUTPUT CONFIGURATIONS
FOR IMPACTING STAGE

FIG. 2 IMPACTING STAGE

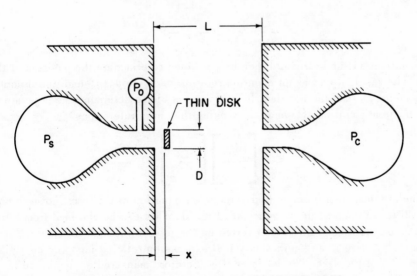

FIG. 3 MODEL FOR ANALYSIS OF IMPACTING JETS

119

2. Analysis of Impacting Amplifier Stage

The flow pattern postulated in Fig. 1 is extremely complex and has not been determined analytically. To analyze the impacting stage, therefore, a simplified model is assumed. The model is shown in Fig. 3. Here, two opposing, aligned, axi-symmetric nozzles are spaced a distance, L, apart. A thin, round, solid, weightless disk, having a diameter equal to the nozzles, is interposed between them. The disk serves as a dividing barrier between the jets, replacing the dividing streamline. The equilibrium position of the disk occurs when the force from the supply side on its left face equals the force from the control side on its right face. The equilibrium position of the disk can be changed by a change in either supply pressure or control pressure. In this analysis the supply pressure is assumed fixed. The consequences of this assumption are discussed in section 4. The equilibrium position of the disk can only be changed, therefore, by changing the control pressure. Each equilibrium position of the disk corresponds to some amount of supply nozzle restriction and a change in output static pressure. The magnitude of the output pressure can be related to the disk position x by using Bernoulli's equation for incompressible flow and the continuity equation. The result is

$$\frac{P_o}{P_s} = 1 - 16 \left(\frac{x}{D}\right)^2 C_d^{\,2} \qquad (0 \leq \frac{x}{D} \leq \frac{1}{4C_d}) \qquad (1)$$

where C_d is the discharge coefficient from the cylindrical area $\pi D x$ between the disk and the nozzle exit. The surrounding region is assumed to be at zero gauge pressure.

Equation (1) is that which would be used in the analysis of a flapper valve. The analysis of the impacting stage can be completed simply by obtaining one more relation. This relation must be of the form

$$\frac{P_c}{P_s} = f \left(\frac{x}{D}, \frac{L}{D}\right) \qquad (2)$$

Equations (1) and (2) could then be combined to eliminate the position of the disk. The result would be an equation relating p_c/p_s to p_o/p_s and would contain the spacing L/D of the nozzles. It is also possible to determine the pressure gain G_p from equations (1) and (2) by using the chain rule. Thus

$$G_p = \left[\frac{dp_o}{dx}\right]\left[\frac{dx}{dp_c}\right] = \frac{dp_o}{dp_c} \qquad (3)$$

The problem, therefore, is to determine an equation of the form shown in equation (2) for the impacting stage model (Fig. 3). This can be obtained from a force balance on the disk if the force exerted by the jets on the disk is known. Unfortunately, there is no known analytical expression relating jet force on a disk to position of the disk. The jet force was therefore measured as described in section 2.1.

120

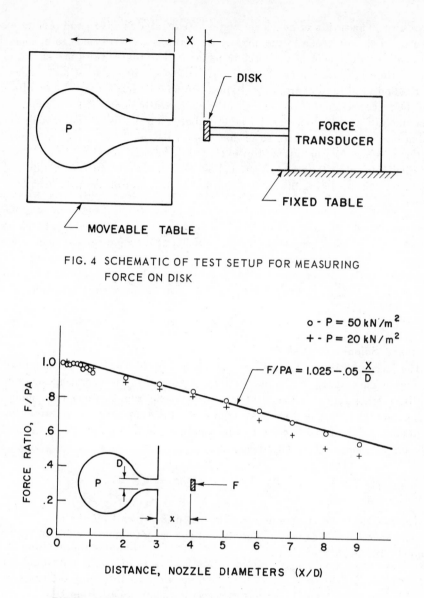

FIG. 4 SCHEMATIC OF TEST SETUP FOR MEASURING
FORCE ON DISK

FIG. 5 FORCE OF A JET ON AN EQUAL DIAMETER DISK

2.1 Force of a Jet on a Disk

A schematic of the test setup to measure the force exerted by a jet on a disk
having the same diameter as the jet is shown in Fig. 4. A 1-mm nozzle was
mounted on a moveable table and directed at a 1-mm diameter disk. The disk was
fastened rigidly to a strain-gage force transducer. The transducer had a full-scale
displacement of 0.4 mm. The distance between jet and disk was adjusted by a
micrometer screw in contact with the moveable table. With this arrangement, distances could be measured to 0.01 mm. The pressure in the jet was maintained at
either 50 kN/m^2 or 20 kN/m^2 as the jet was moved relative to the disk. These
pressure levels caused a maximum displacement of about 0.1 mm on the force

121

transducer. Thus, this arrangement could be expected to give good results except when the disk was close to the nozzle. No corrections were made to account for the small displacement of the force transducer. The test results are shown in Fig. 5. Here the force is nondimensionalized by pA, its value at a distance of 0.1 mm and is plotted against the distance in nozzle diameters. The results show that the force exerted by the jet remained essentially constant for distances less than one-half nozzle diameter; for greater distances the force decreased mono-tonically. The reduction was somewhat greater for the $20\text{-}kN/m^2$ jet pressure than for the $50\text{-}kN/m^2$ jet pressure. However, the difference between them is not great. This indicates that for pressure around $50\ kN/m^2$, the normalized results are reasonably valid. Using these data, the force of the jet on the plate can be ex-pressed as

$$\frac{F}{pA} = 1 \qquad\qquad (0 \leq \frac{x}{D} \leq 0.5) \tag{4}$$

$$\frac{F}{pA} = 1.025 - 0.05\,\frac{x}{D} \qquad (\frac{x}{D} \geq 0.5) \tag{5}$$

2.2 Force Balance on Disk

The forces acting on the disk are shown in Fig. 6. The equilibrium position of the disk occurs where the force functions intersect. In the operating range of the amplifier, the intersection must always occur in the region where the supply force is constant; that is, the disk must be close to the supply nozzle to affect the out-put pressure. The force exerted by the supply jet in this region can be written by referring to equation (4). The result is

$$F_s = p_s A \qquad (0 \leq \frac{x}{D} \leq 0.5) \tag{6}$$

The control force is obtained from equation (5) by shifting the coordinates. This is necessary because the supply and control jets oppose each other. The control force is then written as

$$F_c = p_c A \left[1.025 - 0.05 \left(\frac{L}{D} - 0.50 - \frac{x}{D} \right) \right] \tag{7}$$

$$(\frac{x}{D} \leq \frac{L}{D} - 0.50)$$

Equating the supply and control forces given in equations (6) and (7) yields

$$p_s = p_c \left[1.025 - 0.05\,(\frac{L}{D} - 0.50 - \frac{x}{D}) \right] \tag{8}$$

$$(\,0 \leq \frac{x}{D} \leq 0.50)$$

Equation (8) is a specific form of the functional relation indicated in eq. (2).

122

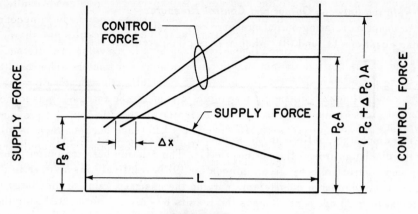

FIG. 6 FORCE OF SUPPLY AND CONTROL JETS ON DISK

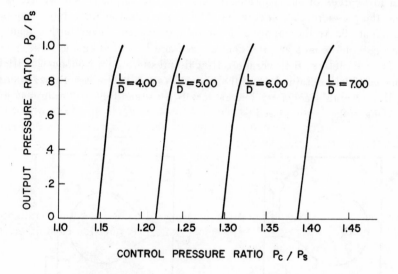

FIG. 7 OUTPUT VERSUS CONTROL FOR VARIOUS SPACINGS

A change in control pressure ΔP_c results in a change in the equilibrium position of the disk Δx. From the force-distance relation shown in Fig. 6 the effect of a change in the jet spacing can be visualized. For example, if the spacing is increased, a higher control pressure is needed to bring the balance point into the sensitive region. In addition, a change in control pressure results in less movement of the balance point since the control forces converge as the distance from the control jet increases. As a consequence, pressure gain decreases as the jet spacing increases.

2.3 Relation between Output and Control Pressures

An equation relating output pressure to control pressure is obtained by combining equations (1) and (8). When x/D is eliminated, the result is

$$\frac{p_c}{p_s} = \left[\frac{1}{1.025 - 0.05\left(L/D - 0.50 - \frac{1}{4C_d}\sqrt{1 - p_o/p_s}\,\right)} \right] \qquad (9)$$

The discharge coefficient C_d is assumed to be 0.6, a value usually assumed for the discharge from a flapper nozzle [1]. The relation between output pressure and control pressure given in equation (9) is relatively insensitive to the value of the discharge coefficient. Varying the assumed value of discharge coefficient by ± 25 per cent changes the results by only ± 1 per cent. Using the discharge coefficient of 0.6, the output pressure ratio p_o/p_s is plotted against the control pressure ratio p_c/p_s in Fig. 7 for cases where the nozzles are 4, 5, 6, and 7 nozzle diameters apart. The pressure gain is the slope of these curves. When the spacing is 4 nozzle diameters, the pressure gain has a maximum value of 50 at low values of output pressure ratio. As the output pressure ratio increases, the pressure gain decreases. The average full-scale value of pressure gain is about 30. As the supply and control nozzles are moved farther apart, the pressure gain decreases and the control pressure level increases. At a spacing of 6 nozzle diameters, the average full-scale pressure gain is about 25. Higher pressure gains are obtained when the spacing is reduced below 4 nozzle diameters. However, this geometry leaves very little space for deflecting jets when a deflecting stage is also used.

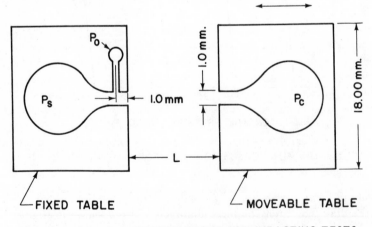

FIG. 8 SCHEMATIC OF TEST SETUP FOR IMPACTING TESTS

3. Experiments on the Impacting Stage

To determine the accuracy of the theoretical model presented in section 2, experiments were conducted on an impacting stage. The experimental setup is shown in Fig. 8. A circular nozzle, 1 mm in diameter, is mounted in a fixed position on a table. The nozzle has a 3-mm straight section at its exit and a static pressure tap is located along this straight section 1 mm from the nozzle exit. A

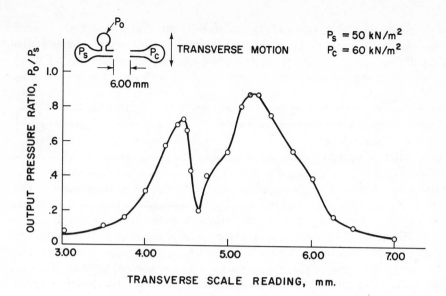

FIG. 9 RESULTS OF TRANSVERSE NOZZLE MOVEMENT

similar nozzle, without a static pressure tap, is mounted on a micro-positioner also fixed to the table. This nozzle can be moved in all three directions by micrometer screws attached to the micro-positioner. The smallest movement of the nozzle is 0.01 mm and the total travel in each direction is 10 mm. Both nozzles were contained in square bars, 18 mm on a side. The control, supply, and output pressures were measured with Bourdon gauges having either 0.50 kN/m^2 or 0.25 kN/m^2 as the smallest scale division.

The bars containing the nozzles were mounted flush with each other when the micrometer screw controlling the axial spacing was set to zero. Thus, the distance between the jets was always the micrometer reading. To check the alignment of the nozzles, traverses were made before the output-control relationship was measured. A traverse was made for each axial position used.

The results of a typical traverse test are shown in Fig. 9 for a jet spacing of 6 nozzle diameters. For this test the power jet pressure was set and maintained at 50 kN/m^2. The control jet pressure was set to a value that would provide a signal above atmospheric pressure at the output static pressure tap. In this case the control pressure was set at 62 kN/m^2. The moveable nozzle was now moved transversely. At each transverse position the supply pressure was readjusted to 50 kN/m^2 before the output pressure was recorded. The control pressure did not change during the traverse. The output pressure ratio shown in Fig. 9 is a double humped curve. The axes of the jets are aligned at the transverse position corresponding to the bottom of the valley between the humps. The experimental data are asymmetrical with respect to supply jet axis. This probably indicates that the nozzles were slightly out of round or that the nozzle axes were not quite perpendicular to the face of the nozzle blocks.

For small transverse misalignments the output pressure ratio increases. This occurs because the balance point is always much closer to the supply nozzle. To visualize this effect, consider that when misalignments occur, part of the supply

125

force does not act on the disk. The force of the control jet on the disk, however, remains almost the same since the control jet has spread over the longer distance. The result is that the balance is shifted toward the supply nozzle and the disk is no longer perpendicular to the axis. The net escape area for the supply fluid is reduced. The output pressure continues to increase with increasing misalignment until the supply nozzle exit area is not sufficiently covered by the disk. From this point on the output pressure decreases.

Using this method, the jet was aligned in both transverse directions. Then the relation between output pressure and control pressure was measured with the jet positions fixed. In these tests, also, the supply pressure had to be adjusted constantly to 50 kN/m^2, since the supply source did not have zero impedance. The results of these tests are shown in Figs. 10, 11, and 12. In Fig. 10 the spacing between the jets was 6 nozzle diameters. Data were taken for the aligned jet and for a misalignment of 0.05 mm. The pressure gain of the aligned jets (slope of the test results) was slightly higher than that of the non-aligned jets, but the output contained larger amplitude fluctuations. The experimental pressure gain was about 15, about 50 per cent of that predicted by theory. The theoretical values from equation 9 are also shown on Fig. 10. The displacement between the experimental and theoretical results is about 2 per cent.

The data for a jet spacing of 5 nozzle diameters are shown in Fig. 11. The experimental pressure gain is about 20 which is 60 per cent of the theoretical value. In this case the theory and experiments are displaced by 10 per cent along the p_c/p_s axis.

Fig. 12 shows the results for a spacing of 4 nozzle diameters. Data taken on the impacting stage of an impact modulator is also shown on this figure. The slopes of the experimental curve made with the test apparatus and the one taken on the impact modulator are approximately equal, but the impact modulator data saturates at lower pressure ratios. This probably is caused by the position of the annular ring, which is located between the jets in the impact modulator. The pressure gain of the experimental data is about 30. Here again, this is lower than the theory predicts and again there is a 10 per cent displacement between theory and experiment.

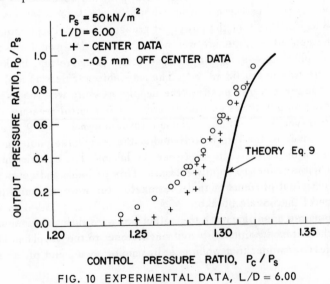

FIG. 10 EXPERIMENTAL DATA, L/D = 6.00

126

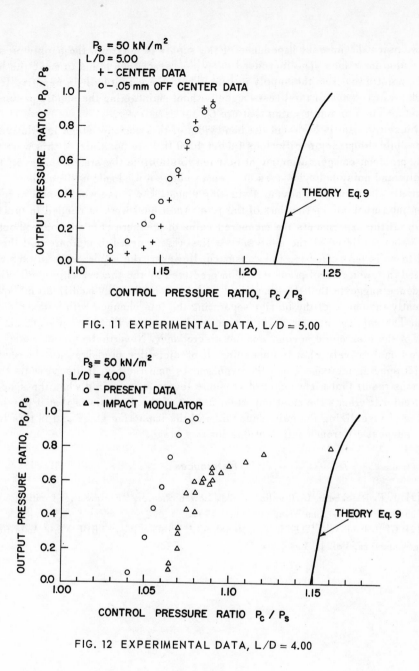

FIG. 11 EXPERIMENTAL DATA, L/D = 5.00

FIG. 12 EXPERIMENTAL DATA, L/D = 4.00

4. Discussion

One of the most troublesome features of the current experiments was the erratic and noisy output pressure signals obtained. This was noticed on both the test setup and the impact modulator. Some of the difficulty is believed to be caused by the inherent pressure feedback of the flapper-valve arrangement. To see how this works, consider that the control pressure increases. Then the balance point moves toward the supply nozzle, tending to restrict the supply flow. Since the internal impedance of the supply is not zero, the supply pressure also increases. The increased supply pressure then tends to move the balance point away from the supply nozzle. Thus, there is a built-in negative feedback. As evidence of this, tests made without maintaining the supply pressure constant yield pressure gains that are 60 per cent lower.

Since the gain is high and the bandwidth of this compact stage is relatively wide, high-frequency oscillations (about 1000 Hz) are possible. If this were the only problem, compensation might be tried to stabilize the stage. However, the erratic and noisy behavior does not seem to have a predominant frequency. Actually, it is audible, having a sizzling sound. The noise would seem to result from the turbulent fluctuations of the jets. Additional work is needed in this area.

In all the experiments the measured value of pressure gain was only about half the value predicted by the analysis. At first this appears to indicate that the control force is less effective than assumed. However, the experiments always resulted in lower control pressures than predicted by the theory. This conflicting evidence suggests that the simplified model selected needs modification. Apparently the shape of the barrier separating the jets changes with balance position. The gain mechanism in this stage is so sensitive that even a small curvature of the disk could account for the discrepancy. Nevertheless, the model shows qualitatively what is happening. It predicts that pressure gain decreases as jet spacing increases, and the experiments confirm this. It also reveals the obvious result that higher control pressure levels are required when the spacing is greater. Perhaps the most important aspect of the analysis is that it provides a way of visualizing the gain mechanism of the impacting stage and in this way may suggest different configurations for this stage.

References

[1] J. F. Blackburn, G. Reethof, and J. Lowen Shearer, "Fluid Power Control," Technology Press — John Wiley and Sons, 1960.

[2] G. B. Bjornsen, "The Impact Modulator," Proceedings of HDL Fluid Amplification Symposium, Vol. II, May 1964.

Flow Characteristics in a Supersonic Fluid Amplifier

Cornelius C. Shih
University of Alabama
Huntsville, Alabama

Abstract

An analytical study of flow characteristics was conducted for a two-dimensional supersonic fluid amplifier. Through the method of characteristics under the inviscid assumption, the supersonic flow including shock waves and free stream boundaries was analyzed numerically with the use of an electronic digital computer. Configurations of shock waves and free stream boundaries are presented graphically under various pressure conditions at the control port and the supply chamber. Detailed illustrations of the pressure, Mach number and the velocity vector distributions, respectively, are given for the flow field in the amplifier under various supply pressures and an ambient pressure at the control port. By quasi-steady approach, configurations of the intersecting shock waves and free stream boundaries are calculated and presented graphically.

A discussion concerning the three flow regimes peculiar to the supersonic amplifier and the switching mechanism is given based on the results of this study.

Nomenclature

u = velocity component along x coordinate

v = velocity component along y coordinate

x, y = Cartesian coordinates

c = sonic velocity

μ = Mach angle

q = velocity

θ = inclination of velocity vector with respect to x coordinate

S = entropy

k = specific heat ratio ($= 1.4$ for air)

129

R = engineering gas constant (= 53.3 ft/lb/lb °R for air)

P_o = supply pressure in air supply chamber (psia)

P_{cl} = pressure of left control port (psia)

P_{cr} = pressure of right control port (psia)

P_{al} = pressure of left output channel (psia)

P_{ar} = pressure of right output channel (psia)

Introduction

The supersonic fluid amplifier has been under development for more than five years by several agencies. This type of amplifier has been found particularly useful for rocket thrust vector control due to its high gain of momentum in the supersonic power jet.

Distinctive features of this amplifier different from those of subsonic amplifiers are the convergent-divergent nozzle located upstream from the control ports for producing a high energy supersonic jet stream and the switching mechanism of the amplifier.

Fluid amplifiers of this type with variations in design have been developed and reported, to the author's knowledge, by the U. S. Army Missile Command, Harry Diamond Laboratory, and Honeywell Company. Details of each of the amplifiers are obtainable from the papers and reports published by Warren and Holmes [1], Holmes and Foxwell [2], U. S. Army Missile Command reports [3], Yalamanchili [4] and [5], Olson and Miller [6]. The literature review shows that most of the previous works on the supersonic fluid amplifier are experimental in nature. Feasibility of the amplifier in each case had been clearly demonstrated through empirical means, but without theoretical analysis. However, an exception has been found in Olson and Miller's work which has some similarity in analytical technique and difference in boundary conditions from this study.

For further advancement of the fluidic technology in this area, more emphasis on theoretical approach to some of the problems is considered essential. Accordingly, a modest step has been taken forward in this direction and results of the work are reported herein.

Most of the supersonic fluid amplifiers are so designed that flow fields in the amplifiers are three-dimensional and extremely complex. Although the flow complexity seems to cause no noticeable deficiency on the amplifier performance, it has imposed a great mathematical difficulty in theoretical analysis of the fluid flow.

Therefore, a simplification of the theoretical analysis was made under the assumption of two-dimensional inviscid flow with the premise that the results might yield some qualitative insights and explanations of the flow problems in some of the existing supersonic fluid amplifiers. Also, it may be argued that the two-dimensional analysis should be particularly useful if a two-dimensional amplifier is to be designed.

The present study is concerned with flow characteristics of the flow field in the two-dimensional supersonic amplifier under various pressure conditions at the control ports and the supply chamber. The flow characteristics to be considered are namely: configurations of shock waves and free stream boundaries; distributions of velocity vectors, pressures, and local Mach numbers; flow separation phenomena in the divergent passage following the sonic throat.

Through the method of characteristics, the flow field downstream from a two-dimensional convergent-divergent nozzle of the power jet was analyzed numerically with the use of an electronic digital computer. For the numerical calculation, the geometry of a typical supersonic fluid amplifier with 30 degree divergent passage is selected as one of the boundary conditions. Results of the numerical calculation of the flow characteristics are presented graphically.

Based on the results of this study and the knowledge obtained from previous studies, a discussion of flow regimes related to performance characteristics and the switching mechanism is given.

The Governing Equations for the Method of Characteristics

The flow field in the amplifier is assumed to be two-dimensional, adiabatic, supersonic, either irrotational or rotational, nonviscous, as well as steady for this simplified analysis. Although, in assumption, there are no viscour and heat conduction effects, the existence of a curved shock wave causes the entropy increase across the shock to vary from one streamline to the other, depending on the corresponding shock strength and angle. As a consequence, the rotational flow is expected to occur in the flow field downstream of the curved shock wave. The stagnation enthalpy is assumed invariant throughout the flow field. The entropy varies from one streamline to the next but is assumed constant on each streamline except at the crossing of the shock wave. The power jet stream from the two-dimensional nozzle is assumed to be an irrotational source flow.

The governing equations are derived by the application of the momentum equation (Euler's), the continuity equation, and the sonic velocity equation.

$$\left[1 - \frac{u^2}{c^2}\right] \frac{\partial u}{\partial x} + \left[1 - \frac{v^2}{c^2}\right] \frac{\partial v}{\partial y} - \frac{uv}{c^2} \left[\frac{\partial v}{\partial x} + \frac{\partial u}{\partial y}\right] = 0 \quad (1)$$

where u and v are the velocity components along the x and y Cartesian coordinates, respectively, and c is the sonic velocity.

Equation (1) can be expressed along the characteristics lines in the following form

$$\cot \mu \, \frac{dq}{q} \mp d\theta + \sin \mu \cos \mu \, \frac{dS}{kR} = 0 \quad (2)$$

along the characteristic lines

$$\tan (\mu \pm \theta) = \frac{dy}{dx} \quad (3)$$

and

$$dS = 0 \quad (4)$$

131

along the streamline defined by

$$\frac{dy}{dx} = \tan \theta \qquad (5)$$

where μ is the Mach angle, q the velocity, θ the inclination of velocity vector with respect to x coordinate, S the entropy, k the specific heat ratio, R the engineering gas constant. Detailed derivations of the above equations are omitted for brevity, but may be found in the reference [6].

Equation (2) is known as the compatibility equation which except for the shock wave describes the variation of flow characteristics along the characteristic lines. Locally the characteristic lines are tangent to the Mach line. Equation (2) is also called the hodograph characteristics for two-dimensional flow.

The equations of the oblique shock waves and Prandtl-Meyer flow at an expansion corner should be incorporated along with Equations (1) through (5) into the analysis of the flow field. Because these equations are derived and discussed in reference [7] and [9], and for the sake of brevity, they are excluded here.

With proper assumptions and boundary conditions, the characteristics equations (2) and (3) can be solved either numerically or graphically.

Several finite-difference numerical procedures have been developed for solving the characteristics equations using the method of characteristics. A nearly complete survey of previous works on the method of characteristics has been made by Strom [8].

For the analysis of flow field in this particular study, the development of a new method for numerical procedure is considered unnecessary since a numerical procedure developed by Prozen [9] is considered suitable and efficient for the study. Detailed descriptions of the numerical procedure and resultant computer program are given in his report. The advantage of the program is the provision of a flexible set of boundary conditions enabling the calculation of the flow fields for nozzles, plumes and other complex internal flows as well as the locations and properties of shock waves and expansion waves.

Presentation of Numerical Results

The numerical calculation of the flow fields was performed on an IBM 7094 at an average time of five minutes for each of the flow fields analyzed. The geometry of a typical supersonic amplifier selected for the analysis is shown in Fig. 1. One of the geometrical elements, a 30-degree divergent two-dimensional nozzle, was modified from the actual 30-degree divergent conical nozzle in order to maintain a two-dimensional flow throughout the amplifier. All of the other elements are in geometrical similarity with the corresponding elements of a supersonic amplifier developed by the Army Missile Command.

In Fig. 2a, pressure contours in psia, shock waves and their reflections at the solid boundary and free stream boundary, and the subsequent Prandtl-Meyer flow are graphically presented. These flow characteristics are calculated with the following basic data and boundary conditions: The supply pressure is 1000 psia; the area expansion ratio of the divergent nozzle exit to the sonic throat is 17.429; one of the control ports and the output channel on the same side are open to the atmosphere ($Pa = 14.2$ psia); the other control port is closed completely; it

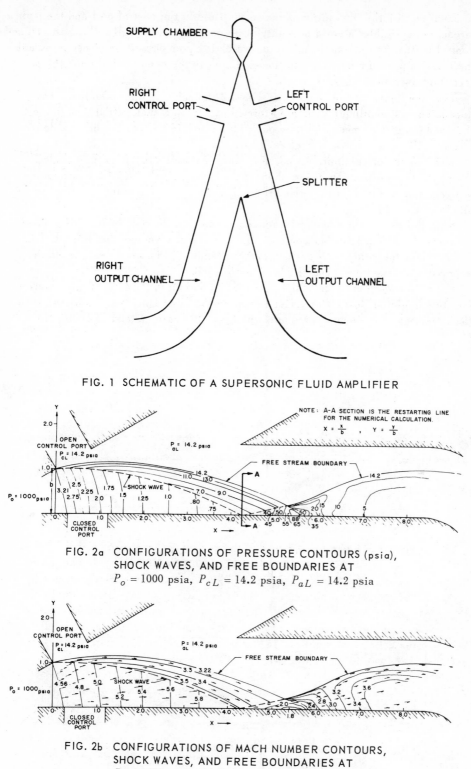

FIG. 1 SCHEMATIC OF A SUPERSONIC FLUID AMPLIFIER

FIG. 2a CONFIGURATIONS OF PRESSURE CONTOURS (psia),
SHOCK WAVES, AND FREE BOUNDARIES AT
$P_o = 1000$ psia, $P_{cL} = 14.2$ psia, $P_{aL} = 14.2$ psia

FIG. 2b CONFIGURATIONS OF MACH NUMBER CONTOURS,
SHOCK WAVES, AND FREE BOUNDARIES AT
$P_o = 1000$ psia, $P_{cL} = 14.2$ psia, $P_{aL} = 14.2$ psia

133

is assumed that the interaction between the fluid in the control port and the main stream is negligible; a solid boundary or an output channel wall follows the closed control port; a free stream boundary on which the pressure of the power jet equals the ambient pressure develops on the side next to the open control port; the perfect fluid used in the amplifier is air.

The coordinate system adopted in Figs. 2 through 6 is dimensionless. The dimensionless coordinate system is formed by dividing each actual coordinate by the normal distance measured from one side of nozzle edge to the other side of nozzle wall, b, as shown in Fig. 2a.

The process of calculation was carried out automatically from the nozzle to the shock wave reflection at the channel wall. A manipulation of the computer program was required for restarting the calculation from the point of reflection as shown in Fig. 2a.

Fig. 2b has the same boundary conditions as Fig. 2a, but, instead of pressure contours, local Mach number contours and the velocity vectors are plotted. The arrows show the velocity directions and the length of the arrows expresses the approximate comparative magnitude of the velocity.

Figs. 3a and 3b are identical with Figs. 2a and 2b in the form of presentation for the calculated flow characteristics and in the input boundary conditions with the exception of the supply pressure which is 1400 psia instead of 1000 psia.

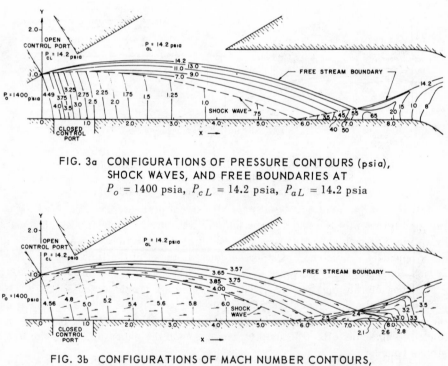

FIG. 3a   CONFIGURATIONS OF PRESSURE CONTOURS (psia),
SHOCK WAVES, AND FREE BOUNDARIES AT
$P_o = 1400$ psia, $P_{cL} = 14.2$ psia, $P_{aL} = 14.2$ psia

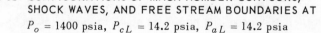

FIG. 3b   CONFIGURATIONS OF MACH NUMBER CONTOURS,
SHOCK WAVES, AND FREE STREAM BOUNDARIES AT
$P_o = 1400$ psia, $P_{cL} = 14.2$ psia, $P_{aL} = 14.2$ psia

134

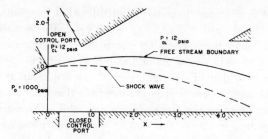

FIG. 4a CONFIGURATIONS OF SHOCK WAVE AND FREE
STREAM BOUNDARY AT P_o = 1000 psia, P_{cL} = 12 psia,
P_{aL} = 12 psia

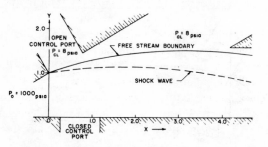

FIG. 4b CONFIGURATIONS OF SHOCK WAVE AND FREE
STREAM BOUNDARY AT P_o = 1000 psia, P_{cL} = 8 psia,
P_{aL} = 8 psia

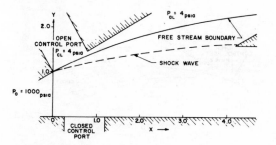

FIG. 4c CONFIGURATIONS OF SHOCK WAVE AND FREE
STREAM BOUNDARY AT P_o = 1000 psia, P_{cL} = 4 psia,
P_{aL} = 4 psia

In Figs. 4a, 4b, and 4c, the effects of ambient pressure upon the configuration and location of the shock wave and the free stream boundary are demonstrated by varying the ambient pressures from 12 psia to 8 psia then to 4 psia, while the other boundary conditions are kept the same as those of the flow case in Figs. 2a and 2b. The supply pressure is maintained at 1000 psia in these cases.

In Figs. 5a, 5b, and 5c, the supply pressures are provided at 1200 psia, 1400 psia, and 1600 psia, respectively, and the pressures in the open control port and the output channel are maintained at 14.2 psia for all three cases. They are intended to show the effect of supply pressure upon the shock wave and the free stream boundary.

In the case of both control ports impressed with different pressures which are higher than the pressure of the power jet near the control ports as shown in Fig.

6, shock waves and free stream boundaries will develop from both nozzle edges. P_{cl} and P_{al} are 14.2 psia and P_{cr} and P_{ar} are 8 psia. The supply pressure is given at 1000 psia. Under these boundary conditions, the degree of over-expansion of the supersonic power jet on the left side where P_{cl} and P_{al} are imposed, is greater than that of the right side of the amplifier. It means that the shock wave strength on the left side is greater than that of the right side.

If the ambient pressure on the right side is assumed to be maintained at 8.0 psia, it may be expected in theory that the weaker shock wave on the right side will extend downstream and intersect with the stronger shock wave. After the intersection, the shock waves will be influenced by each other at different intensities. Due to the mutual influence at the intersection, the stronger shock

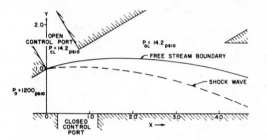

FIG. 5a   CONFIGURATIONS OF SHOCK WAVE AND FREE STREAM BOUNDARY AT $P_o = 1200$ psia, $P_{cL} = 14.2$ psia, $P_{aL} = 14.2$ psia

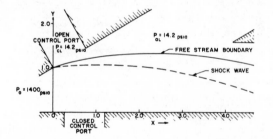

FIG. 5b   CONFIGURATIONS OF SHOCK WAVE AND FREE STREAM BOUNDARY AT $P_o = 1400$ psia, $P_{cL} = 14.2$ psia, $P_{aL} = 14.2$ psia

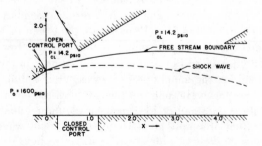

FIG. 5c   CONFIGURATIONS OF SHOCK WAVE AND FREE STREAM BOUNDARY AT $P_o = 1600$ psia, $P_{cL} = 14.2$ psia, $P_{aL} = 14.2$ psia

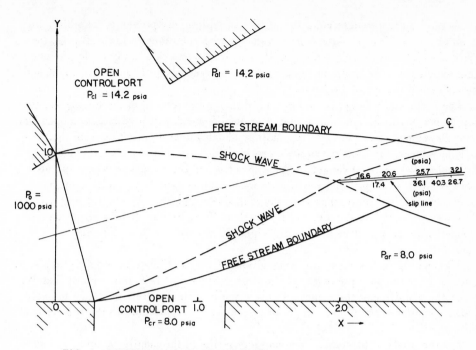

FIG. 6 CONFIGURATIONS OF INTERSECTED SHOCK WAVES AND
FREE BOUNDARIES

wave turns into a weaker one following the intersection and the weaker one
turns into a stronger one with changes in the directions of the waves. These
shock waves proceed to reflect at the free stream boundaries, resulting in
Prandtl-Meyer flow. Between the intersected waves, a slip line initiating from
the point of intersection develops under the following conditions: pressures and
stagnation temperatures along both sides of the slip line are the same; the directions of the velocity vectors along both sides of the slip line are the same,
but the magnitudes or the scalars of the velocity vectors are different. After some
manipulations of the computer program and input boundary conditions, the approximate results of the numerical calculation presented graphically in Fig. 6
were obtained. The numericals given above and below the slip line indicate the
local pressures in psia along the respective sides of the line.

Discussion

Based on the experience and the knowledge from the previous works, it has
been commonly recognized that there are three regimes of operation for a supersonic fluid amplifier.

Regime I – The power jet is overexpanded, but the separation of jet occurs
within the divergent nozzle. Because the supply pressure is lower than the
critical supply pressure, the control of the power jet becomes difficult, and the
power jet is irregularly oscillatory. The critical supply pressure, at which the
power jet is projected from the exit plane of the nozzle without separation inside
the nozzle, has been thoroughly investigated by numerous researchers. Two conclusive works by Arens and Spiegler [10], and Kalt and Badal [11], in recent

years have made the determination of the critical supply pressure possible with good accuracy for most gases. For example, with reference to their results, the critical supply pressure for the amplifier of interest to this study is determined to be approximately 750 psia for air at a temperature of 70 F and an ambient and an ambient pressure of 14.2 psia.

The factors affecting the separation of the power jet within the nozzle are the supply pressure, the ambient pressure or amplifier exhaust pressure, the boundary layer developed in the nozzle, the oblique shock waves interacting with the boundary layer, the nozzle expansion ratio, and the free stream Mach number.

Regime II — The power jet is overexpanded and the supply pressure is sufficiently high to prevent jet separation within the nozzle, but insufficient to cause symmetrical reattachment to the wall downstream of the control ports. In this range of supply pressure, the flow will be fully established in either output channel without a continuous control signal. This type of flow is called a bistable flow.

The amplifiers tested by the Army Missile Command function properly in regime II for the supply pressure ranging from 800 psia to 1800 psia approximately. Since the amplifier of this study is only slightly different from the Army's amplifiers, a similar range of the supply pressure may be applicable to the regime II of this amplifier.

For the study of bi-stable flow characteristics of the amplifier, thus, the supply pressures of 1000 and 1400 psia were selected as shown in Figs. 2a, 2b, 3a, and 3b.

Regime III — The supply pressure in this regime is high enough to cause the power jet leaving the nozzle to become underexpanded. The underexpansion of the power jet is the situation where the pressure in the power jet is higher than the ambient pressure. In this regime, the flow remains completely attached to the diffuser walls of the amplifier past the region of the control ports. This flow is called a tri-stable flow, because, without the control flow, it produces equal exit flow from each output channel. The supply pressure range is determined to be approximately above 1600 psia for this regime.

The inspection of Figs. 2 and 3 confirms the bi-stable nature of flow field in regime II at the supply pressures of 1000 psia and 1400 psia. It is evident that the configuration of the curved shock wave developed from the nozzle edge under the particular boundary conditions tends to rotate the flow direction in the region downstream from the curved shock wave toward the channel wall. This tendency seems to contribute effectively to the bi-stable nature of the flow field in regime II.

One of the boundary conditions which requires discussion and justification is the assumed pressures in the control ports. The previous experiments [3] reported that a supersonic amplifier functions effectively in regime II under atmospheric pressure by merely closing and opening the control ports, and perhaps even better than applying a control jet.

In view of the above report, and in order to provide the theoretical analysis with practical and simplified pressure boundary conditions, the pressure in the open control port is assumed to be atmospheric ($P_{cl} = 14.2$ psia), and the pressure in the output channel on the same side is also assumed to be atmospheric, provided that the output opening is well ventilated. It must be realized, however, that the effects of viscosity and heat conduction may cause some degree of jet

138

mixing with the ambient air. Consequently, a dynamic condition prevailing in the ambient air may cause the ambient pressure to be less than atmospheric, and may result in a limited degree of diffusion of the inviscid free stream boundary.

Nevertheless, the idealized assumptions on the pressure boundary conditions are considered justified because the knowledge from studies on a similar flow, such as the rocket jet plume [12], shows that these effects are negligible in as short a distance as that of the output channel in the amplifier. Moreover, the theoretical analysis with the inviscid assumption is an initial step for the analysis of boundary layer development due to the viscosity and heat conduction effects. The so-called outer edge boundary conditions required for the analysis of boundary layer development along the channel wall usually are provided from the inviscid flow theory. Flow characteristics along the free stream boundary of the power jet can be applied as the boundary conditions for the solution of air entrainment problems occurred along the free jet boundary.

As for the boundary condition at the closed control port, it is assumed that a dynamic equilibrium is attained between the power jet and the air occupying the control port since the port is closed and no air supply is provided. The dynamic equilibrium signifies that the pressure in the closed control port is equal to the pressure along the free stream boundary extending across the port. This assumption is justified only under the condition that the interaction between the power jet and the air in the port, and the subsequent vortices in the port due to viscous effects, are negligibly small. It should be, however, pointed out that an excessive interaction at the port may induce disturbing waves significant enough to influence the flow characteristics in the power jet downstream from the port. The above argument seems to be in essence substantiated by Korst's theory on the cavity flow [13].

In Figs. 2 and 3, only the pressures, Mach numbers, and the directions of velocity vectors are given, but it should be mentioned that the output of the computer program includes, in addition, the temperature, the entropy, the shock angle, density, the Mach angle and others at each mesh point formed by the intersecting characteristic lines.

It is interesting to note that in both Figs. 2b and 3b the Mach numbers are greater than unity throughout the flow field despite the presence of curved shock waves. Also, it is of special interest to observe that the Mach number increases in the flow field downstream from the originating point of the Prandtl-Meyer flow toward the exit of the output channel.

The supply pressures are varied in Figs. 2 and 3 for the purpose of demonstrating the effects of supply pressure upon flow characteristics in the flow field.

The inspection of Figs. 4a, 4b, and 4c, reveals that the effects of the control pressure and the ambient pressure upon the configurations of shock waves and free stream boundaries are significant enough to govern the degree of bi-stability. Fig. 4c shows that the pressures P_{cl} and P_{al} at 4 psia definitely cause a considerable interaction of the power jet with the splitter, generating a complicated series of shock waves following the splitter. In this case, bi-stable flow is obviously impossible, and the flow should be classified as regime III. In Fig. 4b, P_{cl} and P_{al} are set at 8 psia, and the bi-stable flow field may become uncertain if the development of free jet boundary associated with the air entrainment becomes significant in the order of magnitude comparable with the magnitude of the power jet.

139

Fig. 5 demonstrates the effects of the supply pressure upon the shock wave and free stream boundary configurations. The tendency of switching from regime II to regime III is noted as the supply pressure is increased.

It is evident that the analysis of the type shown in Figs. 4 and 5 should be of aid to the design of amplifier, particularly for selecting a best location of the splitter. Also a proper width of the control port may be determined for better operational efficiency through obtaining the knowledge of the entraining flow due to jet mixing along the power jet. This knowledge may be obtained by applying the results of the type of analysis mentioned above as the boundary conditions of first approximation for the solution of boundary layer equations. Such a task is being planned for future project by the author.

Using a quasi-steady approach to the unsteady flow problems at the period of flow switching, an attempt was made to analyze the flow characteristics, in particular the configurations of shock waves and free stream boundaries. Results presented in Fig. 6 for an instant during the period of switching, show the asymmetrical configuration of two intersected shock waves which may indicate a tendency toward a bi-stable flow field.

In Fig. 6, the pressure distributions along the left and right sides of the slip line are not exactly matched, but they are approximately in agreement. Undoubtedly, the analysis must be further improved in order to obtain a better matching of the pressures on both sides along the slip line. However, the directions of free stream boundaries are clearly set toward the right output channel, in which the ambient pressure and the control pressure are less than in the left output channel. This phenomenon seems to indicate that the shock wave system developed in the power jet due to the pressure difference with respect to the ambient air, is one of the important factors governing the switching mechanism of the supersonic amplifier.

Conclusion

A mathematical tool for the analysis of flow characteristics in a supersonic fluid amplifier is introduced with the application Prozan's computer program based on the method of characteristics. The shock wave system developed in the power jet in the case of overexpansion is identified to be one of the main factors governing the bi-stable nature of the flow field and the switching mechanism. Results of the theoretical analysis may yield some constructive suggestions for the design improvement of the amplifier. In order to complete the theoretical analysis of the switching mechanism, solving the unsteady flow equations is essential.

Acknowledgments

The author would like to express his thanks to Messrs. Ray Deep and Billy Jenkins of the Aerodynamics Branch, Advanced System Lab, Directorate of Research and Development, U. S. Army Missile Command for their assistance in providing the digital computer program. This work was conducted under the sponsorship of the Army Inertial Guidance and Control Laboratory, Directorate of Research and Development, U. S. Army Missile Command.

References

[1] R. W. Warren, R. G. Barclay, and A. B. Holmes, "Application of Fluid Amplification to Rocketry," R-RCA-63-2, Harry Diamond Laboratories, Washington, D. C.

[2] A. B. Holmes and J. E. Foxwell, Jr., "Supersonic Fluid Amplification with Various Expansion Ratio Nozzles," Harry Diamond Laboratories, *Proceedings of the Fluid Amplification Symposium*, Vol. IV, p. 123, May, 1964.

[3] Technical reports of U.S. Army Missile Command, "Experimental Design of a Fluid-Controlled Hot Gas Valve," Report No. RE-TR-62-9, December, 1962.

"Development of a Pure Fluid Missile Control System," Report No. RG-TR-65-22, September, 1965.

"The Development of a Hot Gas Reaction Control Valve for an Antitank Missile," J. C. Dunaway, Report No. RG-TR-65-23, September, 1965

[4] J. Yalamanchili, "Supersonic Fluid Amplifier Performance Characteristics," Honeywell Document 6D-F-502, Vol. A, February, 1966.

[5] J. Yalamanchili, "Flow Process in the Turbulent Mixing Region of a Supersonic Fluid Amplifier Using the Free Jet Analysis," Honeywell Document 6D-F-502, Vol. B, February, 1966.

[6] R. C. Olson and D. P. Miller, "Aerodynamic Studies of Free and Attached Jets," United Aircraft Corp., Research Laboratories Report A-1771-24, December 1963.

[7] W. R. Sears, "General Theory of High Speed Aerodynamics," Princeton Series, Vol. VI, Princeton University Press.

[8] C. R. Strom, "The Method of Characteristics for Three-Dimensional Steady and Unsteady Reacting Gas Flow," Ph.D. Dissertation, University of Illinois, 1965.

[9] R. J. Prozan, "Development of a Method of Characteristics Solution of Supersonic Flow of an Ideal, Frozen, or Equilibrium Reacting Gas Mixture," LMSC/HREC A 782535, Lockheed Missiles & Space Company, April, 1966.

[10] M. Arens and E. Spiegler, "Shock-Induced Boundary Layer Separation in Over-expanded Conical Exhaust Nozzles," *Journal AIAA*, Vol. 1, No. 3, pp. 578-581, March, 1963.

[11] S. Kalt and D. L. Badal, "Conical Rocket Nozzle Performance under Flow-Separated Conditions," Journal, *Spacecraft, Engineering Notes*, Vol. 2, No. 3, pp. 447-449, May-June, 1965.

[12] R. C. Farmer, R. J. Prozan, L. R. McGimsey, and A. W. Ratliff, "Verification of a Mathematical Model Which Represent Large, Liquid Rocket-Engine Exhaust Plumes," *AIAA* Paper No. 66-650, AIAA 2nd Propulsion Joint Specialist Conference, June, 1966.

[13] H. H. Korst, "Dynamics and Thermodynamics of Separated Flows," Symposium Proceedings, Single and Multi-Component Flow Processes, Rutgers, The State University, New Brunswick, New Jersey, 1965.

The Effect of Aspect Ratio and Offset on Nozzle Flow and Jet Reattachment

D. I. McRee

H. L. Moses

Corning Glass Works
Raleigh, North Carolina

Abstract

A theoretical analysis of the flow of an incompressible fluid in a convergent nozzle with a finite aspect ratio is presented. A simplified model of the flow is then adopted to predict the effect of aspect ratio on jet reattachment.

Experimental results for the reattachment of a confined jet issuing from nozzles with varying aspect ratios and wall offset are described and compared with the theoretical model. An improved correlation is developed by use of an experimentally determined constant in the analysis.

Nomenclature

A_{ef} = effective

a = distance between side walls

AR = aspect ratio, a/b

b = nozzle exit width

c = distance to virtual origin

D = wall offset

h = nozzle width at any x-position

J = jet momentum per unit depth

J_R = momentum of jet returned at reattachment

k = constant

L = reattachment length

P = static pressure

P_s = supply pressure

P_∞ = atmospheric pressure

P_b = bubble pressure

P_w = wall static pressure

Q = volume flow per unit depth

Q_E = entrained flow from separation bubble

Q_L = total jet flow at reattachment

Q_R = returned flow at reattachment

Q_s = secondary flow

R = radius of jet centerline

R_b = Reynolds number, $U_e\ b/\nu$

s = distance along curved jet

u = shear layer velocity

U = free stream velocity

U_c = jet centerline velocity

x = distance parallel to flow

y = distance normal to flow

$\bar{y}$ = shift of jet centerline from circular arc

z = distance normal to side walls

δ = boundary layer thickness

δ_a = mean boundary layer thickness

δ^* = displacement thickness

δ^{**} = momentum thickness

η = similarity parameter, $\sigma y/x$

$\bar{\eta}$ = reattaching streamline

σ = jet spreading parameter

ρ = fluid density

ν = fluid viscosity

θ = reattaching angle

τ_w = wall shear stress

ξ = distance to convergence point of streamline

Subscripts

0 = conditions at center of span, $z = 0$

1 = curved nozzle wall boundary layers

2 = side wall boundary layers

e = nozzle exit conditions

$2D$ = two-dimensional

Introduction

A study of the literature on jet reattachment revealed that information on geometries directly applicable to fluidic devices was very limited. With the exception of limited data obtained by Sher [3], Wilson [9], and Müller [4] with aspect ratios of 4, 1.6, and 0.6 respectively, all the information found was at aspect ratios of six or greater (1-10). From their results and from the work of Comparin et al [10], and Kantola [11], it was concluded that wall attachment is strongly dependent upon aspect ratio, particularly for small values. Most fluidic devices are designed with an aspect ratio of 4 or less.

The existing data also indicated that there is an effect of Reynolds number on the attachment length. This variation appeared to be significant for Reynolds numbers less than 5000, particularly for small aspect ratios, and relatively unimportant for Reynolds numbers between 5000 and 12,000.

Several analytical models for the attachment distance were found in references [1], [2], [3], [6], [8], [12], and [15] for the two-dimensional case. With the limited amount of experimental data and the difficulty of treating three-dimensional effects, no attempt to solve the three-dimensional case analytically was found. A qualitative discussion of this effect is given by Kantola [11]. It was realized that before a two-dimensional model could be used with confidence, or a three-dimensional model developed, the effects of finite aspect ratio on the attaching phenomena would have to be determined.

This paper presents the effects of varying offset, aspect ratio, and Reynolds number on the wall attachment length.

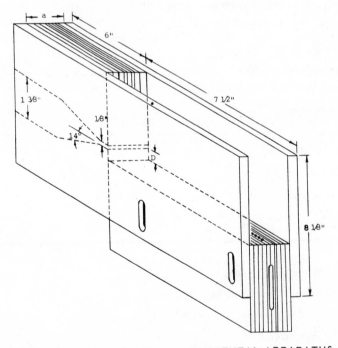

FIG. 1 SCHEMATIC OF THE EXPERIMENTAL APPARATUS

Apparatus and Experiment

A schematic diagram of the test apparatus is shown in Fig. 1. The device is machined of brass in laminated layers so that the aspect ratio can be varied through a range of 1 to 9. The nozzle is 1/8 inch in width at the exit with a convergence angle of 14 degrees. The chamber is 1 3/8 inches wide, resulting in a chamber-to-nozzle area ratio of eleven.

The attachment wall can be moved to vary the offset. Forty static pressure taps 1/32 inch in diameter are located along the attachment wall at a spacing of 1/8 inch. The first static pressure tap is located 1/8 inch from the nozzle exit.

Data was recorded at zero wall angle; aspect ratios of 1, 2, 3, 5, and 9; offsets of 2, 4, 6, and 10 nozzle widths; and Reynolds numbers of 2000, 4000, 8000, and 12,000. Reynolds numbers were calculated using the relation

$$R_b = \left[2 \frac{(P_s - P_e) \, b^2}{\rho \nu^2} \right]^{\frac{1}{2}}$$

and set by adjusting $P_s - P_e$ across the nozzle. The values of P_s and P_e were measured by static pressure taps in the jet chamber (P_s) and at the nozzle exit (P_e).

The attachment was initially determined by two techniques. The first method was to locate closely spaced drops of a silicone oil-carbon black mixture along the attachment wall. The attachment could be observed by a change in direction of the drop motion along the wall. Because of three-dimensional effects, the attachment did not form a straight line, so the attachment length was determined midway between the parallel walls. The second technique was to move a flattened total pressure probe, 0.036 inch in height and 0.080 inch wide, along the centerline of the attachment wall. The total pressure and static pressure along the wall were plotted and the point where the total pressure was equal to the static pressure was considered the attachment point. The silicone oil-lampblack technique and the probe technique for measuring the attachment length agreed within a few per cent. After initial tests to evaluate the probe method of locating the attachment point, this technique was used throughout the remainder of the investigation.

Analysis

Aspect Ratio Effects on Nozzle Flow

To analyze the effect of a finite aspect ratio on the jet reattachment, the wall boundary layers at the nozzle exit must be determined.

With the primary emphasis being boundary layer development in the nozzle, the following assumptions are made:

a. the flow is laminar and incompressible (consistent with the range of experiments);
b. the flow consists of wall boundary layers and an inviscid core;
c. boundary layers on opposite walls are identical;
d. the pressure is constant at any cross section;

e.   secondary flow and corner effects are negligible in the nozzle;

f.   the velocity profile in the boundary layers is given by

$$\frac{u}{U} = 2\frac{y}{\delta} - \left(\frac{y}{\delta}\right)^2 \tag{1}$$

and consequently

$$\frac{\delta^*}{\delta} = \frac{1}{3} \quad \text{and} \quad \frac{\delta^{**}}{\delta} = \frac{2}{15} \quad .$$

The restriction of a constant velocity profile shape, assumption f, is of course unnecessary, but greatly simplifies the problem. With assumptions $a - e$, the boundary layer equation can be solved as accurately as desired. In view of the approximations that must be made to complete the analysis, however, assumption f seems well justified.

From assumptions a and b, the Euler equation may be written for the inviscid core.

$$\frac{dP}{dx} = -\rho U \frac{dU}{dx} \quad . \tag{2}$$

Applying the continuity equation,

$$\frac{dU}{U} + \frac{dA_{ef}}{A_{ef}} = 0 \tag{3}$$

where the effective area, A_{ef}, is given by

$$A_{ef} = (h - 2\delta_1^*)(a - 2\delta_2^*) \quad .$$

The boundary layer on the curved nozzle walls may be determined by use of the momentum integral equation [ref. 13, p. 139].

$$\frac{d\delta_1^{**}}{dx} + (\delta_1^* + 2\delta_1^{**}) \frac{1}{U} \frac{dU}{dx} = \frac{\tau_{w1}}{\rho U^2} \quad . \tag{4}$$

For the assumed velocity profiles,

$$\frac{\tau_w}{\rho U^2} = \frac{\nu}{U^2}\left(\frac{\partial u}{\partial y}\right)_w = \frac{4}{15R_b} \frac{U_e}{U} \frac{b}{\delta^{**}} \quad .$$

In the boundary layer on the side walls, it is assumed that the streamlines converge uniformly; i.e., the flow is collateral. This is consistent with the one-dimensional pressure assumption. The momentum integral equation is then: [ref. 13, p. 586]

$$\frac{d\delta_2^{**}}{dx} - \frac{\delta_2^{**}}{\xi} + (\delta_2^* + 2\delta_2^{**}) \frac{1}{U} \frac{dU}{dx} = \frac{\tau_{w2}}{\rho U^2}$$

146

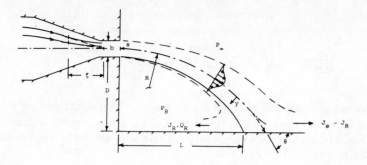

FIG. 2 TWO-DIMENSIONAL MODEL

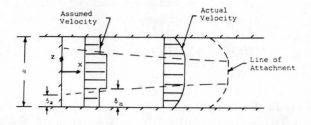

Top View

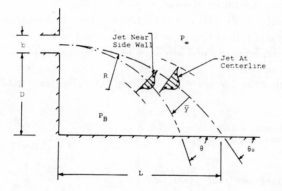

FIG. 3 THREE-DIMENSIONAL MODEL

where ξ is the distance to the point of convergence of the streamline tangents. (see Fig. 2)

From the continuity equation,

$$\frac{1}{\xi} = -\frac{1}{h-2\delta_1^*} \frac{d(h-2\delta_1^*)}{dx} \approx \frac{1}{U}\frac{dU}{dx} \; .$$

Then

$$\frac{d\delta_2^{**}}{dx} + \left(\delta_2^* + \delta_2^{**}\right) \frac{1}{U}\frac{dU}{dx} = \frac{\tau_{w_2}}{\rho U^2} \ . \tag{5}$$

Equations (3), (4), and (5) form a set of differential equations for the two boundary layer thicknesses and the velocity, U. These equations have been solved numerically for the experimental nozzle with the following results at the nozzle exit: $(AR = 3)$

R_b	δ_1/b	δ_2/b
2000	.148	.154
4000	.111	.115
8000	.080	.083
12000	.066	.068

Two-Dimensional Jet Reattachment

Since a number of approximate models have been proposed, the analysis starts with the two-dimensional case. The primary interest, however, is the effect of a finite aspect ratio, so one of the simplest two-dimensional models that agrees with the data is adopted. The three-dimensional effects are then treated as a correction to the two-dimensional case.

Except for equations (6), (7), and (14), the analysis is essentially that of Borque and Newman [1] (first theory, attachment point model). It is briefly described here for completeness and arranged in a form more convenient to the three-dimensional model.

It is assumed that the jet velocity profile in the fully developed region can be expressed by

$$\frac{u}{U_c} = \text{sech}^2 \eta \ , \qquad \text{where} \quad \eta = \frac{\sigma y}{s+c} \ .$$

The free jet conserves momentum, or

$$J = J_e = \int_{-\infty}^{\infty} \rho u^2 \, dy = \frac{4}{3} \rho \frac{U_c^2}{\sigma} (s+c)$$

then

$$U_c = \frac{1}{2}\sqrt{\frac{3\sigma J_e}{\rho(s+c)}} \ .$$

The volume flow is given by

$$Q = \int_{-\infty}^{\infty} u\,dy = U_e b \sqrt{\frac{3(s+c)}{\sigma b}} \ .$$

148

Simson [14] indicates that the jet becomes fully developed at approximately five nozzle widths downstream of the exit. This approximation depends on a reasonably flat profile at the exit and to some extent on the Reynolds number, but for the range considered, the attachment length is nearly independent of Reynolds number for large aspect ratios.

Conserving momentum with $U_c = U_e$ at the end of the core region, the virtual origin can be determined.

$$c = \frac{3}{4}\,\sigma b - 5b \quad . \tag{6}$$

This approach is slightly different from that of Borque and Newman [1], who assume that the rate of entrainment is the same in both regions, but gives the same result when $\sigma = 12$.

The total length of entrainment as a function of θ, is given from geometrical considerations, approximately (see Fig. 2)

$$\frac{S}{b} \approx \frac{D}{b}\,\frac{\theta}{1-\cos\theta} \quad . \tag{7}$$

This length is shorter and more nearly equals the actual entrainment edge length than does the jet centerline, which was used by Borque and Newman [1]. Furthermore, the entrainment length should be decreased because of the rising pressure near attachment.

Then, the total volume flow at reattachment is

$$\frac{Q_L}{Q_e} = \frac{3}{2}\sqrt{1 + \frac{4}{3\sigma}\left(\frac{D}{b}\,\frac{\theta}{1-\cos\theta} - 5\right)} \quad , \tag{8}$$

and the flow entrained from the separation bubble is

$$\frac{Q_E}{Q_L} = \frac{1}{2}\left[1 - \frac{Q_e}{Q_L}\right] \quad . \tag{9}$$

The entrained flow for the two-dimensional jet is shown in Fig. 4 for several values of D/b.

For a momentum balance at reattachment [ref. 1]

$$\frac{J_R}{J_e} = \frac{1-\cos\theta}{2} \quad , \tag{10}$$

but from integration of the velocity profiles

$$\frac{J_R}{J_e} = \left[\frac{1}{2} - \frac{3}{4}\tanh\eta + \frac{1}{4}\tanh^3\eta\right] \tag{11}$$

149

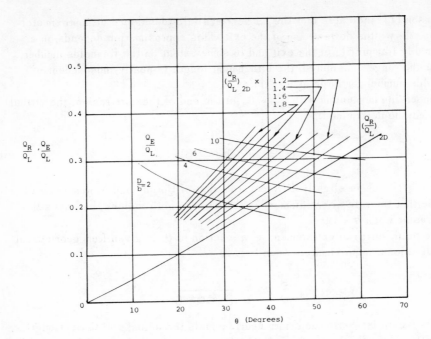

FIG. 4 GRAPHICAL SOLUTION OF ATTACHMENT ANGLE

and

$$\frac{Q_R}{Q_L} = \frac{1}{2}\left[1 - \tanh \bar{\eta}\right]. \tag{12}$$

Thus, by eliminating $\bar{\eta}$ and using equation (10), the return flow is only a function of the angle, θ. (see Fig. 4)

$$\frac{Q_R}{Q_L} = f(\theta) \approx k\theta . \tag{13}$$

Finally the solution is obtained by equating the entrained flow to the return flow.

$$\frac{Q_R}{Q_L} = \frac{Q_E}{Q_L} .$$

The attachment length, then, is approximately

$$\frac{L}{b} \approx \frac{D}{b} \tan\left(\frac{180 - \theta}{2}\right) . \tag{14}$$

This result is simpler but more approximate than that of Bourque and Newman [1].

Fig. 5 shows the attachment length for two values of σ compared with experimental data.

150

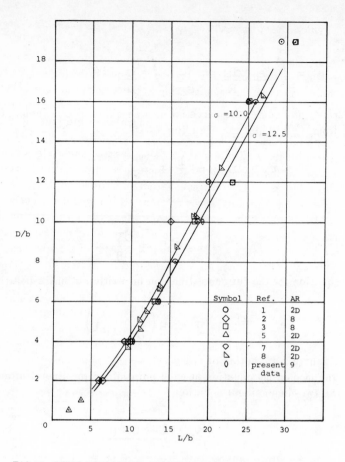

FIG. 5 COMPARISON OF TWO-DIMENSIONAL ANALYTICAL
ATTACHMENT LENGTH WITH EXPERIMENT

Reattachment of Jet with Finite Aspect Ratio

General Analysis:

As with the two-dimensional jet, it is assumed that the bubble pressure is constant, and for a momentum balance in the radial direction

$$P_\infty - P_b = \frac{J_e}{R} = J \text{ x curvature.} \qquad (15)$$

Since the momentum per unit depth of jet, J, is less near the side walls because of friction, the curvature of the jet centerline must be greater. The curvature of the jet centerline must be greater. The curvature can be expressed in terms of the angle, θ,

$$\text{curvature} = \frac{d\theta}{ds} \quad .$$

151

Then,

$$\theta = \int_0^S \frac{J_e}{J} \frac{ds}{R} = \frac{\theta_o}{S_o} \int_0^S \frac{J_e}{J} \, ds \ .$$ (16)

As an alternate procedure, the curvature can be expressed in terms of a small deviation, $\bar{y}$, from the circular arc of radius R.

$$\text{curvature} = \frac{1}{R} + \frac{\bar{y}''}{R^2} + \frac{\bar{y}}{R^2}$$ (17)

where

$$\bar{y}' = \frac{d\bar{y}}{d\theta} \ .$$

Then the equation for the jet centerline can be written at any z-position.

$$\bar{y}'' + \bar{y} = R\left(\frac{J_e}{J} - 1\right)$$ (18)

where J is, in general, a function of x and z.

Assuming the momentum equation at each point along the line of attachment is the same as the two-dimensional equation,

$$\frac{J_R}{J} = \frac{1-\cos\theta}{2} \ .$$ (19)

Since the attachment angle is larger near the side walls, the return flow as a fraction of the total jet flow is larger.

$$\frac{Q_R}{Q_L} = f(\theta) \approx k\theta \ .$$ (20)

With no control flow and steady state conditions,

$$2\int_0^{a/2} Q_R \, dz = 2\int_0^{a/2} Q_L f(\theta) \, dz = 2\int_0^{a/2} Q_E \, dz \ .$$ (21)

In order to complete the solution, a relation for the jet entrainment and momentum loss near the side walls must be introduced.

Approximate Solution:

In carrying out an approximate solution the following assumptions are made:

a) the jet centerline velocity, U_c/U_{co}, decays as a turbulent boundary layer on the side walls;

152

b) in calculating the secondary flow an average boundary layer may be assumed

$$\frac{U_c}{U_{co}} = 0.7 \qquad 0 < z - a/2 < \delta_a$$

$$= 1.0 \qquad \delta_a < z - a/2 < a/2 \quad ;$$

c) the jet momentum is proportional to the square of the centerline velocity in the boundary layer

$$\frac{J}{J_e} = (\frac{U_c}{U_{co}})^2 \approx 0.5 \qquad .$$

d) the entrainment is equal to that of the two-dimensional jet (with $\sigma = 12.5$). With assumption c), equation (16) can be integrated

$$\theta = \theta_o \frac{J_e}{J} \frac{s}{s_o} \approx 2\theta_o \frac{s}{s_o} \qquad .$$

As a first approximation, the jet length, s, is assumed constant and equal to s_o, thus

$$\theta \approx 2\theta_o \qquad 0 < z - a/2 < \delta_a$$

$$= \theta_o \qquad \delta_a < z - a/2 < a/2 \quad .$$

A more exact expression for s gives

$$\theta = \cos^{-1} \left[1 - \frac{2b}{R}(\frac{D}{b} + \frac{1}{2}) \right] \qquad .$$

With assumption d), equation (21) can be integrated

$$\frac{Q_E}{Q_L} = \int_0^{a/2} f(\theta)\,dz \Big/ \int_0^{a/2} dz \qquad ,$$

but

$$\int_0^{a/2} f(\theta)\,dz = f(\theta)\frac{a}{2}\left(1 + \frac{2\delta_a}{a}\right) \qquad ,$$

and

$$f(\theta) = \left(\frac{Q_R}{Q_L}\right)_{2D} \quad ,$$

then

$$\frac{Q_E}{Q_L} \approx \left(\frac{Q_R}{Q_L}\right)_{2D} \left[1 + \frac{2\delta_a}{a}\right] \qquad (22)$$

where $\left(\frac{Q_R}{Q_L}\right)_{2D}$ is the return flow ratio for two-dimensional flow.

The boundary layer thickness on the side walls can be approximated by using the flat plate relation, [ref. 13, p. 537]

$$\frac{\delta^{**}}{b} = .036 \left(\frac{s+c}{b}\right)^{4/5} R_b^{-1/5} \qquad (23)$$

where the virtual origin is determined from the nozzle exit boundary layer

$$\frac{c}{b} = \left(\frac{\delta_2}{b}\right)^{5/4} R_b^{1/4} \quad .$$

For the step boundary layer, assumption b, $\delta \approx 5\delta^{**}$ and the average,

$$\delta_a = 5 \left(\frac{\delta_2^{**} + \delta^{**}}{2}\right) \quad .$$

Thus, assuming $s \approx s_o$, the average boundary layer thickness can be determined as a function of the attachment angle, θ.

Equation (22) is then used to modify the two-dimensional analysis, as shown graphically in Fig. 4. Equation (14) completes the approximate solution, Fig. 6.

Correlation with Experimental Results:

Equation (22) relates the entrained flow to the flow returned at the attachment point, with the last term accounting for the additional return flow near the side wall, or secondary flow. Since a number of approximations are made in its derivation, an empirical equation of the same form is adopted.

$$\frac{Q_E}{Q_L} = \left(\frac{Q_R}{Q_L}\right)_{2D} \left[1 + \frac{Q_s}{Q_R}\right] \qquad (24)$$

154

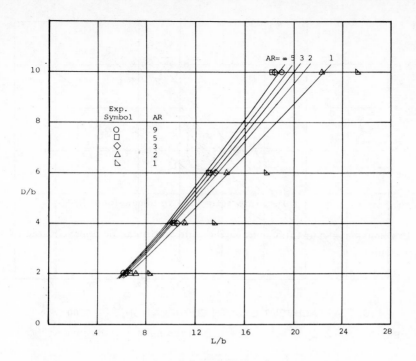

FIG. 6 APPROXIMATE CALCULATION OF ATTACHMENT
LENGTH COMPARED WITH EXPERIMENT $R_b = 8000$

As indicated in equation (22), the secondary flow should be proportional to
the ratio of an average boundary layer thickness to the depth, a.

$$\frac{Q_S}{Q_R} = \frac{g(R_b, D/b)}{AR} \quad .$$

Using the experimental data, a reasonably good correlation is found with the
expression,

$$\frac{Q_S}{Q_R} = \frac{40}{AR \sqrt{R_b}} \quad . \tag{25}$$

Equation (24), then, is used to modify the two-dimensional model, as shown
graphically in Fig. 4. The resulting correlation is shown in Figs. 7, 8, 9, and 10.

Discussion

Since the primary objective of this work is to determine the effect of finite
aspect ratios on jet reattachment, there is no attempt to improve existing two-
dimensional models. One of the simplest models, essentially that given by
Borque and Newman [1], is adopted for large aspect ratios. Some of the assumptions of this analysis have been improved by more recent authors, but perhaps
the weakest and most convenient assumption is that of constant bubble pressure.

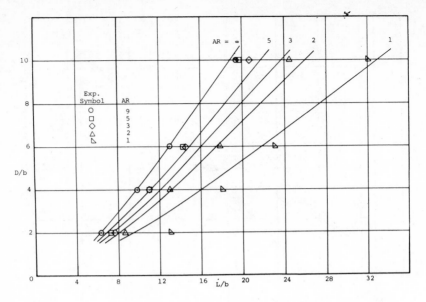

FIG. 7 ATTACHMENT LENGTH CORRELATION, $R_b = 2000$

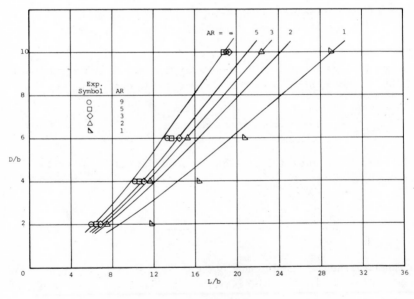

FIG. 8 ATTACHMENT LENGTH CORRELATION, $R_b = 4000$

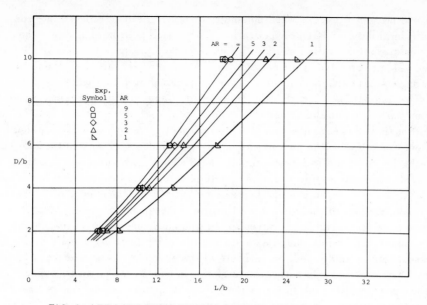

FIG. 9 ATTACHMENT LENGTH CORRELATION, R_b = 8000

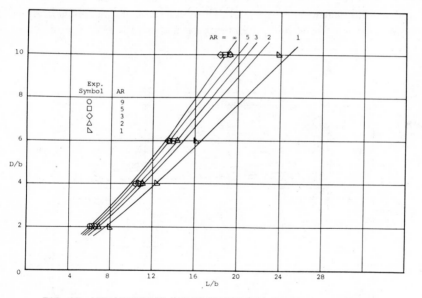

FIG. 10 ATTACHMENT LENGTH CORRELATION, R_b = 12,000

157

In the present work, a spread parameter, $\sigma = 12.5$, is used to correlate the experimental data for large aspect ratios. This value is somewhat larger than that found experimentally for a free jet as the model assumes ($\sigma = 7.7$ for the assumed velocity profiles in a free jet). Several reasons for this discrepancy have been suggested, such as reduced entrainment caused by jet curvature and increasing pressure near attachment. However, the analysis is approximate and σ is simply *used* to correlate the experimental data.

With a finite aspect ratio, the jet loses momentum near the side walls due to friction. Since the bubble pressure is nearly constant, especially in the z-direction, the jet curvature is increased near the walls. This results in a larger attachment angle and a larger fraction of return to total jet flow near the walls and a smaller fraction in the center, thus moving the attachment point downstream. The relative effect of this secondary flow increases with decreasing aspect ratio.

By assuming that the jet behaves as a turbulent boundary layer on the side walls, which can be introduced as a step in the velocity profile, and that the entrainment rate is unaffected, an estimate of the secondary flow effect can be made. The results of this estimate are shown in Fig. 6. As might be expected from the complexity of the flow and the nature of approximations, an estimate that makes no recourse to experimental data is not completely satisfactory. The predicted effect of secondary flow does show the correct trend, but is considerably less than the actual effect. One reason for a secondary flow larger than predicted is the high pressure at the attachment point of the center flow, which is downstream of the attachment near the wall. This high pressure causes more flow to be returned near the walls than predicted by equation (18).

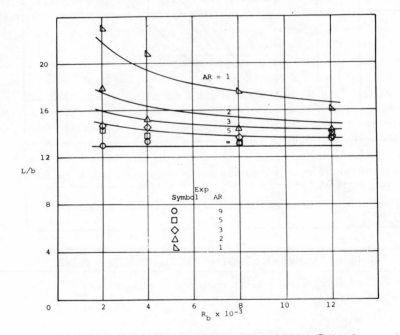

FIG. 11 ATTACHMENT LENGTH CORRELATION, $D/b = 6$

158

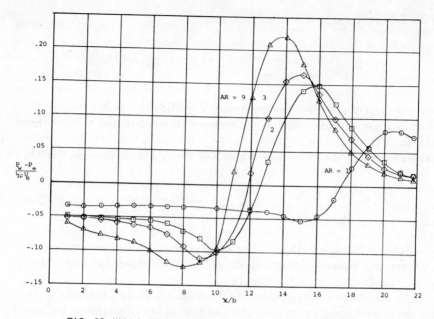

FIG. 12 WALL STATIC PRESSURE DISTRIBUTION FOR
$D/b = 6$ AND $R_b = 4000$

Perhaps the main result of the analysis is to provide a framework in which to attempt an experimental correlation. It is assumed that the form of equation (22) is correct; i.e., the return flow, which must equal the entrained flow, is increased by secondary flow. It is further assumed that the relative secondary flow is inversely proportional to the product of aspect ratio and the square root of the Reynolds number, and not dependent upon offset. The effect of nozzle shape should not be important if the exit boundary layers are relatively thin.

The final results of the experimental correlation are shown in Figs. 7, 8, 9, 10, and 11. As with all analyses of this type, the introduction of an experimental constant gives rise to the question of generality. The comparison simply indicates the degree to which the data *correlates* with a limited number of experimental constants. Considering the complexity of the flow and the fact that the attempted correction is usually regarded as a second order effect, the correlation is quite satisfactory.

The effect of aspect ratio on the wall static pressure distribution is shown in Fig. 12.

Summary and Conclusions

1) For the two-dimensional jet, the entrained flow is given by

$$\frac{Q_E}{Q_L} = \frac{1}{2} - \frac{1}{3\sqrt{1 + \frac{4}{3\sigma}(\frac{D}{b}\frac{\theta}{1 - \cos\theta} - 5)}}$$

and the flow returned at the attachment point

$$(\frac{Q_R}{Q_L})_{2D} = f(\theta) \approx k\theta$$

where $f(\theta)$ depends on the assumed velocity profiles ($k \approx 0.305$ radians^{-1}).

Equating the entrained flow to the returned flow determines the attachment angle, θ.

The attachment length is then determined from the approximate relation,

$$\frac{L}{b} = \frac{D}{b} \tan (\frac{180-\theta}{2}) \quad .$$

2) Jet attachment length is increased greatly at small aspect ratios (as much as 100 per cent increase for an aspect ratio of one compared to nine). The effect is dependent on Reynolds number.

3) An analytical model developed independently of the experimental data predicts the correct trend but gives values somewhat less than the actual effect of aspect ratios.

4) Assuming the form of the equation developed in the analysis to modify the return flow,

$$\frac{Q_R}{Q_L} = (\frac{Q_R}{Q_L})_{2D} \left[1 + g(AR, R_b, D/b) \right]$$

the data correlates quite satisfactorily with

$$g = \frac{40}{AR \sqrt{R_b}} \quad ,$$

assuming Q_E/Q_L is the same as that for the two-dimensional case.

References

[1] C. Bourque and B. G. Newman, "Reattachment of a Two-Dimensional Incompressible Jet to an Adjacent Flat Plate." The Aeronautical Quarterly, Vol. XI, August 1960.

[2] Seldon G. Levin and Francis M. Manion, "Jet Attachment Distance as a Function of Adjacent Wall Offset and Angle." Fluid Amplification 5, Harry Diamond Laboratories, December 31, 1962.

[3] Neil C. Sher, "Jet Attachment and Switching in Bistable Fluid Amplifiers." ASME Publication 64-FE-19.

[4] H. R. Müller, "A Study of the Dynamic Features of a Wall-Reattachment Fluid Amplifier." ASME 64-FE-10.

[5] Thomas J. Mueller, "An Experimental Investigation of the Reattachment of Compressible Two-Dimensional Jets." ASME 64-FE-18.

[6] R. E. Olson and Y. T. Chen, "Studies of Reattaching Jet Flows in Fluid-State Devices." Fluid Amplification 17, AD623911, September 1965.

[7] John R. C. Pedersen, "The Flow of Turbulent Incompressible Two-Dimensional Jets Over Ventilated Cavities." Proceedings of the Fluid Amplification Symposium, October 1965, Vol. 1.

[8] R. A. Sawyer, "The Flow Due to A Two-Dimensional Jet Issuing Parallel to a Flat Plate," May 1960.

[9] James N. Wilson, "A Fluid Analog to Digital Conversion System." Report No. EDC 7-64-4, Case Institute of Technology, Engineering Design Center.

[10] R. A. Comparin, *et al*, "Fluid Switching Elements and Amplifiers." IBM Research, Research Report R2-94, July 23, 1962.

[11] Robert A. Kantola, "Development Aspects of a Miniature Fluid Counter," General Electric Company, Schenectady, New York.

[12] R. A. Sawyer, "Two-Dimensional Reattaching Jet Flows Including the Effects of Curvature on Entrainment." Journal of Fluid Mechanics, May 1963.

[13] H. Schlicting, "Boundary Layer Theory," McGraw-Hill, New York, N. Y., 1960, Fourth Edition.

[14] A. K. Simson, "A Theoretical Study of the Design Parameters of Subsonic Pressure Controlled, Fluid Jet Amplifiers." Ph.D. Thesis, M.I.T., 1963.

[15] F. T. Brown, "Pneumatic Pulse Transmission with Bistable-Jet-Relay Reception and Amplification." Sc.O. Thesis, M.I.T., 1962.

Feasibility Study
of a Laminar NOR Unit

M. Lucius Walker, Jr.

Howard University
Washington, D.C.

R. Pierce Trask, II

Harry Diamond Laboratories
Washington, D.C.

Abstract

Analytical·and experimental investigations are made into the feasibility of miniature flueric NOR elements operating in the laminar flow regime for developing
low power logic circuits.

The results of the analytical investigation based on a simplified physical
model indicate that fan-out ratios of about 10 might be achieved.

A basic NOR element was constructed and the influence of geometric parameters excluded from the theoretical analysis was systematically investigated.

NOR units were then designed incorporating the results of the preliminary experimental and theoretical considerations and tested for static operating characteristics under various loading conditions. The trends observed experimentally
were found to be in general agreement with the theoretical results.

The fan-out ratios obtained from the tests indicate the feasibility of the design for a low power consumption element for flueric logic circuits.

Nomenclature

A = area

a,b = constants, accounting for the wall jet and free jet development lengths

C = nozzle coefficient

$F(\xi)$ = free jet similarity function

$f(\eta)$ = wall jet similarity function

H = depth of element

L = distance between power jet nozzle and collector

N = fan-out ratio

n = empirical exponent related to receiver characteristics

P = pressure

Q = flow per unit depth

R = ratio of pressures at receiver used to define off mode

R_e = Reynolds number

R_e* = effective Reynolds number = R_e (W_j/x)

U = uniform velocity distribution at nozzle

u = velocity distribution

W = nozzle width

x, y = spatial coordinates within element

θ = prescribed angle of deflection of power jet

η, ξ = similarity parameters

ρ = density

τ = effective flow width

Subscripts

B = bleed

bl = infinite resistance load

c = control jet

fj = effective free jet

j = power jet nozzle

nl = zero resistance load

o = output receiver

opt = optimized

p = fractional

v = vent

Introduction

Low power consumption and rapid switching time are features desirable in logic circuits composed of large numbers of fluid elements. A third important feature, compactness, is related to the first two, since power consumption is proportional to the cube of the Reynolds number and switching time is proportional to a length dimension of the element. Combining these features into one element suggests that the flow phenomena within that element should be in the laminar regime rather than in the turbulent regime, as commonly prevails today.

The purpose of this investigation is to explore the feasibility of a two-input NOR element based on the assumption that the flow remains laminar throughout its range of operation. A NOR element was selected for this study because it is generic to any type of logic system, either combinatorial or sequential.

Geometry and Operation of the NOR Element

The basic geometry of the NOR element considered in the study is illustrated in Fig. 1. The power jet issues from the nozzle W_j and either is recovered at the

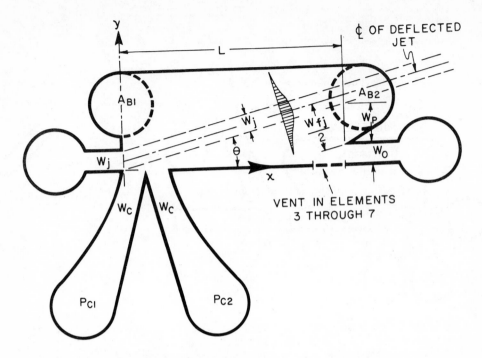

FIG. 1 THE BASIC GEOMETRY CONSIDERED IN THIS INVESTIGATION

collector, W_o, or is diverted from it. The latter, shown in Fig. 1, is effected by the application of a control pressure signal to one or both of the control ports P_{c1} or P_{c2}, while the former occurs in the absence of any signal.

It is noted that the design of this element differs from that of many other fluid elements in that the power jet flows straight into the receiver without having to change direction because of adjacent wall setback or angle. Although this design sacrifices some deflection of the power jet for a given control pressure, as shown in the work of Powell [1], it was found that, in terms of the overall performance of a NOR element, the increased control flow resistance more than compensates for the loss in deflection angle.

The flow collected by the output receiver of any one element in a circuit is admitted to one of the control ports of several subsequent elements in that circuit and serves to deflect the power jets of the subsequent elements driving them into an off mode as shown in Fig. 2. The number of subsequent elements that may be driven in this manner by one element is known as the fan-out ratio N of the driving element. This ratio must be greater than or equal to two for an element to operate in a system without the undesirable addition of buffer amplifier elements.

Theoretical Investigation

Two conditions must be satisfied for the system sketched in Fig. 2 to remain in equilibrium with the driven elements in the off position. The flow received in the output aperture of the driving element must just balance the flow into the control ports of the actuated elements and, simultaneously, the pressure developed at those controls must be sufficient to maintain the prescribed deflection.

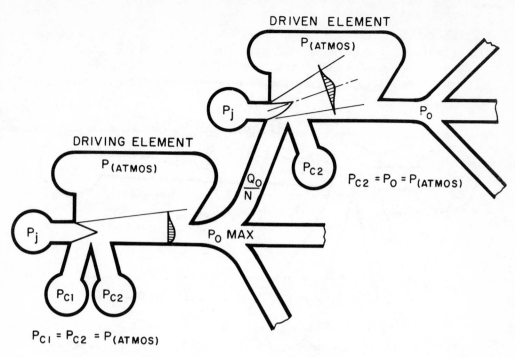

FIG. 2 OPERATION OF NOR ELEMENT

Mathematically the continuity condition may be expressed as

$$Q_o = N Q_c \tag{1}$$

The study of receiver-diffuser combinations by Reid [2] suggests that the output characteristics of a diffuser may be typically represented by the following empirical relationship between recovered pressure and volume flow rate

$$\frac{P_o}{P_{i\ell}} = 1 - \left(\frac{Q_o}{Q_{n\ell}}\right)^n \tag{2}$$

Assuming that the pressure drop along the manifold is negligible ($P_c \doteq P_o$), the flow out of a control may be written as

$$Q_c = C_c \tau \sqrt{\frac{2 P_o}{\rho}} \tag{3}$$

where C_c is a discharge coefficient expressing the losses in the control nozzle and in the clearance region between the power jet and the straight wall.

Substituting equations (2) and (3) into equation (1) yields an expression for the number of elements being actuated by a driving element

$$N = \frac{Q_{n\ell} \left(1 - \frac{P_o}{P_{i\ell}}\right)^{\frac{1}{n}}}{C_c \tau \sqrt{\frac{2 P_o}{\rho}}} \tag{4}$$

165

This number becomes the fan-out ratio of the driving element when pressure P_o is sufficient to maintain the other power jets at some prescribed angle θ for which they are considered off. The tangent of the deflection angle θ may be approximately expressed in terms of the power jet pressure and the control pressure as

$$\tan \theta = \frac{P_c \, W_c}{2 \, C_j^2 \, P_j \, W_j} \tag{5}$$

Solving for the required control pressure and substituting it into equation (4) gives the fan-out ratio of the element $(P_c \doteq P_o)$.

$$N = \frac{Q_{n\ell}\left(1 - \dfrac{2 C_j^2 \, P_j \, W_j \tan \theta}{P_{r\ell} \, W_c}\right)^{\frac{1}{n}}}{C_c \, W_c \tan \theta \left(\dfrac{4 C_j^2 \, P_j \, W_j \tan \theta}{f \, W_c}\right)^{\frac{1}{2}}} \tag{6}$$

in which the clearance between the jet and the wall has been approximated by $W_c \tan \theta$.

The variables appearing in equation (6) are independent of the control nozzle width (with the possible exception of C_c) and N may be optimized with respect to this quantity.

setting $\dfrac{dN}{dW_c} = 0$ yields

$$W_{c \, opt} = \left(\frac{n+2}{n}\right)\left(\frac{2 C_j^2 \, P_j \, W_j \tan \theta}{P_{b\ell}}\right) \tag{7}$$

Substituting this equation into equation (6) gives the maximum value of the fan-out ratio with respect to W_c

$$N_{opt} = \frac{1}{2 C_c C_j} \left(\frac{2}{n+2}\right)^{\frac{2+n}{2n}} \left(\frac{n}{2}\right)^{\frac{1}{2}} \left(\tan \theta\right)^{-2} \left(\frac{Q_{n\ell}}{Q_j}\right)\left(\frac{P_{r\ell}}{P_j}\right)^{\frac{1}{2}} \tag{8}$$

Equations (7) and (8) afford a much clearer insight into the role that the various physical quantities play in determining the fan-out ratio than equations (5) and (6). The performance of a particular element is seen to involve a trade-off between the infinite resistance load pressure recovery, the zero resistance load flow recovery, and the deflection angle required for the driven element to be in the off mode of operation.

166

Estimation of Optimum Fan-Out for Laminar Flow

By making several simplifying assumptions, an estimate of the fan-out ratio for laminar flow may be made. These assumptions are that:

1) The flow at the exit plane of the power nozzle is uniform;

2) The flow in the element is plane, two-dimensional flow;

3) The wall adjacent to the jet extends from the nozzle exit to the receiver entrance;

4) The power jet behaves as a free jet when deflected to the off position.

The quantities that must be evaluated in equations (7) and (8) are the infinite resistance load pressure P_{bl} the zero resistance load flow Q_{nl}, and the tangent of the deflection angle θ. Also, a criterion must be established for an element being in the off position.

The first two quantities may be established from the solution of Glauert [3] for the wall jet. Glauert shows that the velocity distribution for a developed plane wall jet is of the form

$$ u = U_j \left(\frac{5}{4} \, \overline{R_e^*} \right)^{1/2} f'(\eta) \tag{9} $$

where

$$ \eta = \left(\frac{5}{64} \right)^{1/4} \frac{y}{W_j} \left(\overline{R_e^*} \right)^{3/4} $$

is the wall jet similarity variable

$$ \overline{R_e^*} = \frac{R_e}{1 + a R_e} $$

is a modified effective Reynolds number in which a[1] accounts for the development length of the flow, and

$$ \eta = \ln \frac{(1 + \sqrt{f} + f)^{1/2}}{1 - \sqrt{f}} + \sqrt{3} \tan^{-1} \frac{\sqrt{3f}}{2 + \sqrt{f}} $$

is the implicit solution derived from the Prandtl boundary layer equations which relates the similarity variable to the similarity function.

---

[1] The constants a and b accounting for the wall jet and free jet development lengths, respectively, were determined by standard integral techniques for obtaining approximate solutions to the Prandtl boundary layer equations. They were found to have the following values: $a = 0.11$, $b = 0.08$.

By making the assumptions commonly used for the interaction of a free jet and a receiver, the infinite resistance load pressure and the zero resistance load flow rate are given respectively by

$$P_{irl} = \frac{1}{2W_o} \int_o^{W_o} \rho u^2 dy$$

$$= \rho U_j^2 \left(\frac{125}{4} \overline{Re} \right)^{\frac{1}{4}} \left(\frac{2f^{3/2} - f^3}{9} \right) \left(\frac{W_j}{W_o} \right) \tag{10}$$

and

$$Q_{nc} = \int_o^{W_o} u \, dy$$

$$= U_j W_j \left(\frac{20}{Re} \right)^{\frac{1}{4}} f(\eta_1) \tag{11}$$

where

$$\eta_1 = \left(\frac{5}{64} \right)^{\frac{1}{4}} \frac{W_o}{W_j} \overline{Re}^{\frac{3}{4}} \tag{12}$$

The tangent of the deflection angle θ may be evaluated from geometrical considerations. From Fig. 1 it is seen to be

$$\tan \theta = \frac{W_o + W_p}{L} \tag{13}$$

It can also be seen be seen from Fig. 1 that for small θ, the width W_p that must be added to the width of receiver in equation (13) is approximately one-half the effective width of the free jet at the receiver location minus one-half the width of the power jet, or mathematically

$$W_p = \frac{1}{2} \left(W_{fj} - W_j \right) \tag{14}$$

The effective width of the free jet is defined by the classical solution of the laminar free jet made by Schlichting [4] and by the criterion for the deflected jet being in the off position. The very conservative assumption is made that the off-position occurs when the ratio of the available infinite resistance load pressure of the deflected jet at the receiver station to the infinite resistance load pressure of the undeflected jet is less than some small prescribed ratio R.

From the solution of Schlichting and equation (10), this ratio may be expressed as

$$R = \frac{P_{b\ell}(\text{FREE JET})}{P_{b\ell}(\text{WALL JET})} = \frac{1 - \frac{3}{2}F(1 - F^3/3)}{\frac{2}{9}\left(\frac{125}{4}\overline{Re}\right)^{1/4}(2f^{3/2} - f^3)} \tag{15}$$

where

$$\xi = 0.275 \frac{y}{W_j}\overline{Re}^{2/3}$$

is the free jet similarity variable,

$$\overline{Re} = \frac{Re}{1 + bRe}$$

is a modified effective Reynolds number, in which b accounts for the free jet development length, and

$$\xi = \tan^{-1}F$$

is the solution for the similarity function.

For R to be much less than 1, the free jet must be deflected to a position where most of the momentum flux lies above the top edge of the receiver or $F = 1 - \delta$ where $\delta \ll 1$. Neglecting terms of order δ^3, the similarity variable ξ_1 may be obtained explicitly in terms of the other quantities appearing in equation (15); i.e.,

$$\xi_1 = -\frac{1}{4}\ln\left[R\left(\frac{125}{4}\overline{Re}\right)^{1/4}\frac{2f^{3/2} - f^3}{27}\right] \tag{16}$$

Now in terms of ξ_1, width W_p may be expressed as

$$\frac{W_p}{W_j} = \frac{\xi_1}{0.275}\left(\overline{Re^*}\right)^{-2/3} - \frac{1}{2} \tag{17}$$

When equations (10) and (11) are substituted into equation (8) (with $C_j = C_c = n = 1$), the fan-out ratio for plane laminar flow is given by

$$N_{opt} = 0.214\, Re^2\left[\frac{2f^{7/2} - f^5}{\ln\left[\frac{(1 + \sqrt{f} + f)^{1/2}}{1 - \sqrt{f}}\right] + \sqrt{3}\tan^{-1}\frac{\sqrt{3f}}{2 + f}}\right]^{1/2}\left[\frac{Re^{*\frac{1}{8}}}{\frac{W_o}{W_j}} + \frac{Re^*}{\frac{W_p}{W_j}}\right]^2 \tag{18}$$

in which W_o/W_j and W_p/W_j are functions of R, f, and R_e^*, given by equations (12) and (17).

169

Theoretical Results

Inspection of equation (18) reveals that the fan-out ratio has the following functional form

$$\frac{N_{opt}}{R_e^2} = G\left(f, R_e, R\right) \qquad (19)$$

This equation was numerically evaluated over a range of values of R, f, and R_e^* and the results were tabulated along with the corresponding values of W_o/W_j, which is obtained from equation (12), and $W_c R_e/W_j$, which is obtained when equations (10) and (13) are substituted into equation (7). Typical results are illustrated in Table 1 for an assumed cut-off ratio R of 5 per cent.

TABLE 1
The Solution of Equation (18) for Various Values of f and R_e^*.

f	R_e^*	(N/R_e^2)	W_o/W_j	$(W_c R_e/W_j)$	Element
0.5	15	$0.919 \times (10)^{-4}$	1.21	$0.492 \times (10)^3$	
0.6	15	1.01	1.39	0.486	
0.7	15	1.03	1.59	0.515	5
0.8	15	0.965	1.85	0.591	
0.5	20	0.663	1.12	0.537	
0.6	20	0.731	1.29	0.537	
0.7	20	0.743	1.48	0.565	6
0.8	20	0.688	1.71	0.649	
0.5	30	0.395	1.03	0.644	
0.6	30	0.434	1.18	0.639	
0.7	30	0.439	1.36	0.680	7
0.8	30	0.404	1.58	0.783	

The following observations may be made from the results:

1. Since the fan-out ratio is proportional to the square of the Reynolds number, the element should be operated at the maximum Reynolds number corresponding to laminar flow if the maximum fan-out ratio is desired.

2. A maximum fan-out occurs with respect to the similarity function at f approximately equal to 0.7; however, there is no maximum corresponding to changes in the modified Reynolds number R_e^*. Reducing R_e^* for all values of f gives an increasing value of the fan-out ratio.

For a given Reynolds number, reducing R_e^* corresponds to moving the receiver in the downstream direction. Practically, a limit to the increase of the fan-out ratio with receiver location exists, owing to the buildup of static pressure in the element, which causes appreciably more jet spreading downstream than accounted for in the plane model.

3. For a fixed Reynolds number, it is noted that moving the receiver downstream requires an increase in receiver width and a decrease in control width in order to maintain the maximum value of fan-out with respect to the similarity function.

Experimental Setup and Procedure

Elements having the basic geometry illustrated in Fig. 1 were constructed in Dycril and tested using the experimental setup shown in Fig. 3. The test element was loaded with a number of elements similar to itself. These load elements were themselves loaded with orifices so that effectually the test element was being fed into a complete circuit.

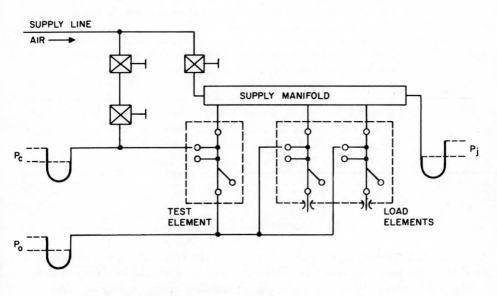

FIG. 3 EXPERIMENTAL SETUP WITH TEST ELEMENT
AND TWO LOAD ELEMENTS

The power jet, control, and receiver pressures were measured and recorded for the power element. Also, the receiver pressures of the driven elements were monitored to give an indication that switching of these elements followed from the application of a control signal to the power element.

Concurrent with the theoretical feasibility study, tests were run on a series of four preliminary designs described in Table 2. For each of these elements the dimensions $H = 0.431$ mm, $W_j = 0.508$ mm $= W_c = W_o$, and $L = 12 W_j$ were held constant. The objectives of these tests were to

1) determine the range of power jet pressures over which the elements operate in the laminar regime;
2) establish the influence of geometrical parameters that could not readily be accounted for in the theoretical model.

171

Finally, three elements were designed incorporating the results of the preliminary experimental work and the theoretical study. The nozzle dimensions and locations for these elements were derived from Table 1 using $R_e = 300$ and $W_j = 0.508$ mm. These were then tested for maximum fan-out ratios and power consumption. The experiments were conducted by applying a control signal to one control and leaving the other control port open to atmosphere.

TABLE 2

Description of the Geometries of the Four Elements Tested in the
First Phase of the Experimental Study.

Element	General Description
1	Basic element with two small bleed areas as shown in Fig. 1. $A_{B1} = A_{B2} = \pi\,(2W_j)^2$
2	Basic element having increased downstream bleed area $A_{B2} = \pi\,(2W_j)^2 + \pi\,(4W_j)^2$. This is accomplished by adding a second bleed hole adjacent to the existing one.
3	Basic element having increased bleed area as in element 2 and a vent added in straight wall immediately before collector. $W_v = 3W_j$
4	Basic element having increased downstream bleed area similar to element 2 and having vent similar to element 3. However, the upstream bleed area is closed off and the wall setback is decreased to $1W_j$ and given an angle of 30 degrees.

Experimental Results

In Fig. 4, a typical curve is given illustrating the variation of recovery pressure ratio with power jet pressure. Turbulent flow is identified by a marked flattening of the curve with increasing power jet pressure corresponding to the reduced influence of Reynolds number on boundary layer growth in the turbulent regime. For the particular elements tested, the laminar range of operation is seen to extend to a power jet pressure of about 10 cm H_2O or a Reynolds number of approximately 665 based on the power jet pressure and power nozzle width.

In Figs. 5 and 6 the receiver pressure is given as a function of control pressure for seven of the elements that have been tested. Each curve in these figures is obtained for a given element loaded with two elements similar to itself and all data are normalized with respect to the maximum recovery pressure. This normalization affords a convenient means of determining whether or not a particular element has the desired fan-out characteristics. When the control pressure necessary to bring P_o to zero is less than $P_{o\ max}$ for a given element and load, then the curve for that element will have a horizontal intercept less than one and the maximum possible fan-out ratio will be at least equal to the number of load elements. Of course, if the intercept is greater than one, the opposite is true.

172

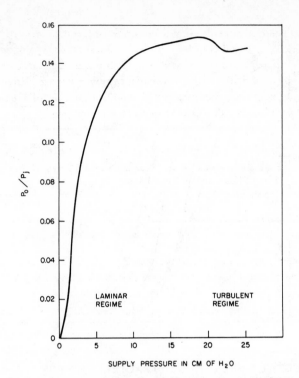

SUPPLY PRESSURE IN CM OF H$_2$O

FIG. 4 TYPICAL RECOVERY CURVE FOR NOR ELEMENTS
STUDIED IN THIS INVESTIGATION

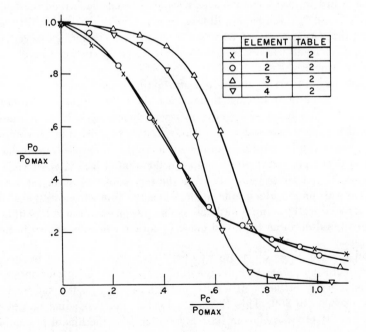

	ELEMENT	TABLE
X	1	2
O	2	2
△	3	2
▽	4	2

FIG. 5 STATIC OPERATING CHARACTERISTICS FOR THE
ELEMENTS IN THE FIRST PHASE OF THE EXPERI-
MENTAL INVESTIGATION

173

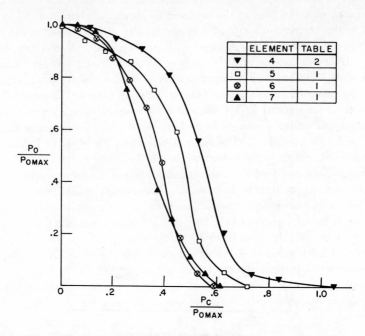

	ELEMENT	TABLE
▼	4	2
□	5	1
⊗	6	1
▲	7	1

FIG. 6 STATIC OPERATING CHARACTERISTICS FOR THE
ELEMENTS IN THE SECOND PHASE OF THE EXPERI-
MENTAL INVESTIGATION

Each curve in Fig. 5 represents data from an element described in Table 2.
For elements 1 and 2 which have solid walls adjacent to the jet but different
bleed areas, the output pressure curves are seen to be similar. However, the
larger bleed of element 2 is necessary to allow for adequate dumping of power
jet and control flows.

A vent was added to element 3 in the straight wall immediately upstream from
the receiver entrance in an attempt to decrease the static pressure buildup along
the wall. This results in an improved cutoff performance as well as a significant
increase in the recovery pressure. Additional tests revealed that the width of the
vent nozzle has an optimum size — too small a width has no effect; too large a
width results in the power jet bleeding out of the vent. Finally, an attempt was
made to reduce the static pressure level in the region of the power jet nozzle by
modifying the wall on the bleed side of the element. In a series of tests, it was
found that a bleed wall having a setback of one power nozzle width and an angle
of 30 degrees resulted in an improved cut-off characteristic as shown in the curve
for element 4.

A second group of three elements was developed from element 4 by modifying
it to conform with the parameters designated in Table 1. These elements were designed for each value of the modified Reynolds number at $f = 0.7$ and for a power
jet Reynolds number of 300. This Reynolds number, corresponding to a power jet
pressure of 2cm H_2O, was chosen first in keeping with the aim of producing an
element having low power consumption and second to afford a range of operating
pressures prior to the transition to turbulence. This range is desired to insure
that optimum performance may be achieved, despite the impossibility of having a
design exactly satisfying the assumptions underlying the theory.

174

Fig. 6 shows typical operating characteristics of the elements in the second group compared with the best of the preliminary designs (element 4). The improvement of the performance effected by the modifications based on the theory is obvious. Since the horizontal intercepts in Fig. 6 are all less than one, these elements will have a fan-out of at least two, the number of load elements.

Similar tests were run with a larger number of load elements in an attempt to determine the maximum values of the fan-out for each element. Elements 5, 6, and 7 have theoretical fan-outs of 3.95, 6.68, and 9.23, respectively; whereas, experimentally the maximum values appeared to be between 3 and 4 for elements 5 and 6 and between 2 and 3 for element 7. The large discrepancy for element 7, having a receiver location 20 nozzle widths downstream, is believed to be due to increased jet spreading at low modified Reynolds numbers where static pressure effects become significant, as previously discussed in the theoretical results.

One unfortunate aspect of the basic geometry is the control mismatching. The second control, located closer to the receiver, causes a reduction in the maximum fan-out by a factor ranging from 10 to 30 per cent.

Inherent in a laminar jet is a decreased fluid velocity. The effect of this on the dynamic response of these elements is not yet determined. However, this fact should weigh against the compactness of the element, and it might be expected that the dynamic response will be somewhat less than presently obtainable.

System Performance

To explore the information-handling capabilities of these elements, preliminary tests were run on bread-boarded half and full-adder circuits containing 6 and 15 elements respectively. As a factor of safety, no element was fanned out to more than two other elements. In both circuits the systems accomplished the truth table functions accurately and reliably for values of supply pressures ranging from 3 to 10 cm H_2O.

Measurements taken from the full adder circuit at $P_j = 5$ cm H_2O indicate power consumption of 0.03 watts or 0.002 watts per element compared with a power consumption of approximately 50 times this magnitude for present state-of-the-art devices.

Summary

In this investigation a NOR element was developed satisfying the criteria that the flow phenomena remain laminar, that the element be compact, have a fan-out of at least two, and operate on low power levels.

It is shown that for the elements tested, laminar operation is possible for values of supply pressure less than 10 cm H_2O.

Independent parameters for these laminar units are expressed as nondimensional quantities. Although the elements tested had $W_j = 0.508$ mm and $H = 0.413$ mm, it is possible to apply results to smaller elements.

The experimentally determined fan-out is shown to be in good agreement with the theoretical predictions for those elements having their receiver located between 10 and 15 nozzle widths downstream from the power nozzle exit. It is demonstrated that practical fan-out ratios are about 3.

Measurements were made that indicated power consumption levels to be 2 per cent of those of present state-of-the-art devices.

Research is being continued to see whether further improvements in the fan-out characteristics can be achieved, and to learn more about the dynamic characteristics of these elements.

Acknowledgment

The authors wish to thank Mr. Silas Katz, Research and Development Supervisor at Harry Diamond Laboratories, for his original suggestions which led to this study and for his continued help and interest throughout the investigation.

References

[1] A. Powell, "Characteristics and Control of Free Laminar Jets," *Proceedings of the Fluid Amplification Symposium*, Vol. I, Harry Diamond Laboratories, October, 1962, pp. 289-299.

[2] K. N. Reid, Jr., "Static and Dynamic Interaction of a Fluid Jet and a Receiver-Diffuser," Sc. D. Thesis, Department of Mechanical Engineering, Massachusetts Institute of Technology, Cambridge, Mass., September, 1964.

[3] M. B. Glauert, "The Wall Jet," *Journal of Fluid Mechanics*, Vol. I, 1956, pp. 625-643.

[4] H. Schlichting, *Boundary Layer Theory*, McGraw-Hill Book Company, New York, N. Y., pp. 164-168.

Analytical Method for Predicting Power Jet Reattachment Characteristics in Wall-Attachment-Type Fluidic Devices

R. E. Olson
R. C. Stoeffler
United Aircraft Research Laboratories
East Hartford, Connecticut

Abstract

A semiempirical analytical method capable of predicting the effect of control flow on the power jet reattachment location and the pressure in the separation bubble enclosed by the power jet for wall-attachment-type fluidic devices is outlined together with experimental verification of all the empirical formulations employed in the analysis. A comparison with experimental results is presented and good correlation is shown for the limited range for which the comparisons were made. Additional comparisons are required to demonstrate that the analytical method is applicable over a wide range of conditions.

Nomenclature

F = Correlation function (see Fig. 4)

h_{i_c} = Distance between jet centerline and inner wall of nozzle at nozzle exit (see Fig. 1)

h_{o_c} = Distance between jet centerline and outer wall of nozzle at nozzle exit (see Fig. 1)

I_o = Initial jet momentum per unit depth

L_R = Distance between nozzle exit and reattachment location measured along boundary wall

L_W = Distance along boundary wall measured from nozzle exit

M = Mach number

M_C = Control flow Mach number

P = Static pressure

P_i = Mean static pressure in separation bubble

R = Jet centerline radius of curvature (see Fig. 1)

S = Distance between boundary wall in inner wall of nozzle at nozzle exit (see Fig. 1)

u = Velocity parallel to jet centerline

u_C = Velocity on jet centerline

u_R = Maximum reverse flow velocity

W = Total height of nozzle at exit (see Fig. 1)

W_C = Total height of control nozzle at exit (see Fig. 1)

$\overset{\circ}{W}$ = Weight flow in portion of jet

$\overset{\circ}{W}_C$ = Control jet weight flow

$\overset{\circ}{W}_O$ = Initial jet weight flow

X = Distance along jet centerline measured from nozzle exit

X_c = Distance from nozzle exit to end of inviscid core measured along jet centerline

X_i = Distance from nozzle exit to effective impingement point between jet and control flow measured along jet centerline

X_R = Distance to reattachment measured along jet centerline from nozzle exit

y = Distance from wall measured perpendicular to jet centerline

y_o = Distance from wall measured perpendicular to jet centerline to location in separation bubble where flow direction reverses

Δ = Distance between jet centerline and boundary wall measured perpendicular to jet centerline (see Fig. 1)

θ = Boundary wall angle measured from nozzle centerline (see Fig. 2)

κ_{c_i} = Effective shear stress constant upstream of core for inner boundary of reattaching jet

κ_{c_o} = Effective shear stress constant upstream of core for outer boundary of reattaching jet

λ = Jet deflection angle measured from control jet centerline (see Fig. 2)

ξ = Distance perpendicular to inviscid boundary measured from inner boundary of mixing zone

Subscripts

o = Denotes conditions at nozzle exit

s = Denotes conditions on separating streamline

Superscripts

*   = Denotes conditions where the velocity in the shear layer is one half of the velocity on the edge of the mixing zone

      = Denotes conditions at beginning of recompression (see Fig. 1)

Introduction

The growing interest in the application of fluidic components has placed increased importance on the development of analytical techniques for predicting the performance characteristics of these devices. Development of such techniques for wall-attachment-type digital devices requires a generalized procedure for computing the power jet reattachment location as a function of control flow. Although previous studies such as those in [1], [2], and [3] have provided procedures which have been demonstrated to be adequate under certain circumstances, the general applicability of these procedures must be questioned since the empirical information needed in the procedures to match the analytical and experimental reattachment locations is in some instances inconsistent with experimental evidence. Accordingly the procedure outlined herein was developed under contract with the United States Army, Harry Diamond Laboratories in an attempt to provide a basis for formulating an improved technique for computing jet reattachment location.

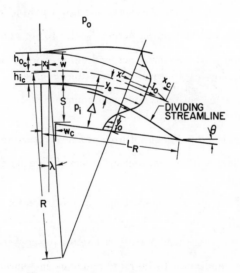

FIG. 1 DETAILED FLOW MODEL FOR JET RE-
ATTACHMENT ANALYSIS

Description of Procedure

The detailed flow model employed in the development of the procedure is presented in Fig. 1. Employing this flow model assuming (1) ideal momentum exchange between the jet and control flow and (2) constant jet momentum in the streamwise direction, the relations for computing the reattachment location as

179

a function of the mean pressure in the separation bubble become (see Appendix for summary of derivation)

$$\frac{\Delta}{W} = \frac{R}{W} -$$

$$\sqrt{\left(\frac{L_w}{W}\cos\theta - \frac{1}{2}\frac{W_c}{W} - \frac{R}{W}\sin\lambda\right)^2 + \left[\frac{R}{W}\cos\lambda + \frac{W_c}{W}\tan\theta - \left(\frac{h_{i_c}}{W} + \frac{S}{W} + \frac{L_w}{W}\sin\theta\right)\right]^2}$$

$$(1)$$

and for $X/W < X_c/W$

$$\frac{\mathring{W}_c}{\mathring{W}_o} = \frac{\kappa_{c_i}}{2C_2}\left(\frac{X}{W}\right)\left\{\frac{1}{f_4(1)}\int_0^{\frac{y_s - h_{i_c}\left(1-\frac{X}{X_c}\right)}{\xi^*}}\frac{u/u_o}{1 + \frac{\gamma-1}{2}M_o^2\left[1-\left(\frac{u}{u_o}\right)^2\right]}d(\xi/\xi^*) - 1\right\}$$

$$(2)$$

or for $X/W > X_c/W$

$$\frac{\mathring{W}_c}{\mathring{W}_o} = \left(\frac{X_c}{W}\right)\frac{1}{2C_2}\left[\kappa_{c_o} + \frac{\kappa_{c_i}}{f_4(U)}\int_0^{y_s/y^*}\frac{U(u/u_c)}{1 + \frac{\gamma-1}{2}M_o^2\left[1-U^2\left(\frac{u}{u_c}\right)^2\right]}d(y/y^*)\right] - 1$$

$$(3)$$

where

$$\frac{X}{W} = \frac{R}{W}\alpha + \frac{1}{2}\frac{W_c}{W}$$

$$(4)$$

and

$$\alpha = \lambda + \tan^{-1}\left[\frac{\frac{L_w}{W}\cos\theta - \frac{1}{2}\frac{W_c}{W} - \frac{R}{W}\sin\lambda}{\frac{R}{W}\cos\lambda + \frac{W_c}{W}\tan\theta - \left(\frac{h_{i_c}}{W} + \frac{S}{W} + \frac{L_w}{W}\sin\theta\right)}\right]$$

$$(5)$$

which must be solved iteratively employing the boundary condition that at reattachment $y_s/W = \Delta/W$. However, an additional constraint is required to determine a unique reattachment location for a particular geometry and jet Mach number. Such a constraint is obtained by postulating that the velocity profiles in the jet boundary enclosing the separation bubble and in the reverse flow in the separation bubble can be generalized in terms of the percentage distance to reattachment. That such a postulation might be reasonable was suggested first by the data of [4] which showed that both the boundary wall static pressure distribution and the spreading rate along the jet boundary enclosing the separation bubble could

180

be generalized in terms of the percentage distance to reattachment and later verified by the velocity profile data of [5]. It follows from the postulation that the relation

$$\left[\frac{d\left(u/u_R\right)}{d\left(y/y_0\right)} \right]_{u=0} \frac{\left(u_R/u_0\right)}{y_0/W} = \left[\frac{d\left(u/u_C\right)}{d\left(\xi/\xi^*\right)} \right]_{u=0} \frac{\left(u_C/u_0\right)}{\xi^*/W} \qquad (6)$$

which expresses the requirement that the slopes of the jet and reverse flow velocity profiles be equal at the point of zero velocity dividing the jet from the reverse flow, can be conveniently employed at the initiation of recompression $(X/X_R \approx 0.65)$ as the required additional constraint. In Eq. (6) $[d\left(u/u_C\right)/d\left(\xi/\xi^*\right)]$ and $[d\left(u/u_R\right)/d\left(y/y_0\right)]$ are the slopes of the generalized jet and reverse flow velocity profiles at the dividing point between the jet and reverse flow. The generalized velocity profile at the initiation of recompression employed in the analysis is presented in Fig. 2 and compared with data of [5] obtained for a range of geometries and control flow rates for a Mach number of 0.66. It is seen that the generalized velocity profile selected as the best fit to

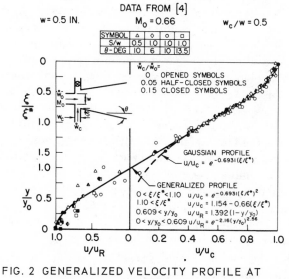

FIG. 2 GENERALIZED VELOCITY PROFILE AT
INITIATION OF RECOMPRESSION $(X/X_R \approx 0.65)$

all the data provides a fair representation of both the jet and reverse flow profiles for the range of flow conditions and geometries for which the data are presented. It appears reasonable to assume that such a generalization would exist for all subsonic Mach numbers over a wider range of geometries. The remaining quantities in Eq. (6) are determined from geometric and flow conditions which can be computed utilizing the generalized velocity profile for the jet and reverse flow.

181

Typical Results and Comparison with Experiment

The procedure outlined for computing jet reattachment location was programmed for machine computation using the convergence criterion expressed in Eq. (6). It was found that the criterion provided an extremely accurate and stable technique for obtaining a reattachment location solution. Typical computed reattachment locations obtained as a function of control flow are presented in Fig. 3 and compared with experimental data.

Computed results for three different values of effective shear stress constant on the inner boundary at the initiation of recompression are presented as the dashed lines. The effective shear stress constant is defined as the shear stress constant (see Eq. (10) in Appendix for definition) which would correctly predict the mixing region width at a given axial distance along the jet centerline if the mixing rate were constant between the nozzle exit and the given axial station. The values were chosen to fall within the band of scatter of the experimental values of effective shear stress constants presented in [4] and [5]. The solid curve in Fig. 3 is a plot of the predicted values of reattachment location obtained when the correlation presented in Fig. 4 is utilized for obtaining the effective shear stress constant on the inner jet boundary. This correlation was obtained from an empirical fit of the values of effective shear stress constant which matched the theoretical and experimental reattachment locations for the range of geometries and flow conditions encompassed by the data considered. The experimental data presented in Fig. 4 were obtained for a spanwise station midway between the side plates and for an axial station corresponding to the initiation of recompression ($X/X_R \approx 0.65$). The correlation appears to be generally substantiated by the experimental data obtained without control flow with somewhat poorer substantiation shown by the data at the higher control flow rates. The correlation employed for obtaining the effective shear stress on the outer jet boundary is presented in Fig. 5. The data presented in Fig. 5 were also obtained for a spanwise station midway between the sideplates and for an axial station corresponding to the initiation of recompression. It appears for the limited amount of data that the shear stress constant correlates reasonably well with the non-dimensional jet curvature (defined as the reciprocal of the local radius of curvature of the jet centerline multiplied by the jet nozzle width).

It is evident from the computed results presented in Fig. 3 that the predicted reattachment locations are extremely sensitive to the value of the inner jet boundary shear stress constant employed in the analysis. It is encouraging, however, that the shear stress constants required to match the predicted reattachment locations to the measured values generally fall within the scatter band of the shear stress constants determined experimentally. Such a result suggests that the flow model utilized in the analysis is substantially correct and that it only remains to determine whether an adequate generalization exists for the shear stress constant on the inner jet boundary and the velocity profile for the jet and reverse flow in the separation bubble at the initiation of recompression. It is encouraging to note in this regard the results of the [4], [5], and [6] investigations suggest that for subsonic Mach numbers the generalized velocity profile for the jet and reverse flow in the separation bubble and the shear stress constants for the inner and outer jet boundaries are essentially Mach number independent. It

182

remains to be shown, however, whether or not such empirical correlations can be sufficiently generalized for a wide range of geometries.

$M_0 = 0.66$ $S/w = 1.0$ $\theta = 10$ DEG
$w_c/w = 0.5$ $w = 0.5$ IN.

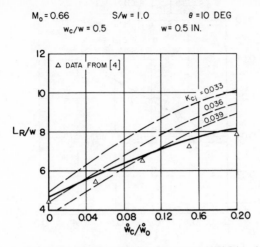

FIG. 3 TYPICAL COMPARISON OF ANALYTICAL AND
EXPERIMENTAL RESULTS

$w = 0.5$ IN. $M_0 = 0.66$
$w_c/w = 0.5$ $X/X_R = 0.65$

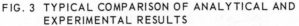

$$F = \left[0.1579 \left\{ (S/w)^{2.69} \theta \right\}^{-0.286} - 0.1565 \left\{ (S/w)^{2.32} \theta \right\}^{-0.525} \left\{ 1 - \frac{\overset{\circ}{w}_c}{\overset{\circ}{w}_0} \right\} \right]$$

SYMBOL	O	□	◇	△
θ – DEG	6	10	13.5	10
S/w	1.0	1.0	1.0	0.5

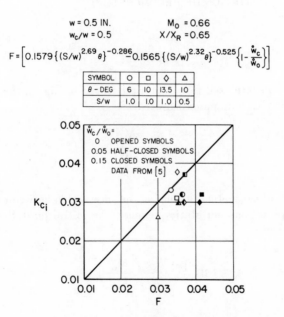

FIG. 4 CORRELATION OF EFFECTIVE SHEAR STRESS
CONSTANT ON INNER JET BOUNDARY AT
INITIATION OF RECOMPRESSION

183

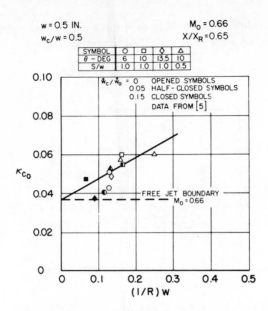

FIG. 5 CORRELATION OF EFFECTIVE SHEAR STRESS
CONSTANT ON OUTER JET BOUNDARY AT
INITIATION OF RECOMPRESSION

Appendix

Referring to the generalized flow model presented in Fig. 1, the jet radius of curvature can be expressed approximately as

$$\frac{R}{W} = \frac{\gamma M_o^2}{1 - \frac{P_i}{P_o}} \tag{7}$$

From conservation of momentum, assuming the interaction between the control flow and jet occurs at constant static pressure, the initial jet deflection angle becomes

$$\lambda = \tan^{-1}\left[\frac{W_c}{W}\left(\frac{M_c}{M_o}\right)^2\right] \tag{8}$$

The position of the jet centerline relative to the inner and outer inviscid jet boundaries (jet boundaries for no mixing) can be written respectively as

$$\frac{h_{i_c}}{W} = \frac{\kappa_{c_i}}{\kappa_{c_i} + \kappa_{c_o}} \quad \text{AND} \quad \frac{h_{o_c}}{W} = \frac{\kappa_{c_o}}{\kappa_{c_i} + \kappa_{c_o}} \tag{9}$$

184

where κ_{c_o} and κ_{c_i} are the shear stress constants on the inner and outer bound- aries of the jet respectively defined in Prandtl's expression for the turbulent eddy viscosity, namely,

$$\epsilon = \kappa \xi^* \frac{h}{2} \tag{10}$$

Equations (1), (4), and (5) in the text can now be obtained from geometry referring to Fig. 1.

To compute the position of the separation streamline, consideration is given to the mass flow distribution in the jet boundary mixing zone. For isoenergetic mixing, the position of the separation streamline as a function of control flow can be expressed as in Eqs. (2) and (3) of the text for the core and developed regions respectively. In these expressions

$$\frac{X_c}{W} = \frac{2C_2}{\kappa_{c_i} + \kappa_{c_o}} \tag{11}$$

where

$$C_2 = \frac{0.5\left[f_2(1) + f_4(1)\right] - f_1(1)}{2 f_3(1) f_4(1)} \tag{12}$$

and

$$f_1(U) = \int_0^1 \frac{U^2\left(\dfrac{u}{u_c}\right)^2}{1 + \dfrac{\gamma-1}{2} M_0^2 \left[1 - U^2\left(\dfrac{u}{u_c}\right)^2\right]} \, d\left(\frac{y}{y^*}\right) \tag{13}$$

$$f_2(U) = \int_0^1 \frac{U\left(\dfrac{u}{u_c}\right)}{1 + \dfrac{\gamma-1}{2} M_0^2 \left[1 - U^2\left(\dfrac{u}{u_c}\right)^2\right]} \, d\left(\frac{y}{y^*}\right) \tag{14}$$

$$f_3(U) = \frac{0.6931}{2}\left[\frac{U^2}{1 + \dfrac{\gamma-1}{2} M_0^2(1 - 0.25 U^2)}\right] \tag{15}$$

$$f_4(U) = \int_0^\infty \frac{U^2\left(\dfrac{u}{u_c}\right)^2}{1 + \dfrac{\gamma-1}{2} M_0^2 \left[1 - U^2\left(\dfrac{u}{u_c}\right)^2\right]} \, d\left(\frac{y}{y^*}\right) \tag{16}$$

185

$$U = \left(\frac{1}{x/x_c}\right)^{0.5} \qquad \text{(for subsonic Mach numbers)} \qquad (17)$$

$$\frac{u}{u_c} = e^{-0.6931(y/y^*)^2} \qquad (18)$$

A more detailed derivation of Eqs. (1) through (5) in the text is given in [4].

References

[1] R. A. Sawyer, "Two-Dimensional Reattaching Jet Flows Including the Effects of Curvature on Entrainment." Journal of Fluid Mechanics, Vol. 17, December 1963.

[2] C. Bourque and B. G. Newman, "Reattachment of a Two-Dimensional, Incompressible Jet to an Adjacent Flat Plate." The Aeronautical Quarterly, Vol. XI, August 1960.

[3] N. C. Sher, "Jet Attachment and Switching in Bistable Fluid Amplifiers." ASME Paper No. 64-FE-19, presented at Fluid Engineering Conference, May 1964.

[4] R. E. Olson, and Y. T. Chin, "Studies of Reattaching Jet Flows in Fluid-State Wall-Attachment Devices." Report No. 17, Fluid Amplification, Harry Diamond Laboratories, Washington, D. C., September 30, 1965.

[5] R. E. Olson, and R. C. Stoeffler, "Supplemental Studies of Reattaching Jet Flows in Fluid-State Wall-Attachment Devices. United Aircraft Research Laboratories Report E910263-25, September 1966.

[6] R. E. Olson, and D. P. Miller, "Aerodynamic Studies of Free and Attached Jets." Report No. 6, Fluid Amplification Series, Harry Diamond Laboratories, Washington, D. C., June 16, 1963.

Wall Attachment
Crossover "AND" Gate

R. F. Hellbaum

NASA Langley Research Center
Langley Station, Hampton, Va.

Abstract

A new and improved flueric "and" gate, using the wall attachment principle, has been constructed and tested. The principle of operation and static performance data are presented in this report. Tests indicate its performance is not adversely affected by normal dimensional variations encountered in fabrication and it will operate throughout the full range of loading from fully open to fully blocked output.

Introduction

There are currently available several functional "and" gate configurations [1], but each has limitations which restrict its application. For satisfactory operation of an "and" gate, certain requirements must be met. They are: 1) The "and" function must be available at the output throughout a considerable variation in magnitude of the two input signals; 2) The unit should operate throughout the range from zero to infinite load in order to eliminate impedance matching problems; 3) Output signal should not vary proportionally with a change in input signal magnitude; 4) Power losses in the unit should not exceed those of a conventional fluidic amplifier; and, 5) The unit should have no critical dimensions which would create production difficulties or make costs excessive.

Design Theory

This new "and" gate resulted from removing the supply input and one control port from each of two identical monostable wall attachment amplifiers and joining the two units so that the result is a passive element with two inputs and three outputs. The monostable amplifier used is shown in Fig. 1 and the mirror image is joined along the dashed line to form the "and." In the basic amplifier, the supply is A and the control port is B. Since this active amplifier is monostable, flow from A attaches to wall C when signal B is present. If A is always present

187

the outputs indicate B or $\bar{B}$. If the unit is considered passive with inputs A and B, then the outputs indicate A·B or A·$\bar{B}$. The foregoing indicates the inherent ability of the monostable wall attachment unit to perform the "and" function.

Joining two of the basic amplifiers along the dotted line shown in Fig. 1 and combining the internal vents will result in a unit as shown in Fig. 2. Note the dotted line of symmetry. By providing a summing junction for channels I and J the unit shown in Fig. 3 will be produced. Walls C and D and input channels A and B form a monostable device as in Fig. 1 so that B acts as the control of supply A. Walls E and F and input channels A and B form another monostable device which is the mirror image of that in Fig. 1 where A now acts as the control for supply B. Since the configuration is monostable, flow from A only, at-

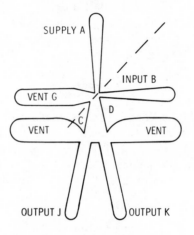

FIG. 1 SCHEMATIC OF A BASIC MONOSTABLE
WALL ATTACHMENT AMPLIFIER

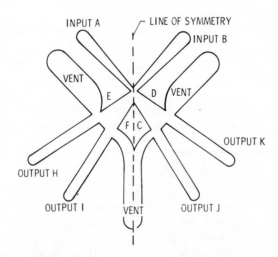

FIG. 2 SCHEMATIC OF A PASSIVE "AND" GATE
CREATED BY THE JOINING OF TWO MONO-
STABLE WALL ATTACHMENT AMPLIFIERS

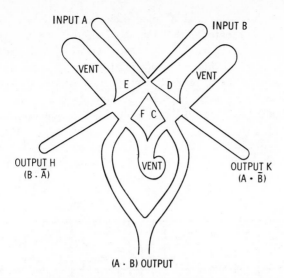

FIG. 3 SCHEMATIC OF "AND" GATE WITH SUMMING
JUNCTION FOR (A · B) OUTPUT

taches to wall D, leaving through port K, and yielding function A·$\bar{\text{B}}$. Also, a flow appearing only at B would attach to wall E leaving via port H yielding logic functions $\bar{\text{A}}$·B. When both A and B appear, simultaneous attachment to walls C and F is obtained, thereby forming the "and" function A·B at outputs I and J. Combining these two channels gives this unit the attractive feature of providing an "and" output when either input signal is considerably weaker than the other. A simple "Y" connection has been used successfully but it is possible that channel modifications would improve the summed output of channels I and J.

Characteristics and Performance

Three essential features of this fluid "and" gate are: 1) The flow from one control must be sufficiently monostable to allow initial attachment and upon switching, return to the outer wall; 2) The flow splitter which is formed by the interior attachment walls must be close to the input streams to prevent flow oscillations across it; and 3) Venting must be adequate. Fig. 3 shows a practical modification of the original vent, as shown in Fig. 2. Most monostable fluidic amplifiers can be utilized to produce workable "and" gates, and in general the "and" gate produced will have the output and switching characteristics of the amplifier used to produce it.

Fig. 4 shows the outline of an operational "and" gate superimposed on a grid to illustrate unit dimensions. The grid has eight lines per inch in both axes and the outline is 6 times actual gate size. The gate will function with the ratio of the two input signal pressures going as high as five to one. Per cent pressure recovery (100 × output pressure/input pressure), per cent flow recovery (100 × output flow/input flow), and per cent power recovery (per cent pressure recovery × per cent flow recovery/100) are shown in Figs. 5 and 6. Loading of the gate will cause no degradation in performance.

189

The design does not have the critical dimensions associated with many fluidic components. A unit was fabricated with a throat width of 5.08×10^{-4} m (0.020 in.), and the depth of 1.0×10^{-4} m (0.04 in.), and the outer attachment wall was moved 1.0×10^{-5} m (0.004 in.) toward the center of the element. This unit produced no noticeable variation in unit operational characteristics. Since this is normally the most critical dimension in the basic amplifier configuration, it is assumed that a production tolerance of 10 per cent of throat width in unit dimensions will be acceptable.

The switching time of this device has not yet been measured, but should be comparable with that of the monostable amplifier used as the basis of the design.

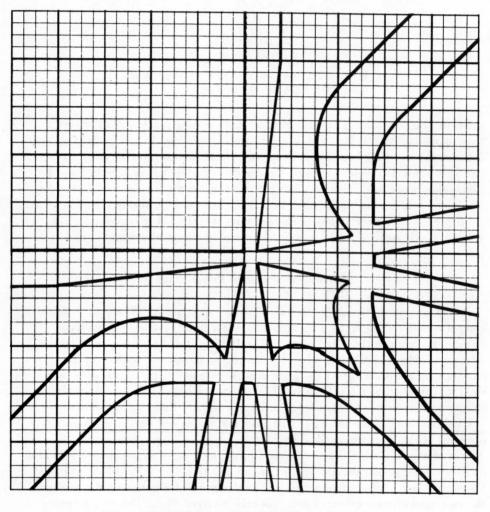

FIG. 4 OUTLINE OF OPERATIONAL "AND" GATE
MAGNIFIED SIX TIMES AND PLACED ON AN
8 × 8 GRID

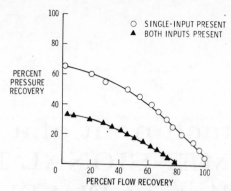

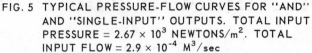

FIG. 5 TYPICAL PRESSURE-FLOW CURVES FOR "AND"
AND "SINGLE-INPUT" OUTPUTS. TOTAL INPUT
PRESSURE = 2.67×10^3 NEWTONS/m^2. TOTAL
INPUT FLOW = 2.9×10^{-4} M^3/sec

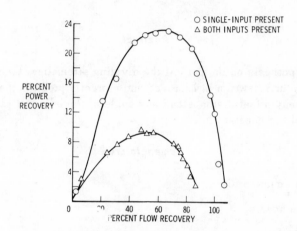

FIG. 6 TYPICAL POWER RECOVERY CURVES FOR "AND"
AND "SINGLE-INPUT" OUTPUTS. TOTAL INPUT
POWER = 4.2 WATTS. TOTAL INPUT FLOW = 2.9 ×
10^{-4} M^3/sec

Conclusions

A fluid "and" gate has been developed which operates through the range from
zero to infinite load and with wide variation in input signal levels. Power losses
in the unit are nominal, and it has no critical dimensions which would create production difficulties or make cost excessive.

Reference

[1] Joseph M. Iseman, "Fluerics (Fluid Amplification) — 9. Fluid Digital
Logic Elements and Circuits." TR-1302, Harry Diamond Labs., U. S. Army Materiel
Command, August 16, 1965.

Reattachment of a TWO-DIMENSIONAL JET to an Adjacent Flat Plate

C. Bourque

Laval University
Quebec 10, Canada

Abstract

With a new hypothesis on the path of the dividing streamline, the original theory of Bourque and Newman is improved and correctly predicts the position of reattachment for any offset distance and any angle of the adjacent plate, using the same value of the constant σ.

Nomenclature

a = constant in equation (6)

b = width of the nozzle

D = offset distance

r = vector radius in the equation of the path (6)

R = value of r at reattachment

s = distance along the dividing streamline

s_o = distance of the theoretical origin

S = distance along the jet centerline from the theoretical origin

t = variable defined as $\tanh \dfrac{\sigma y}{S}$

u = velocity at any point in the jet

U_o = velocity at the nozzle exit

x = distance along the plate

y = distance normal to the jet centerline

α = plate angle

β = angle between the dividing streamline and the vector

γ = angle between the dividing streamline and the plate at reattachment

θ = angle between the vector r and the initial direction of the jet

θ_R = value of θ at reattachment

θ_m = maximum possible value of θ

ρ = density

ϕ = variable defined by equation (13)

σ = constant in Goertler's velocity profile

Introduction

In a previous publication, the author and Newman [1] proposed a solution to the problem of finding the position of reattachment of a two-dimensional incompressible turbulent jet on an adjacent flat plate. The theory has been applied to the following two geometries: a plate set at an angle to the initial direction of the jet, without any offset and an offset plate parallel to the initial direction of the jet. The agreement between theory and experiment was not very good in the first case, but was satisfactory in the second as shown in Figs. 1 and 2.

Sawyer [2] and [3] proposed an almost similar theory with some refinements introduced at the cost of more complex calculations.

Levin and Manion [4] applied the solution of Bourque and Newman to the more general case of a flat plate with both incidence and offset. They obtained agreement between the theory and the experimental points by using different values of σ for different geometries. This is equivalent to saying that the theory is not satisfactory.

Other theories have been proposed for the compressible case which is not to be considered in this paper.

This problem of reattachment of a jet, like most others, can be tackled in many different ways. One can, for example, look for a solution that describes as well as possible the physical behavior of the flow. Such a solution will necessarily be complex and difficult to handle. On the other hand, we can look for the simplest possible solution, that will give us the results we are interested in.

If we keep in mind that the solution of this problem is the basis for the solution of other problems such as the effect of the injection of mass and momentum through a control jet and the response time characteristic of these effects, we conclude that it is essential to look for the simplest solution if we want to end up with useful expressions.

By modifying two of the hypotheses in the theory already mentioned at the beginning, a better agreement has been obtained between a theory which is still very simply expressed and the experimental results.

The now widely-used assumption that the path of the jet is a circular arc, which can only be associated with a constant pressure in the bubble, has been replaced by a simple sine function determined with the help of some experimental results. Since this expression is no more than a rough approximation, it can be assumed that it represents the path of the dividing streamline rather than the

193

centerline of the jet. The principal reason for doing this is to obtain an expression as simple as possible for the volume of the enclosed bubble which is necessary for the calculation of the response time. Since with the dividing streamline as bubble boundary, entrainment continues to the wall, it is also possible to eliminate certain terms in the original expressions which were necessary to correct for the fact that the jet centerline does not reach the wall.

Theoretical curves have been compared with experimental points and the agreement is satisfactory for any angle and offset of the plate with the same value of the constant σ.

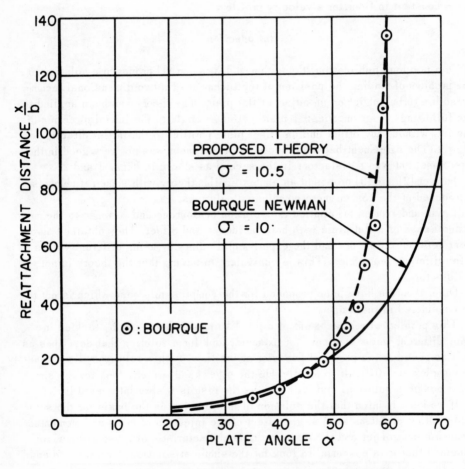

FIG. 1 THE REATTACHMENT DISTANCE ON AN INCLINED
PLATE WITHOUT ANY OFFSET

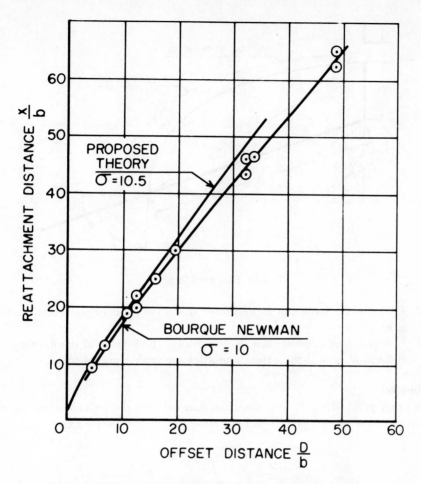

FIG. 2 THE REATTACHMENT DISTANCE ON AN OFFSET
PARALLEL PLATE

Theory

A geometrical model of the flow is shown in Fig. 3, with the important notations. The jet emerges through a two-dimensional nozzle of width b. The dividing
streamline between the flow that proceeds downstream and the flow that is re-
circulated in the bubble reaches the wall at a distance x from its origin. The offset distance of the plate is D and its angle of inclination is α.

The angle that the dividing streamline makes with the wall at reattachment
is γ.

The theory is also based on the following assumptions:
1) The flow is everywhere two-dimensional and incompressible.
2) The entrainment ceases at the point where the dividing streamline reaches
   the wall.
3) The distance measured along the dividing streamline is the same as the
   distance measured along the jet centerline.
4) The velocity profile just before reattachment is a free jet profile.

195

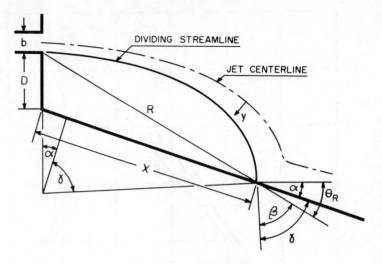

FIG. 3 FLOW MODEL

5) The pressure force can be neglected in the momentum equation at reattachment.
6) At reattachment, momentum is conserved on both sides of the dividing streamline even if the velocity profiles are highly perturbed.

Continuity:

At every point along the jet, the mass flow between the jet centerline and the dividing streamline is equal to half the mass flow at the nozzle exit.

$$\frac{\rho U_o b}{2} = \int_0^y \rho u\, dy$$

With Goertler's profile for the jet, this becomes

$$\frac{S}{b} = \frac{\sigma}{3t^2} \tag{1}$$

where

$$t = \tanh \frac{\sigma y}{S}$$

Since the theoretical origin of the jet is a distance s_o upstream of the nozzle exit, we can write

$$S = s_o + s \tag{2}$$

The value of s_o can be determined if we note that the mass flow at the nozzle exit is equal to the mass flow in a jet at a distance s_o from its origin

$$\rho U_o b = \int_{-\infty}^{\infty} \rho u\, dy$$

196

Again with Goertler's profile this reduces to

$$s_o = \frac{\sigma b}{3} \tag{3}$$

The final form of the continuity equation is obtained when we introduce equations (2) and (3) into equation (1)

$$\frac{s}{b} = \frac{\sigma}{3} \left(\frac{1}{t^2} - 1 \right) \tag{4}$$

Momentum :

When the pressure force is neglected and the momentum is assumed to be conserved on both sides of the dividing streamline the following momentum equation can be written around the reattachment point. Fig. 3.

$$\cos \gamma \int_{-\infty}^{\infty} \rho u^2 dy = \int_{-\infty}^{y} \rho u^2 dy - \int_{y}^{\infty} \rho u^2 dy$$

Using Goertler's profile once more, this reduces to

$$\cos \gamma = \frac{3t}{2} - \frac{t^3}{2} \tag{5}$$

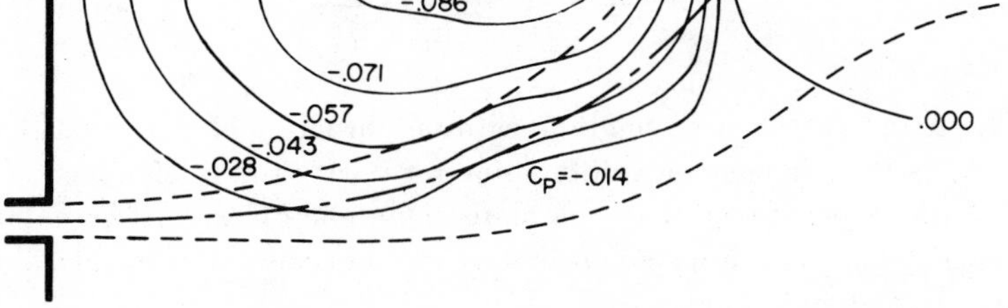

FIG. 4 PRESSURE DISTRIBUTION INSIDE AN ENCLOSED BUBBLE

Path of the dividing streamline of the jet:

It is now well known that the pressure in the bubble is not constant. Fig. 4, reproduced from [1], gives a good idea of the pressure field inside such a bubble. It is to be noted that the pressure coefficient along the offset wall decreases with distance and then increases rapidly to become positive just before the point of reattachment. The point of minimum pressure inside the bubble is closer to the point of reattachment than to the nozzle lip.

197

Since the pressure coefficient along an inclined plate without offset [1] varies in much the same way, it is reasonable to assume that in this case also the point of minimum pressure is closer to reattachment than to the nozzle. In other words, the whole pressure field should be qualitatively the same.

The path of the jet being tightly linked with the pressure field, the ideal solutions would give the two simultaneously. Unfortunately, no simple solution of this kind can be foreseen at the moment and a function representing the path of the jet has to be assumed with the help of some experimental results.

It is seen on Fig. 4 that the difference in pressure across the jet increases along about 70 per cent of the distance between the nozzle and the point of reattachment and that it is not possible to tell how it varies along the remaining 30 per cent. It will be assumed for simplicity that the pressure difference across the jet increases up to the point of reattachment, which means that the curvature of the path also increases up to the reattachment.

The jet intersects the adjacent plate at a certain angle which is a function of the plate angle and offset and of the unknown path. A limiting value can nevertheless be determined with Fig. 1 which shows the reattachment distance as function of the plate angle for the case of no offset. An extrapolation of these experimental results shows that the reattachment distance would become infinite for a plate angle of about 67 degrees. From the continuity equation (4), reattachment will occur at infinity if t is equal to zero and the momentum equation (5) then becomes

$$\cos \gamma = 0$$

This tells us that when reattachment is at infinity the reattachment angle must always be 90 degrees. Thus when a plate, without any offset is set at an angle of 67 degrees, the jet should intersect this plate at right angle. This, of course, is impossible with a circular arc path.

The following function for the path has been proposed by Rodrigue in his thesis [5]. It satisfies the conditions of increasing curvature and of right angle intersection when the plate is set at an angle of 67 degrees:

$$\frac{r}{b} = \frac{a}{b} \, \sin \frac{\pi}{2} \, \frac{\theta}{\theta_m} \tag{6}$$

where r is the radius vector at an angle θ with the direction of the jet at the nozzle exit and θ_m is the maximum possible value for θ which is 67 degrees. The scale factor a, which is a function of the plate angle and offset will be determined with the continuity and momentum equations. It will become infinite when the jet intersects the plate at right angle.

Since this expression is no more than a rough approximation, it can be assumed, for simplicity of the geometric relations, that it represents the path of the dividing streamline rather than the centerline of the jet. For a plate set at an angle at the nozzle lip, the value of θ at reattachment becomes the plate angle α and the scale factor a will vary from zero to infinity as α varies from zero to 67 degrees.

In fluidics devices, there is always an offset distance between the plate and the nozzle lip. The reattachment then goes to infinity for a smaller plate angle; and at the limit, when the offset distance D/b becomes infinite, the reattachment is at infinity on a plate at zero incidence.

198

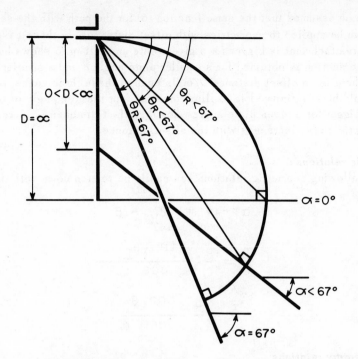

FIG. 5 REATTACHMENT AT INFINITY FOR DIFFERENT OFFSET
         DISTANCES

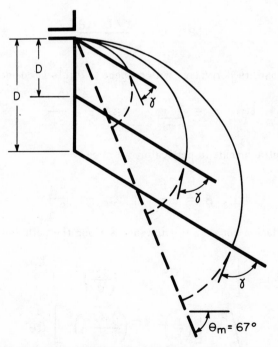

FIG. 6 ANGLE OF REATTACHMENT AS FUNCTION OF
         OFFSET DISTANCE

It can be assumed that the same function (6) for the path with the same value of θ_m can be applied to geometries with offset distances. In these cases, the angle of reattachment is bigger for a given plate angle. Fig. 5 shows how a right angle intersection is obtained for a smaller plate angle α and a smaller value of θ when there is an offset distance D/b. In each of these three cases, reattachment would be at infinity. Fig. 6 illustrates the fact that the angle of reattachment is bigger for a given plate angle when the offset distance is increased. The scale factor a also increases with the offset distance.

Geometric relations:

The following geometric relations can easily be written down with the help of Fig. 3.

$$\alpha + \gamma = \theta_R + \beta \tag{7}$$

$$\frac{D}{b} = \frac{R}{b} \frac{\sin(\theta_R - \alpha)}{\cos \alpha} \tag{8}$$

$$\frac{X}{b} = \frac{R}{b} \frac{\cos \theta_R}{\cos \alpha} \tag{9}$$

Supplementary relations

An expression for the angle β is obtained with the equation of the path.
The angle between the vector radius r and the path is everywhere

$$\tan \beta = \frac{r/b \; d\theta}{d \; r/b} \tag{10}$$

With equation (6) and its derivative with respect to θ this becomes

$$\tan \beta = \frac{2\theta_m}{\pi} \tan \frac{\pi}{2} \frac{\theta}{\theta_m}$$

At the point of reattachment, in particular, we have

$$\tan \beta = \frac{2\theta_m}{\pi} \tan \frac{\pi}{2} \frac{\theta_R}{\theta_m} \tag{11}$$

We also need a relation between the distance s along the path and the angle θ

$$d \frac{s}{b} = \left[\left(\frac{r}{b} d\theta \right)^2 + \left(\frac{dr}{b} \right)^2 \right]^{1/2}$$

$$\frac{s}{b} = \int_0^\theta \left[\left(\frac{r}{b} \right)^2 + \left(\frac{dr/b}{d\theta} \right)^2 \right]^{1/2} d\theta \tag{12}$$

Introducing again equation (6) and its derivative, we obtain

$$\frac{s}{b} = \frac{a}{b} \frac{\pi}{2} \int_{0}^{\theta/\theta_m} \left[1 - \left(1 - \left(\frac{2\theta_m}{\pi}\right)^2 \right) \sin^2 \frac{\pi}{2} \frac{\theta}{\theta_m} \right]^{1/2} d\frac{\theta}{\theta_m}$$

If we write:

$$\varphi = \frac{\pi}{2} \frac{\theta}{\theta_m} \tag{13}$$

this reduces to

$$\frac{s}{a} = \int_{0}^{\varphi} \left[1 - \left(1 - \left(\frac{2\theta_m}{\pi}\right)^2 \right) \sin^2 \varphi \right]^{1/2} d\varphi \tag{14}$$

which is an elliptic integral whose value can be found in tables. The upper limit of integration is of course to be taken as

$$\varphi = \frac{\pi}{2} \frac{\theta_R}{\theta_m}$$

Solution

Unfortunately, the distance of reattachment x/b cannot be written explicitly in terms of the parameters D/b and α. It is necessary to solve simultaneously the equations (4), (5), (6), (7), (8), (9), (11) and (14). The simplest method is to try a value for θ_R, get β from (11), γ from (7), t from (5), s/b from (4), s/a from (14) and so a/b, R/b from (6), D/b from (8) and x/b from (9). This is straightforward except when D/b is to be taken as parameter. In this case, we have to try different values for θ_R until we end up with the desired value for D/b.

Comparison of the theory with experimental results

The theory has been compared with experimental results of Bourque [1], of Rodrigue [5] and of Leven and Manion [4].

Fig. 1 presents the reattachment distance as function of the plate angle α for the case where $D/b = 0$. The improvement over the theory of reference [1] is evident.

In Figs. 2 and 7, we see x/b as function of D/b when α is zero. Rodrigue's results are limited to small values of D/b which are interesting for fluidic devices while Bourque's results are for higher values. The agreement is reasonably good.

The most interesting figures, as far as fluidics is concerned, are Figs. 8 and 9. We find in these figures the reattachment distance as function of α with D/b as parameter. The range of Rodrigue's results is again limited to values of D/b and of α used in fluidic devices. The agreement with theory is very good and we note that the small discrepancy at $\alpha = 0$ is in agreement with Fig. 7. For higher values of D/b and α, the agreement is good with the experimental results of Levin and Manion.

It is to be noted that all the theoretical curves have been calculated with the same values of the constant σ and of θ_m which were taken as 10.5 and 67 degrees.

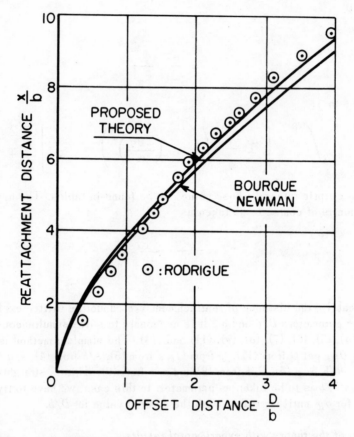

FIG. 7 THE REATTACHMENT DISTANCE ON AN OFFSET PARALLEL
PLATE WITH SMALL OFFSET VALUES

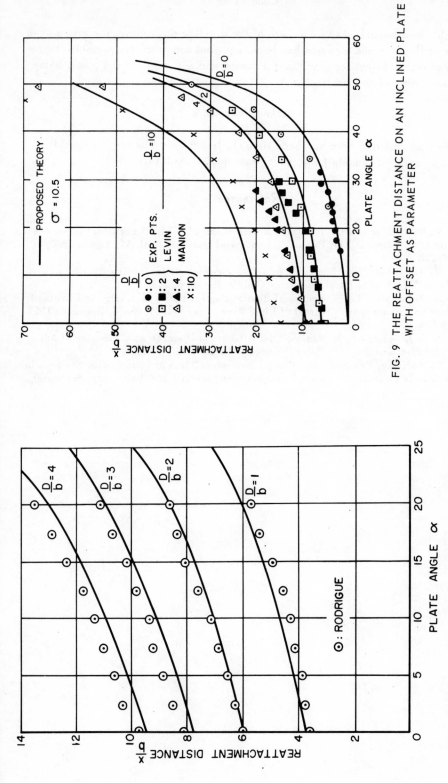

FIG. 9   THE REATTACHMENT DISTANCE ON AN INCLINED PLATE
         WITH OFFSET AS PARAMETER

FIG. 8   THE REATTACHMENT DISTANCE ON AN INCLINED PLATE
         WITH OFFSET AS PARAMETER

Conclusion

With a new hypothesis on the path of the dividing streamline, the original theory of Bourque and Newman has been improved and correctly predicts the position of reattachment for any offset distance and any angle of the plate, using the same value of the constant σ.

Acknowledgments

The work reported here has been financially supported by the National Research Council of Canada Ltd, under Grant number A-2714.

References

[1] C. Bourque and B. G. Newman, "Reattachment of a Two-Dimensional Incompressible Jet to an Adjacent Flat Plate." Aeronautical Quarterly, Vol. XI, August 1960, pp. 201-232.

[2] R. A. Sawyer, "The Flow Due to a Two-Dimensional Jet Issuing Parallel to a Flat Plate." Journal of Fluid Mechanics, Vol. 9, Part 4, p. 543.

[3] R. A. Sawyer, "Two-Dimensional Reattaching Jet Flows Including the Effects of Curvature on Entrainment." Journal of Fluid Mechanics, Vol. 17, No. 4, December 1963, pp. 481-498.

[4] S. G. Levin and F. M. Manion, "Jet Attachment Distance as a Function of Adjacent Wall Offset and Angle." Harry Diamond Laboratories, TR-1087.

[5] G. Rodrigue, "Recollement d'un jet incompressible à une paroi adjacente avec injection dans la bulle de séparation." Thesis submitted at Laval University, September 1966.

Two-Dimensional Jet Attachment

C. C. Perry

W. M. Chace Company
1600 Beard Avenue
Detroit, Michigan

Abstract

The Bourque and Newman model for two-dimensional jet attachment is briefly re-examined, principally with respect to generalizing the Görtler jet-spread parameter. It is shown that by a simple improvement in the "control-volume" model, a single value of the jet-spread parameter suffices for a wide range of geometric conditions.

Experimental data are presented to support the theory and to demonstrate that attachment distance is unaffected by the presence or lack of a second, symmetrically disposed sidewall, and is also unaffected by the nozzle aspect ratio for ratios between 1 and 100.

Nomenclature

b = Nozzle width

C_P' = Pressure coefficient defining base pressure

D = Sidewall offset in nozzle exit plane

h = Nozzle depth

J = Momentum per unit of jet depth

P_B = Average bubble pressure

P_B' = Average base pressure in nozzle exit plane

P_∞ = Pressure of fluid in receiving chamber

R = Radius of jet centerline

t' = Dimensionless parameter

x = Attachment distance, measured along sidewall from nozzle exit plane

α = Sidewall angle with respect to nozzle axis

θ = Angle of intersection between extended jet centerline and sidewall

σ = Görtler jet-spread parameter, references [4], [7], and [8]

Introduction

Analyses of the turbulent two-dimensional attached jet, based upon very similar models, have been given by Bourque and Newman [1], Sawyer [2], and Levin and Manion [3]. These studies include the derivation of equations for predicting the attachment distance in terms of the system geometry. It is assumed in each case that the velocity profile of the attached curved jet can be described by the Görtler expression for the velocity distribution in a free straight jet.

The Görtler solution [4] includes an undetermined constant, or "jet-spread" parameter σ, to be evaluated experimentally. From Reichardt's experimental observations [5], it can be demonstrated that for a straight jet the spread parameter is in fact a constant and equal to approximately 7.7. In the curved-jet studies referred to above, the spread parameter is again left undetermined. There are, however, more severe physical constraints on the attached curved jet than on the unattached jet, and the authors have elected to employ the jet-spread parameter not only as a coefficient for experimental evaluation but also as a reservoir for accumulating the effects of the approximations and inaccuracies embodied in the analytical model.

Unfortunately, these effects vary with the system geometry and, as a result, the spread parameter must also be taken as a function of system geometry in order to bring the theoretical predictions into harmony with observed attachment distances. While this is not unexpected, particularly in the light of the complexity of the problem, it develops that the range and extreme magnitudes of σ required to rationalize the theoretical and experimental data are so inordinate that this factor completely loses its identity and significance as a spread parameter and becomes instead an ungeneralized empirical coefficient.

This study briefly re-examines the role of the jet-spread parameter and attempts to restore it to its primary function by a different allocation of model error effects, leading to modified equations for predicting the attachment distance. The attachment distance is computed as a function of system geometry and other parameters. Experiments were conducted with a two-dimensional water tunnel to study the effects of sidewall offset and angle on the attachment distance, and these data are compared with the modified theory. Other experiments included studies of nozzle aspect-ratio and sidewall-symmetry effects.

Prediction Relationships

Fig. 1 is a photograph of the attached jet, and Fig. 2 is the combined mathematical and physical model. It is characteristically assumed that the flow is incompressible and two-dimensional; that the velocity distribution at the nozzle discharge and the pressure distribution throughout the separation bubble are both uniform; that the jet forms a circular arc of radius R which is large with respect to the jet width; and that the jet is turbulent and entrains fluid from the surroundings in a manner similar to a straight jet.

FIG. 1 CHARACTERISTIC FLOW PATTERN WITH JET
ATTACHED TO ADJACENT WALL

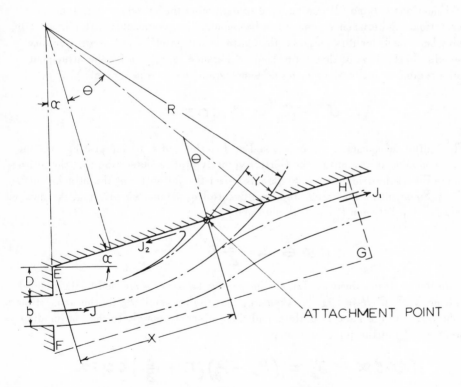

FIG. 2 PHYSICAL AND MATHEMATICAL MODEL FOR
ANALYSIS OF ATTACHMENT DISTANCE

207

With these assumptions the earlier authors have derived the following equations:

$$\frac{D}{b} = \frac{\sigma}{3(\theta+\alpha)} \left(\frac{1}{t'^2} - 1\right)\left(1 - \frac{\cos\theta}{\cos\alpha}\right) - \frac{1}{2} \tag{1}$$

$$\frac{x}{b} = \frac{\sigma}{3(\theta+\alpha)} \left(\frac{1}{t'^2} - 1\right)(\sin\theta + \sin\alpha)$$

$$-\left(\frac{D}{b} + \frac{1}{2}\right)\sin\alpha - \frac{\tanh^{-1} t'}{3t'^2 \sin\theta} \tag{2}$$

where:

$$t' = \tanh \frac{\sigma y'}{s + \frac{\sigma b}{3}}$$

Equations (1) and (2) can be used to determine the attachment distance x/b if a relationship between t' and θ can be found. Two presumably different models have been used for this purpose, the "attachment-point" and "control-volume" models. In the first of these a momentum balance is written for the attachment-point region as follows, ignoring pressure gradients in this region:

$$J_1 - J_2 = J \cos\theta \tag{3}$$

The individual momenta are expressed as functions of t' by integrating over the corresponding fragments of the Görtler velocity profile, assuming that these fragments retain their identity and character after the jet splits at the attachment point. Substituting the integrated results into Eq. (3) and simplifying, the desired relationship between t' and θ is obtained:

$$\cos\theta = \frac{3}{2}t' - \frac{t'^3}{2} \tag{4}$$

In the control-volume model, the momentum balance is applied to the control volume E-F-G-H in Fig. 2. Assuming that the pressure P_B in the separation bubble and on the base is uniform and rises discontinuously to the surrounding pressure P_∞ at the jet centerline,

$$J\cos\alpha - J_1 = (P_\infty - P_B)\left(D + \frac{b}{2}\right)\cos\alpha$$

Letting the pressure difference $(P_\infty - P_B) = J/R$, substituting the geometric conditions, integrating and simplifying as before,

$$\cos\theta = \frac{1}{2} + \frac{3}{4}t' - \frac{t'^3}{4} \tag{5}$$

208

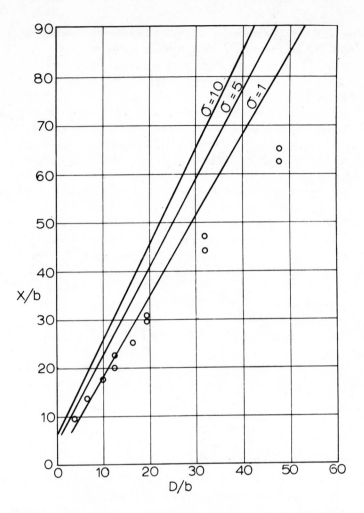

FIG. 3 COMPARISON OF CONTROL-VOLUME MODEL THEORY
EXPERIMENTAL DATA. AFTER BOURQUE AND NEWMAN

With either Eq. (4) or Eq. (5) the wall offset distance D/b and the attachment distance x/b can now be calculated in terms of the jet-spread parameter σ for arbitrary values of the parameter t'. This allows tabulating D/b and x/b as functions of t' and σ, and then plotting x/b versus D/b, since an explicit solution is not feasible.

Although the attachment-point model correlates quite well with experimental data for parallel sidewalls, Levin and Manion find it grossly inaccurate as the included angle of divergence between the walls is increased beyond about 60 degrees. The control-volume model, on the other hand, holds more appeal in terms of the capacity for fundamental representation of the flow and appears to offer greater promise for analytical refinement. However, Fig. 3, after Bourque and Newman, illustrates that the latter model fails completely to predict attachment distances, even for parallel sidewalls. In order to rationalize the theoretical and experimental data, the spread parameter σ would have to be varied from some very small fraction of unity to a value of about 5. Furthermore, since jet spreading

209

varies inversely with σ, there is the unexpected implication of greater jet diffusion in the attached jet than in the free, straight jet for which σ is known to be approximately 7.7. When divergent sidewalls are considered, the range of σ required to bring the theoretical and experimental results together is still greater. While it is presumably possible to write an empirical expression for $\sigma(\alpha, D/b)$ as suggested by Levin and Manion, the result would have little or no physical meaning and would not in any way enhance the validity of the theory.

It is evident that the control-volume model incorporates some significant inaccuracies the correction of which, even approximately, should greatly improve the representation of the model. One fairly obvious source of error in the control-volume model is the assumption that the base pressure, which might be called P_B', is equal to the bubble pressure P_B, assumed uniform throughout the separation bubble. Pressure measurements by Bourque and Newman and by Sawyer have shown that this is far from true and that the base pressure is noticeably higher than either the average pressure in the separation bubble or the pressure on the isobar roughly coincident with the concave edge of the curved jet. As a result $(P_\infty - P_B')$ is considerably less than $(P_\infty - P_B)$. This difference is in the proper direction to at least partially account for the deviation between theory and experiment shown in Fig. 3.

Ignoring the errors inherent in the relationship $(P_\infty - P_B) = J/R$ (i.e., in reality the jet curvature is not constant, the width of the jet is not in general small with respect to the radius, and the pressure difference across the jet is not constant along the jet), an approximate correction for the base pressure can still be made. By definition,

$$ \frac{P_\infty - P_B}{P_\infty - P_B'} \equiv C_p' \tag{6} $$

where the coefficient C_p' may be a function of D/b and α.

Replacing $(P_\infty - P_B)$ by the equivalent of $(P_\infty - P_B')$ in the momentum equation for the control-volume model,

$$ J\cos\alpha - J_1 = (P_\infty - P_B)\frac{1}{C_p'}\left(D + \frac{b}{2}\right) \tag{7} $$

Equation (7) yields a new relationship between t' and θ. That is,

$$ \cos\alpha - \left(\frac{1}{2} + \frac{3}{4}t' - \frac{t'^3}{4}\right) = (\cos\alpha - \cos\theta)\frac{1}{C_p'} $$

Or,

$$ \cos\theta = \cos\alpha\left(1 - C_p'\right) + C_p'\left(\frac{1}{2} + \frac{3}{4}t' - \frac{t'^3}{4}\right) \tag{8} $$

There are now two undetermined coefficients, C_p' and σ, left to be inferred from experiments. However, the spread parameter is subject to relatively direct experimental measurement and, if desired, the remaining inaccuracies in the model can be accumulated in the coefficient, C_P', along with the base pressure correction.

It can be presumed that the entrainment process which produces jet diffusion is inhibited on the concave side of a curved jet and augmented on the convex side because of the response in each case of a deviating particle to the pressure gradient in which it finds itself. Since the attachment distance is primarily affected by the entrainment and spreading rate on the concave side of the jet, it can be expected that the apparent change in σ in going from a straight jet to a curved jet will be an increase, corresponding to reduced jet diffusion on that side. Although it appears obvious that σ should not be a function of D/b or α directly, it is perhaps a function of jet curvature, b/R. Sawyer [2], through detailed observation and analysis of the velocity distribution in an attached jet, determined the value of σ as approximately 10 for one particular set of conditions. Velocity profile measurements over the practical range of the independent variables are needed to definitively establish this relationship.

The general nature of the base-pressure correction can be inferred from the pressure measurements reported in the references [1] and [2]. It is evident from these data that C_P' should be greater than unity and possibly 1.5 or higher for the parallel-wall configuration. Since the shape of the separation bubble does not change radically with the offset for parallel walls, C_P' should be relatively independent of D/b. For diverging walls, however, the shape of the separation bubble is strongly affected, and C_P' can be expected to vary as the ratio $\alpha/(D/b)$ increases. Additional variation of C_P' will arise, of course, to the degree that this coefficient absorbs the effects of other differences between the model and the actual flow.

An application of Eqs. (1), (2), and (8) can be made to the Bourque and Newman data for parallel sidewalls. Arbitrarily selecting σ as 10, it is found that a value of C_P' equal to 2 produces excellent agreement between theory and experiment as shown in Fig. 4. It is worth noting, however, that with $\alpha = 0$ and $C_P' = 2$, Eq. (8) reduces to

$$\cos\theta = \frac{3}{2}t' - \frac{t'^3}{2}$$

which is the attachment-point model relationship between t' and θ. In other words, the control-volume model, when pressure-corrected in the above manner, reduces to the attachment-point model in the case of parallel walls.

Chaplin [6], in studying the related problem of the two-dimensional "annular" jet for ground-effect machines, derived what at first glance might appear to be an independent expression for the base pressure, employing both the attachment-point and control-volume concepts. In effect, however, Chaplin merely substituted the momentum equation for the attachment-point model into that for the control-volume model and solved for the base pressure. All this does is define a base pressure such that the control-volume model satisfies and reduces to the attachment-point model. Since the attachment-point model is inadequate for predicting attachment distances in the presence of diverging walls, it appears that the pressure coefficient C_P' must be left for experimental determination. Published experimental data suitable for evaluating $C_P'(\alpha, D/b)$ have not been found. For the limited range of wall divergence and offset included in this research, the values of C_p' required to correlate the theoretical and observed data are given in the following section of the paper.

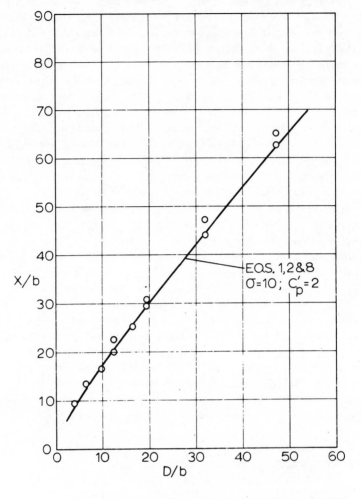

FIG. 4 BASE-PRESSURE CORRECTED CONTROL-VOLUME
MODEL THEORY COMPARED WITH BOURQUE AND
NEWMAN EXPERIMENTAL DATA

Experimental Program

Experiments for measuring jet attachment distances with parallel and diverging walls were conducted in a novel two-dimensional water tunnel described elsewhere [9]. These experiments were undertaken primarily to determine jet attachment distances under conditions not treated by earlier investigations (1), (2), (3); that is in the presence of oppositely disposed sidewalls and with small nozzle aspect ratios. The data for symmetrical parallel and diverging sidewalls are compared in this section to the modified theory consisting of the base-pressure corrected control-volume model.

212

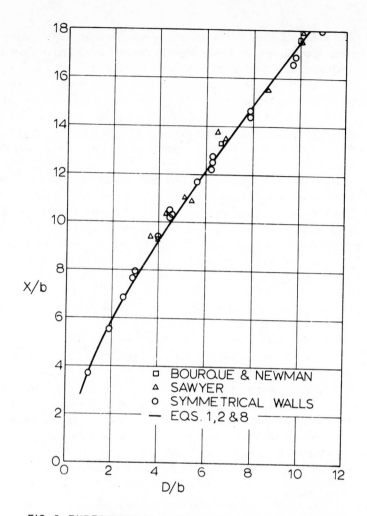

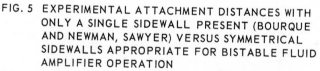

FIG. 5 EXPERIMENTAL ATTACHMENT DISTANCES WITH
ONLY A SINGLE SIDEWALL PRESENT (BOURQUE
AND NEWMAN, SAWYER) VERSUS SYMMETRICAL
SIDEWALLS APPROPRIATE FOR BISTABLE FLUID
AMPLIFIER OPERATION

    One of the features of the water tunnel used in these experiments was a free-
surface section, downstream from the test section, permitting the insertion upstream and the free manipulation of probes for air bubble removal, velocity
measurement, flow direction indication, and the like. Validation tests indicated
that the presence of the free-surface section did not affect attachment distances.
After experimenting with a variety of different methods of measuring the attachment distance, the technique finally selected, on the basis of repeatability and
convenience, involved a small nylon tuft at the end of a slender probe. The tuft
was moved slowly back and forth along the calibrated sidewall and the average
point of direction reversal was taken as the attachment point. Attachment distances measured in this manner were repeatable to within ± 3%.

    Because of the importance in fluid amplifiers of the bistable mode of opera-
tion and because previous experimental work was limited to systems con-

taining only one sidewall, attachment distances were measured in a variety of opposed-wall configurations. The basic experiments were conducted with parallel sidewalls, starting with the walls symmetrically located at an offset, D/b, of unity. The wall opposite that on which attachment took place was successively moved to larger offsets until the limit of the system was reached. Within the limit of experimental errors, no effect of the presence or location of the opposing sidewall could be detected. Fig. 5 compares the attachment distances for symmetrically located pairs of sidewalls with single-sidewall data from Bourque and Newman, and from Sawyer.

The reason for the insensitivity of the attachment distance to the presence or location of the opposite sidewall may be inferred from the general nature of the flow. A detailed study of still and motion pictures of attached flow, including velocity measurements, demonstrates that the flux of momentum returned to the jet region from the convex side is so small with respect to the jet momentum that differences in the direction of the return flow due to the presence and location of the second wall have a negligible effect on jet curvature and the attachment distance.

Another prominent difference between the experiments reported here and earlier work lies in the nozzle aspect ratio — the ratio of the depth to the width of the nozzle opening. To assure themselves of a close approximation to two-dimensionality, Bourque and Newman, and Sawyer, employed very high nozzle aspect ratios, up to 100 and 75 respectively.

From purely practical considerations of manufacturing and operational reliability, it is preferable that the nozzle aspect ratio of a fluid amplifier be as close to unity as is consistent with the required jet attachment and switching characteristics. Because of the importance of small aspect ratios, experiments were performed to determine the effect of aspect ratio on attachment distance. The evidence as shown in Fig. 6, is again essentially negative; that is, no

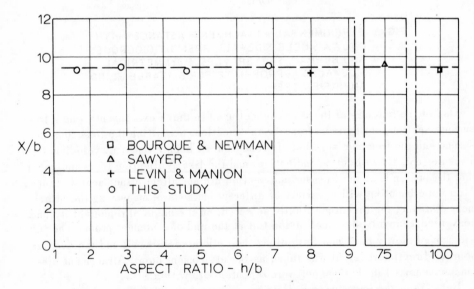

FIG. 6 EFFECT OF NOZZLE ASPECT RATIO ON ATTACH-
MENT DISTANCE FOR $D/b = 4$, $N_r = 1.3 \times 10^4$.

measurable effect of aspect ratio was observed. The data in Fig. 6 from this study were taken with symmetrically disposed sidewalls, while that from references [1], [2], and [3] were with single sidewalls. Detailed probing with direction and velocity-sensitive probes and photographs taken in different planes, demonstrated that the flow was always substantially two-dimensional, irrespective of nozzle aspect ratio.

To provide experimental data on jet attachment distances under conditions more closely akin to those of practical interest in fluid amplifier design than earlier studies, observations were made with symmetrical sidewalls, a modest nozzle aspect ratio, wall offsets between approximately 1 and 10 nozzle widths, and wall inclinations from 0 to 25 degrees with respect to the nozzle axis. The results of these experiments are given in Fig. 7. In Fig. 8, the data are cross-plotted in a manner convenient for comparison with the modified theory corresponding to the base-pressure corrected control-volume model, employing $\sigma = 10$ and $C\acute{p} = 2$. It can be seen from this figure, and from Fig. 4, that for the range

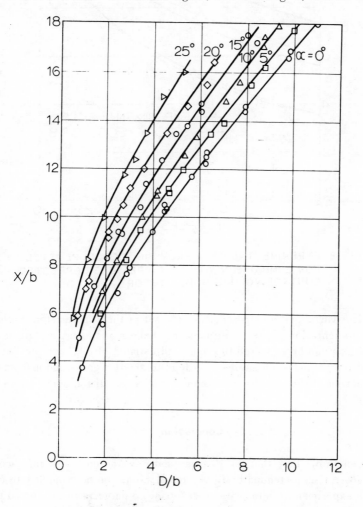

FIG. 7 ATTACHMENT DISTANCE VERSUS ANGLE AND
OFFSET OF SIDEWALL

215

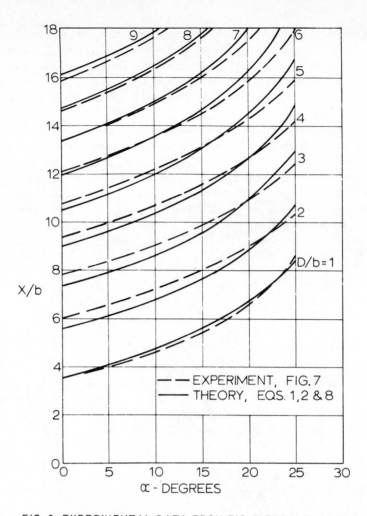

FIG. 8 EXPERIMENTAL DATA FROM FIG. 7 CROSS-PLOTTED
FOR COMPARISON WITH BASE-PRESSURE CORRECTED
CONTROL-VOLUME MODEL THEORY

of independent variables considered, a single set of these parameters yields an adequate representation of the jet attachment phenomenon. Larger wall inclination angles can be expected to require adjustment of the base-pressure correction coefficient, but such angles also lead to smaller gains and much more critical variation of the attachment distance with small dimensional errors in offset or angle.

Conclusion

It has been shown here that the Bourque and Newman control-volume model for jet attachment, as extended by Levin and Manion, can be brought into conformity with experimental data, without resorting to unrealistic jet-spread parameters, by correcting the base pressure in the direction indicated by experimentally observed pressure distributions. The experimental work reported here has

216

demonstrated that data observed with a single sidewall and with large nozzle aspect ratios are equally applicable, within the limits of their respective experimental errors, to symmetrical wall configurations and small nozzle aspect ratios. Experimental data are also provided for a range of wall offsets and divergence angles which should be of practical interest to fluid amplifier designers.

Acknowledgments

The author gratefully acknowledges the counsel and stimulation provided by Dr. A. G. Hansen, now Dean, College of Engineering, Georgia Insititute of Technology, and Prof. R. B. Keller, Mechanical Engineering Department, University of Michigan. He also expresses his gratitude to the technical staff of the University of Michigan Fluids Laboratory for invaluable assistance in the fabrication of experimental equipment and in performing the experiments, the results of which are partially reported here.

The research reported here was done in partial fulfillment of the requirements for the Ph.D. degree in the Mechanical Engineering Department, University of Michigan.

References

[1] C. Bourque and B. G. Newman, "Reattachment of a Two-Dimensional Jet to an Adjacent Flat Plate," *The Aeronautical Quarterly*, Vol. XI, August, 1960, pp. 201-232.

[2] R. A. Sawyer, "The Flow Due to a Two-Dimensional Jet Issuing Parallel to a Flat Plate," *Journal of Fluid Mechanics*, Vol. 9, Part 4, December, 1960, pp. 543-561.

[3] I. Levin and F. M. Manion, "Fluid Amplification 5. Jet Attachment Distance as a Function of Adjacent Wall Offset and Angle," Harry Diamond Laboratory, TR-1087, December, 1962, p. 32.

[4] H. Gortler, "Berechnung von Aufgaben der freien Turbulenz auf Grund eines neuen Naherungsansatzes," *Zeitschrift fur angewandte Mathematik und Mechanik*, Vol. 22, October, 1942, pp. 244-254.

[5] H. Reichardt, "Gesetsmassigkeiten der freien Turbulenz," *Vereines Deutscher Ingenieure, Forschungsheft*, Vol. 414, 1942.

[6] H. R. Chaplin, "Effect of Jet Mixing on the Annular Jet," David Taylor Model Basin Report No. 1375, February, 1959, p. 28.

[7] H. Schlichting, *Boundary Layer Theory*, McGraw-Hill Book Co., New York, N.Y., fourth edition, 1960, pp. 592-607.

[8] R. A. Sawyer, "Two-Dimensional Reattaching Jet Flows Including the Effects of Curvature on Entrainment," *Journal of Fluid Mechanics*, Vol. 17, Part 4, December, 1963, pp. 481-498.

[9] C. C. Perry, "Two-Dimensional Jet Attachment," Ph.D. dissertation, University of Michigan, Mechanical Engineering Department, 1967.

A Theoretical and Experimental Study of Vortex Rate Gyro

Turgut Sarpkaya
University of Nebraska
Lincoln, Neb.

John M. Goto and Joseph M. Kirshner
Harry Diamond Laboratories
Washington, D. C.

Abstract

The performance characteristics of a pneumatic angular rate sensor were studied both theoretically and experimentally. The boundary layer equations for the radial flow were solved and the results were compared with those obtained through the momentum-integral equation. The shear stress and velocity expressions were used to determine the theoretical efficiency of the sensor. Experiments were conducted with a prototype and model and it was found that the experimental viscous efficiencies compare favorably well with those obtained theoretically.

Nomenclature

b	= half of disk spacing
E	= viscous efficiency, Γ_r/Γ_o
f, g, h	= functions
K	= a parameter, $\dfrac{\theta^2}{\nu} \dfrac{dU}{dx}$
K_1, K_2	= constants
p	= pressure
Δp	= differential pressure
Q	= total flow rate through the sensor
r	= radial distance
r_{po}	= radial distance from the sink tube axis to the pressure pickoff hole

218

R	= radius of the sensor
T	= torque
u	= radial component of velocity
U	= potential velocity, $U(r)$ or $U(x)$
U_o	= entrance velocity at $r = R$
U_s	= average sink tube velocity
v_{rt}	= relative tangential velocity
w	= axial component of velocity
x	= radial direction measured from the coupling
z	= axial direction
Γ_r	= circulation at r
Γ_o	= circulation at $r = R$
δ^*	= displacement thickness
ϵ	$= \dfrac{r}{R} \sqrt{\dfrac{\nu R}{U_o b^2}}$
η	= similarity parameter
θ	= momentum thickness
μ	= dynamic viscosity of fluid
ν	= kinematic viscosity of fluid
ρ	= density of fluid
τ_{or}	= radial component of shear stress
τ_{ot}	= tangential component of shear stress
ψ	= stream function
ω	= angular velocity

Introduction

The purpose of the theoretical and experimental investigation described herein is to determine the efficiency and the boundary layer characteristics of a pneumatic angular rate sensor.

The sensor consists basically of two coaxial disks separated by a cylindrical coupling ring, two outlet sinks, and a suitable pickoff element. The gaseous fluid flows through the coupling element of uniform length and porosity and discharges at the two sink tubes. The radial flow between the two coaxial disks is modified by the viscous shear and by a vortex created by the rotation of the unit about an axis parallel to its axis of symmetry. Consequently, the determination of the viscous efficiency of the sensor or in other words the fraction of the angular momentum which the fluid retains at the pickoff location requires a detailed analysis of the resulting boundary layers.

219

In recent years, steady axisymmetric vortex flows have been the subject of extensive investigation. Because a general analysis of radial flow between two parallel rotating disks present certain complexities, various analyses have been carried out with varying degrees of success and with specific objectives in mind. Invariably, all of the solutions are approximate. Some are mere mathematical exercises and appear to be bizarre from a practical viewpoint. A brief review of the subject up to 1962 has been given by Lewellen [1]. None of these analyses treats the problem presently under consideration. Vogelpohl [2] was perhaps the first investigator to attempt an analysis of a confined vortex. His solution is not, however, an accurate representation of the vortex flow between two parallel disks [3]. The works of Lewellen [1], Rosenzweigh, Lewellen and Ross [4], and Mack [5] are confined to the case where the tangential velocity is considerably larger than the radial velocity and the distance between the plates is larger than the radius of the plates. Granger [6] studied the steady three-dimensional vortex flow for a specified vorticity distribution along the axis of rotation and for large spacings between the disks. Ostrach and Loper [3] analyzed the vortex motion between two closely spaced disks. The vortex is assumed to be driven by the tangential injection of fluid at an outer radius and is withdrawn at an inner radius. This analysis too is not applicable to the rate-sensor flow because in the sensor the tangential velocity relative to the sensor at the coupling is zero whereas in the analysis of Ostrach and Loper the relative tangential velocity has a definite finite magnitude; i.e. this particular analysis is carried out for different boundary conditions.

Recently Peube and Kreith [7] studied the steady viscous fluid motion between two infinitely large rotating disks through the use of suitable series expansions. A line source is assumed at the axis and no coupling element at any radius. Because of these significant differences, the results of this analysis are not applicable to the vortex-sink angular rate sensor.

The radial flow between the two coaxial disks has been previously analyzed by Sarpkaya [8] by using the two-dimensional equations as a first approximation. It was found that the boundary layer thickness decreases linearly from a maximum value at the coupling to zero thickness at the center of the disks. Recently, Fiebig [9] studied the response of the radial flow to harmonic oscillations or impulsive rotations of the sensor by approximating the transport flow by a family of "parabolic" profiles which satisfy the equation of continuity but not the equation of momentum.

Egli [10] and Sarpkaya [11] have independently analyzed the radial flow boundary layer on a circular flat disk. In these analyses the drain was approximated by a line sink and the radial potential flow was assumed to be unaffected by the boundary layer.

Boundary Layer Analysis of Radial Flow

The type of flow present in the rate sensor is a combination of a strong sink flow and a weak confined vortex flow. Because of the difficulty of obtaining a closed solution of the Navier-Stokes equations for the confined vortex, the problem is divided into analyzing the radial flow by use of the boundary layer and integral-momentum equations and then extending the solution to flows with a weak swirl by use of suitable perturbation methods.

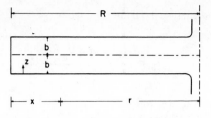

FIG. 1 DEFINITION SKETCH

The boundary layer equation for axisymmetric radial flow is given by (see Fig. 1),

$$u \frac{\partial u}{\partial r} + w \frac{\partial u}{\partial z} = U \frac{dU}{dr} + \nu \frac{\partial^2 u}{\partial z^2} \tag{1}$$

and the equation of continuity by

$$\frac{\partial ur}{\partial r} + \frac{\partial wr}{\partial z} = 0 \tag{2}$$

A stream function ψ may be defined by

$$u = \frac{1}{r} \frac{\partial \psi}{\partial z} \quad \text{and} \quad w = - \frac{1}{r} \frac{\partial \psi}{\partial r} \tag{3}$$

so that the equation of continuity is automatically satisfied. The velocity outside the boundary layer for the unconfined radial flow is given by

$$U(r) = - \frac{U_o R}{r} \tag{4}$$

In a confined radial flow, however, the presence of two symmetrical boundary layers modify the variation of the potential velocity with r. This may be taken care of by introducing the displacement thickness δ^*. From the conservation of radial mass flow, we have

$$U(r) = - \frac{U_o R}{r} \frac{b}{b - \delta^*} \tag{5}$$

which may be expanded to a series in terms of ϵ where[1] $\epsilon = \frac{r}{R} \sqrt{\frac{\nu R}{U_o b^2}}$

$$U(r) = - \frac{U_o R}{r} (1 + K_1 \epsilon + K_2 \epsilon^2 + \dots) \tag{6}$$

where K_1, K_2, etc., remain to be determined.

---

[1] The first order analysis [8] has shown that δ^* is proportional to ϵ.

Now introducing the similarity transformation

$$\eta = \frac{z}{r} \sqrt{\frac{U_0 R}{\nu}} \tag{7}$$

the stream function may be written as

$$\psi = -r \sqrt{U_0 R \nu} \left[f(\eta) + \epsilon K_1 g(\eta) + \epsilon^2 K_2 h(\eta) + \ldots \right] \tag{8}$$

Evaluating u, w, and their derivatives, and making use of Eq. (6), and combining the resulting terms in terms of ϵ and ϵ^2, one has the following two differential equations:

$$f'^2 + ff'' - f''' - 1 = 0 \tag{9}$$

and

$$f'g' + 2f''g + fg'' - g''' - 1 = 0 \tag{10}$$

which are to be solved with the boundary conditions

$$
\begin{array}{lllll}
z = 0 & u = w = 0 & f' = 0 & f''(0) = ? \\
z = \infty & u = U(r) & f' = g' = 1 & g''(0) = ?
\end{array} \tag{11}
$$

It should be noted that the second set of the boundary conditions are to be satisfied at $z = \infty$ rather than at $z = b$. This is justified on the basis of a previous analysis [8] which has shown that for large radial mass flows, the boundary layer becomes thin and velocity gradients become large toward the axis of symmetry. The present analysis too shows that the boundary-layer blockage effects are small and can further be reduced by increasing the radial mass flow within the limitations imposed by other conditions such as noise, stability, and the economical use of available mass flow.

Equation (9) is of Falkner-Skan type and was solved numerically by Terrill as reported by Rosenhead [12]. He found $f''(0) = 1.086$ and $\eta = 7$ for $f' = 0.99$. The displacement thickness for an approximation in the order of ϵ, i.e., through the results of Eq. (9), reduces to:

$$\frac{\delta^*}{b} = \frac{r}{R} \sqrt{\frac{\nu R}{U_0 b^2}} \lim_{\eta \to \infty} \{\eta - f(\eta)\} = 0.88 \frac{r}{R} \sqrt{\frac{\nu R}{U_0 b^2}} \tag{12}$$

where

$$\lim_{\eta \to \infty} \{\eta - f(\eta)\} = K_1 = 0.88$$

222

Equation (10) is solved numerically through the use of a computer and making use of Eq. (9). It is found that $g''(0) = 0.9343$, and $\lim_{\eta \to \infty} (f - g) \simeq 0.50$. Hence, the velocity distribution reduces to

$$\frac{u}{U(r)} = \frac{f' + K_1 \epsilon g'}{1 + K_1 \epsilon} \tag{13}$$

and the displacement thickness is given by

$$\frac{\delta^*}{b} = \frac{r}{R} \sqrt{\frac{\nu R}{U_0 b^2}} \lim_{\eta \to \infty} \{(\eta - f(\eta)) + K_1 \epsilon (f - g)\}$$

or

$$\frac{\delta^*}{b} = K_1 \epsilon \left(1 + \frac{\epsilon}{2}\right) \tag{14}$$

The result is that the displacement thickness is essentially unchanged, for the correction due to second order analysis is in the order of ϵ^2. The displacement thickness, as given by Eq. (12), is shown in Fig. 2. It is apparent that the radial boundary layer thickness decreases as the inward radial flow velocity along the disk increases.

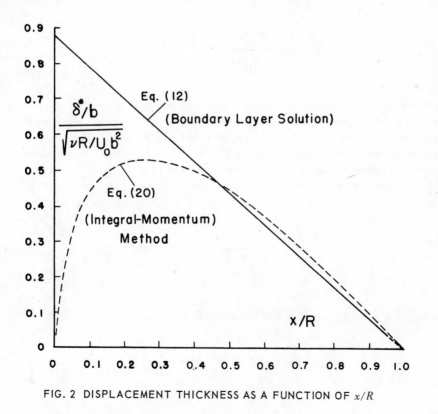

FIG. 2 DISPLACEMENT THICKNESS AS A FUNCTION OF x/R

The weakness of the foregoing analysis is its inability to predict a zero boundary layer thickness at the inner face of the coupling, i.e., at $r = R$. The leading edge of the disk is a ring of singularity. Despite that, the boundary layer thickness should be zero at the leading edge, increase to a maximum, and then decrease toward the center of the disk as predicted by the foregoing analysis. The reason for this anomaly is in the specified form of the free stream velocity. This situation may be remedied in several ways. One method would be to abandon the similarity hypothesis and the other to use an integral-momentum technique.

Radial Flow Analysis Through Integral-Momentum Method

Thwaites [12] analyzing many exact solutions, accurate computations, and approximate methods, has shown that $\dfrac{U}{\nu}\dfrac{d\theta^2}{dx}$ may be expressed as a linear function of $\dfrac{\theta^2}{\nu}\dfrac{dU}{dx}$, namely

$$\frac{U}{\nu}\frac{d\theta^2}{dx} = m - n\frac{\theta^2}{\nu}\frac{dU}{dx} \tag{15}$$

where m and n are constants and depend only on the chosen form of the velocity profile in the boundary layer.

Rott and Crabtree [13], using Thwaites' suggestion, have shown that the momentum thickness for the boundary layer on bodies of revolution may be written as

$$\frac{U\theta^2}{\nu} = \frac{m}{r^2 U^{n-1}} \int_0^x r^2 U^{n-1} dx \tag{16}$$

For flows with weak pressure gradients $m = 0.45$ and $n = 6$.

For the case under consideration, however, the radial flow pressure gradient is quite large (apprx. $\propto U_o^2 R^2/r^3$), and the constants m and n will have to be modified accordingly. Using Launder's [14] modification of the Holstein and Bohlen [15] tables for large pressure gradients and plotting $\dfrac{U}{\nu}\dfrac{d\theta^2}{dx}$ as a function of $\dfrac{\theta^2}{\nu}\dfrac{dU}{dx}$, one has $m = 0.40$ and $n = 5$, or

$$\frac{U\theta^2}{\nu} = \frac{0.40}{r^2 U^4} \int_0^x r^2 U^4 dx \tag{17}$$

Inserting Eq. (4) into Eq. (17) and integrating, one finds

$$\frac{U\theta^2}{\nu} = 0.4\, r\left(1 - \frac{r}{R}\right) \tag{18}$$

The displacement thickness δ^* may be calculated through the use of tabulated values of a function called $f_1(K)$ which depends only on the form of the polynomial or polynomials assumed for the velocity distribution in the boundary layer. For a detailed discussion of this function (see Ref. [12], p. 292 and Ref. [14]). Writing, therefore,

$$\frac{\delta^*}{\theta} = f_1(K) \qquad \text{and} \qquad K = \frac{\theta^2 U}{\nu} \frac{1}{U} \frac{dU}{dx}$$

and making use of Eqs. (4) and (18), one obtains

$$K = 0.4 \left(1 - \frac{r}{R}\right) \tag{19}$$

and

$$\frac{\delta^*/b}{\sqrt{\nu R/U_0 b^2}} = 0.63 \frac{r}{R} \sqrt{1 - \frac{r}{R}} \quad f_1(K) = \frac{r}{R} \sqrt{K} \quad f_1(K) \tag{20}$$

The displacement thickness was calculated from Eq. (20) through the use of Eq. (19) and the $f_1(K)$ values tabulated by Launder [14]. The results are presented in Fig. 2 together with that obtained from the similarity hypothesis. It is seen that the displacement thickness reaches a maximum value at about $x/R = 0.25$ and near the coupling element it is considerably smaller than that predicted from the boundary layer equations.

A second order momentum analysis, not presented herein, was carried out using the modified velocity distribution given by Eq. (5). The lengthy analysis showed that the correction on the displacement thickness is in the order of ϵ^2. This conclusion is not only in conformity with that reached in connection with Eq. (14) but also an indication of the fact that the boundary layers do not appreciably modify the free-stream velocity.

Tangential Velocity for Flow with Weak Swirl

In the foregoing, the development of the boundary layer and the velocity components for only the radial sink flow were discussed. The tangential component of velocity for weak swirls, i.e., for low rates of rotation may be determined either through a perturbation analysis of the equations of motion written for the tangential direction or through the assumption of the similarity of the radial and tangential boundary layers. The latter method, which is considerably simpler than the first, shows that the inclination of the relative streamlines within the boundary layer with respect to the radial direction — if the wall is imagined at rest and the fluid is taken to rotate a large distance from the wall — is equal to the inclination of the relative streamlines outside the boundary layer. This hypothesis, which could be shown to be identical to ignoring the w component of velocity within the boundary layer, yields

$$v_{rt} = \frac{\omega R}{U_o} \left(\frac{\Gamma_r}{\Gamma_o} - \frac{r^2}{R^2} \right) u \tag{21}$$

in which Γ_r and Γ_o represent the strength of the vortex at radial distances r and R, respectively, and u the radial component of velocity. If the strength of the vortex were not diminished by the shear stress on the walls, the ratio Γ_r/Γ_o would have been equal to unity. Obviously, Γ_r/Γ_o represents the ratio of the angular momentum which the fluid retains at a radial distance r to that imparted at the coupling, i.e., the viscous efficiency of the sensor.

Viscous Efficiency of the Sensor

The circumferential component of the shear stress is given by

$$\tau_{ot} = \mu \left| \frac{dv_{rt}}{dz} \right|_{z=0} = \mu \frac{\omega R}{U_o} \left(\frac{\Gamma_r}{\Gamma_o} - \frac{r^2}{R^2} \right) \left| \frac{\partial u}{\partial z} \right|_{z=0} \tag{22}$$

Defining

$$\frac{\tau_{or} \cdot \theta}{\mu U(r)} = \cdot f_2(K) \tag{23}$$

where $\tau_{or} = \mu \left| \frac{du}{dz} \right|_{z=0}$, one obtains

$$\tau_{ot} = \mu \omega \frac{R^2}{r} \left(\frac{\Gamma_r}{\Gamma_o} - \frac{r^2}{R^2} \right) \frac{1}{\theta} f_2(K) \tag{24}$$

The function $f_2(K)$ like the function $f_1(K)$ is tabulated [15] in terms of K.

Considering the torque acting on the two sides of an annulus of fluid mass dM, $(dM = 4\pi\rho b r dr)$, we have

$$dT = 4\pi r^2 \tau_{ot} dr \tag{25}$$

Since

$$\frac{dT}{dM} = \frac{\partial(\Gamma_r/2\pi)}{\partial t} = \frac{\partial(\Gamma_r/2\pi)}{\partial r} \frac{dr}{dt} \tag{26}$$

226

we have

$$\frac{\partial (\Gamma_r/2\pi)}{\partial r} = \frac{r}{b}\frac{\tau_{ot}}{u} \tag{27}$$

Hence, the viscous efficiency may be written as

$$E = \frac{\Gamma_r}{\Gamma_o} = \frac{1}{\rho b \omega R^2} \int_{r_{po}}^{R} \frac{\tau_{ot}\, r}{u}\, dr \tag{28}$$

or replacing u by the average radial velocity $U(r)$ and combining with Eq. (24), one obtains

$$\frac{dE}{d(r/R)} = \sqrt{\frac{\nu\, R}{U_o b^2}}\left(E - \frac{r^2}{R^2}\right)\frac{f_2(K)}{\sqrt{U\theta^2/\nu r}} \tag{29}$$

or in terms of the total flow rate $Q = 4\pi R b U_o$, one has

$$\frac{dE}{d(r/R)} = 4\pi \sqrt{\frac{\nu R^2}{Qb}}\left(E - \frac{r^2}{R^2}\right)\frac{f_2(K)}{\sqrt{U\theta^2/\nu r}} \tag{30}$$

Equation (30) is integrated numerically through the use of Eq. (18) and the tables for $f_2(K)$ for various values of $\sqrt{Qb/\nu R^2}$ and the results are shown in Fig. 3.

Experimental Equipment and Procedure

The sensor was made of plexiglass for ease of machining and for flow visualization. Two 1 in. thick disks 20 in. in diameter were held coaxially at a distance 0.55 in. The porous wall, located around the circumference of the test section, was made of two 30 mesh brass strainer cloth rings one having 12 in. diameter and the other 15 in. diameter. A porous foam annulus was inserted between the brass screens. The purpose of the porous wall was to assure uniform flow at the periphery of the coupling element by eliminating the cross-currents which may be present in the outer region of the pancake assembly, (see Fig. 4).

A sink hole of 0.25 in. diameter was drilled at the center line of one of the disks, the entrance was rounded and the inside surface of the hole was polished. A hole of 2 in. diameter was cut in the other disk to receive the removable sink tube body. A shoulder was cut at the inside face of the pancake wall to insure good alignment with the sink tube body.

The sink tube was machined and fitted with a threaded collar to tighten the body against the shoulder of the pancake wall recess. A sink hole of 0.25 in.

Figure 3 is plotted for $r_{po}/R \simeq 0$ only since r_{po} is a very small fraction of R, ($r_{po}/R = 0.003 \, \sim\sim 0.006$). For this range of r_{po}/R, Fig. 3 remains unchanged.

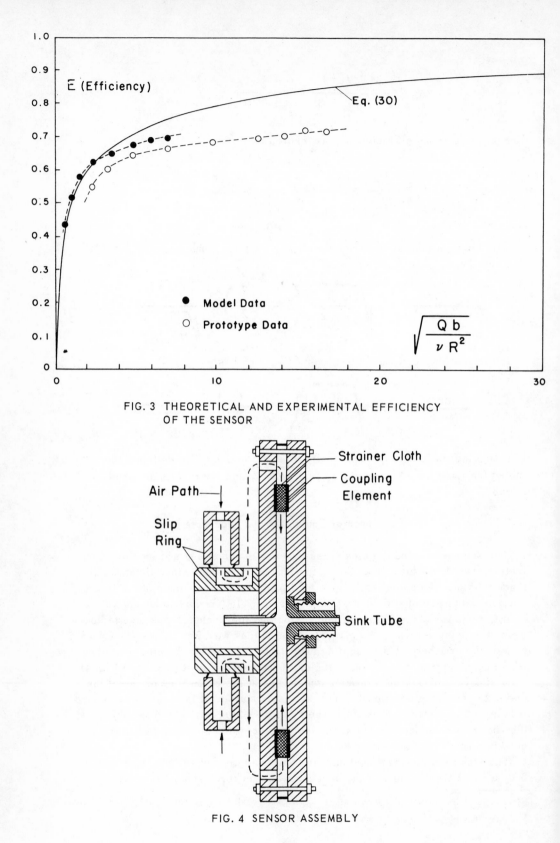

FIG. 3 THEORETICAL AND EXPERIMENTAL EFFICIENCY
OF THE SENSOR

FIG. 4 SENSOR ASSEMBLY

228

diameter was drilled through the body, the entrance was again rounded and polished. A pickoff hole of 0.040 in. diameter at a distance of 0.85 in. from the inside face of the test section was drilled through the sink tube normal to the sink tube axis.

A slip-ring was used to supply the air from stationary lines to the rotating sensor assembly as shown in Fig. 4. Uniform distribution of flow to the porous wall was obtained by the supply line spacing of 60 degrees.

The pickoff element used in the sink tube is shown in Fig. 5. A dividing wall was placed in the tube at the midsection, and two 0.013 in. diameter pressure pickoff holes were drilled on either side of and equidistant from the dividing wall along one side of the tube wall in line with the tube axis and 0.040 in. apart. The pickoff holes were positioned at 45 deg. from the axis of the sink tube and from the direction of flow in the sink tube. It has been shown previously [8] that positioning of the holes 45 deg. from the direction of flow gives maximum theoretical pressure differential across the two pressure pickoff holes.

The pickoff tube was also centered with respect to the sink tube axis, i.e., the pickoff tube was shifted until the two pressure pickoff holes were equal distance away from the center line of the sink tube and until there was no differential pressure output within the range of flow rates used when the sensor was at rest. The null signal for flow rates from 2 to 22 SCFM was less than 0.0017 psi.

For a flow rate of 22 SCFM the maximum null signal corresponded to an equivalent rate of rotation of 0.03 deg/sec. Since this was in the order of the noise level of the sensor output, experiments were conducted by electronically suppressing the small null signal. It is also important to note that the accuracy of the measurement of the rate of rotation of the sensor was in the same order of magnitude, i.e., ± 0.04 deg/sec. There was, therefore, no need at this time for special concern for the observed null signal in the absence of rotation.

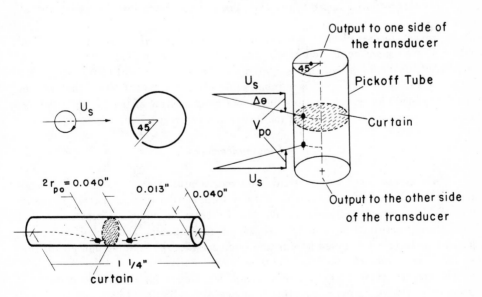

FIG. 5 VELOCITY COMPONENTS AT THE PICKOFF HOLES

Experimental Efficiency of the Sensor

When the pickoff holes are located 45 deg. from the direction of sink flow, the differential pressure *between the two ends* of the pickoff tube is given by [8]

$$|\Delta p| = 2\{ 4 \, \frac{\rho U_s^2}{2} \, \Delta\theta \} \tag{31}$$

Writing $\Delta\theta = V_{po}/U_s$ and $\Gamma_r/\Gamma_o = E$, we have

$$\frac{\Delta p}{\rho \, U_s^2/2} = 8 \, \frac{\omega R}{U_s} \, \frac{R}{r_{po}} \, E \tag{32}$$

or

$$E = \frac{|\Delta p|/\rho U_s^2/2}{8\omega R^2/U_s r_{po}} = F\left(\frac{Qb}{\nu R^2} , \frac{R}{r_{po}} \right) \tag{33}$$

The experimental viscous efficiency is calculated from Eq. (33) for various flows and rates of rotation and plotted in Fig. 3 together with the theoretical curve for the purpose of comparison. It is apparent that the experimental values, although quite consistent among themselves, are lower than those predicted theoretically. This is partly due to the exclusion, from the theoretical analysis, of the energy losses occurring in the sink tube, partly due to various assumptions made in the determination of the shear stress and circulation, partly due to the modifications of the vortex along the sink tube and pickoff, and partly due to experimental errors. The significant fact, however, is that the efficiency of the sensor can be predicted theoretically and that the experimental values follow the same general trend.

In order to further check the experimentally predicted efficiencies, a half-size model of the sensor described herein was built. Only the pickoff tube, due to its very small dimensions, was not scaled down. The experimental efficiency of the model, also shown in Fig. 3, was found to be about 7 per cent larger than that of the prototype. The correlation is considered good in view of the fact that the same pickoff element was used both in the model and prototype.

Closing Remarks

This work has been a theoretical and experimental attempt toward understanding the complex three-dimensional confined fluid motion in a pneumatic gyroscope and acquiring specific information on its efficiency. In addition, experiments were carried out to determine the optimum pancake spacing and pickoff location. For the prototype discussed herein, the otpimum pancake spacing and pickoff location were found to be 0.55 in. and 0.85 in. respectively.

The determination of the optimum pickoff location requires a better understanding of the evolution of swirling flow in short cylindical tubes and of the swirling flow past a bluff body. The experimental verification of the existence of an optimum pancake spacing points out that E is a function of, among other parameters, the ratio b/R. The dependency of E on b/R could have easily been brought out had the Eqs. (6) and (13) rather than Eq. (4) been used in Eqs. (21) and (28). The detailed calculations based on such a relatively more accurate procedure as well as the experiments conducted for various b/R ratios ($R = 6$ in., and 3 in.; $b = 0.25$ in., 0.55 in., 0.65 in., 0.75 in., and 1.0 in.) have shown that E is a rather weak function of b/R. The efficiency E did not vary more than 6 per cent, for a given Reynolds number, for the range of b/R ratios tested. It is for this reason that Eq. (4) was used in Eqs. (21) and (28). This procedure, though obscured the dependency of E on b/R, greatly simplified the resulting calculations.

Despite the inroads made toward the prediction of the performance characteristics of the vortex-sink angular rate sensor still much remains to be done. The understanding of the flow characteristics in the entrance region into the sink tube, evolution of the swirling flow in the sink tube, swirling flow about the pickoff element, frequency response of the sensor, noise level and its reduction through proper streamlining of the pickoff and the sink tube, rate sensor-fluid amplifier matching are but a few of the problems which require additional investigation.

Acknowledgment

This investigation was carried out under the financial sponsorship of the Harry Diamond Laboratories of the U.S. Army Material Command, Washington, D.C. Experiments were conducted in the Hydrodynamics Laboratory of the Department of Mechanical Engineering of the University of Nebraska.

References

[1] W. S. Lewellen, "Linearized Vortex Flows," AIAA Journal, Vol. 3, No. 1, January 1965.

[2] G. Vogelpohl, "Die Strömung der Wirbelquelle zwischen ebenen Wänden mit Berücksichtigung der Wandreibung," ZAMM, Vol. 24, No. 289, 1944.

[3] S. Ostrach and D. E. Loper, "An Analysis of Confined Vortex Flows," (to be published in AIAA Journal), presented at 4th AIAA Aerospace Sciences Meeting, N.Y., 1966.

[4] M. I. Rosenzweig, W. S. Lewellen, and D. A. Ross, "Confined Vortex Flows with Boundary-Layer Interaction," Aerospace Corp., Report No. ATN-64(9227)-2, 1964.

[5] L. M. Mack, "The Laminar Boundary Layer on a Disk of Finite Radius in a Rotating Flow; Part 1: Numerical Integration of the Momentum-Integral Equations and Application of the Results to the Flow in a Vortex Chamber," Tech. Report No. 32-224, JPL, May 20, 1962.

[6] R. Granger, "Steady Three-Dimensional Vortex Flow,' J. Fluid Mech., Vol. 25, Part 3, 1966.

[7] J. L. Peube and F. Kreith, "Ecoulement permanent d'un fluide visqueux incompressible entre deux disques paralleles en rotation," Journal de Mecanique, Vol. 5, No. 2, 1966.

[8] T. Sarpkaya, "A Theoretical and Experimental Investigation of the Vortex-Sink Angular Rate Sensor," Proceedings of the HDL Fluid Amplification Symposium, Vol. II, October 1965.

[9] M. Fiebig, "On the Motion within Fluid Gyroscopes," AIAA Journal, Vol. 4, No. 4, April 1966.

231

[10] W. H. Egli, (contributor), "Study of Vortex Gyro, Part I — Fluid Vortex Rate Sensor," Honeywell, Inc. Technical Documentary Report No. AL-TDR-65-50, Part I, June 1964.

[11] T. Sarpkaya, "A Theoretical and Experimental Study of Swirling Flow in Axisymmetric Systems," Annual Report to HDL, NU Hydro-Report No. 026-TS, July 1966.

[12] L. Rosenhead, (Editor), "Laminar Boundary Layers," Oxford University Press, 1963.

[13] N. Rott and L. F. Crabtree, "Simplified Laminar Boundary Layer Calculations for Bodies of Revolution and for Yawed Wings," Jour. Aero. Sci., Vol. 19, 1952, p. 553.

[14] B. E. Launder, "An Improved Pohlhausen-Type Method of Calculating the Two-Dimensional Laminar Boundary Layer in a Pressure Gradient," Jour. Heat Transfer C86, 1964.

[15] H. Holstein and T. Bohlen, "Ein einfaches Verfahren zur Berechnung laminarer Reibungsschichten, die dem Näherungsansatz von K. Pohlhausen genugen," Lilienthal-Bericht S-10, 1940. (see also: *Boundary Layer Theory*, by H. Schlichting, 4th ed., McGraw-Hill, N. Y., p. 249).

Large-Signal Vortex Valve Analysis

Endre A. Mayer

The Bendix Corporation
Southfield, Michigan

Abstract

This paper presents an analysis based on an experimental curve that accurately describes the nonlinear flow characteristics of the vortex valve over a wide range of operating conditions. A single, nondimensional function defines the effect of swirl on the vortex valve flow characteristics. The mathematical model is suited for describing the nonlinear behavior of the vortex valve in circuits and for predicting the combined performance of such fluid circuits over a wide range of operating pressures. Application of the analytical model to a simple circuit and to evaluating vortex valve parameters is demonstrated.

Nomenclature

A	=	flow area, in.^{2}
A_2	=	outlet area, in.^{2}
A_{c1}	=	control orifice area, in.^{2}
C_1	=	flow coefficient, $(\text{in.}/^\circ R)^{1/2}/\text{sec}$
C_{d2}	=	outlet orifice coefficient
Cd_{c1}	=	control orifice flow coefficient
D_1	=	vortex chamber diameter, in.
D_2	=	outlet orifice diameter, in.
D_c	=	control port diameter, in.
D_L	=	load orifice diameter, in.
$f_1\left(\dfrac{P_v}{P_s}\right)$	=	flow function
g	=	gravitational constant, in./sec^2

k = ratio of specific heats

ℓ = vortex chamber length, in.

n = empirical exponent

P_{c1} = control pressure, psia

P_m = flowmeter pressure, psia

P_s = vortex chamber supply pressure, psia

P_v = vent pressure, psia

R = gas constant, in./°R

r_i = radial dimension within vortex chamber, in.

r_o = vortex chamber radius, in.

T_{c1} = control gas temperature, °R

T_s = vortex chamber supply temperature, °R

V_c = control flow velocity, in./sec

V_{c1} = control flow velocity, in./sec

V_{c2} = control flow velocity, in./sec

V_r = radial flow velocity at outer wall, in./sec

V_t = tangential flow velocity at outer wall, in./sec

V_{ti} = tangential velocity at radius r_i, in./sec

V_{to} = tangential velocity at outer wall, in./sec

W_{c1} = control weight flow, lb/sec

W_{c2} = control weight flow, lb/sec

W_o = outlet weight flow, lb/sec

W_s = supply weight flow, lb/sec

W_N = dimensionless flow variable

ρ = gas density, lb/in.^{3}

ψ = flow vector angle – from tangential direction, degree

Introduction

Analytical performance prediction of the vortex valve depends very strongly on how accurately the tangential velocity distribution within the vortex chamber is known. Over the full operating range of the vortex valve, the tangential velocity at the outer wall of the chamber ranges from zero to near sonic velocity. The velocity distribution changes very significantly over this range, and thus nonlinearities handicap any purely analytical performance prediction.

234

The present analysis is based on the use of a single experimental curve to describe vortex chamber behavior. The curve represents the relationship between a dimensionless weight flow through the valve and the vector angle at the outer wall of the vortex chamber. A single curve describes the entire operating range of the vortex valve, and this large-signal model is a valid multi-terminal representation of the vortex valve. In the simplest form, as a five-terminal network, any three of the variables may be specified, and the remaining two can be calculated over the complete operating range of the vortex valve.

Historical Background

A summary graph of the publication rate of various vortex fields is given in Fig. 1. The largest number of vortex publications are related to the Ranque-Hilsch tube. Some of the other significant vortex research areas include the vortex free air thermometer and the power generators, in addition to the vortex valve.

The earliest vortex valve reports date back to 1929 with the work of Thoma[1] and Heim. [2] Possibly because of the lack of connected technological applications, no follow-on interest was found until 1950 when Posey and Hsu [3] investigated the operation of the vortex using water. The first practical application of a vortex valve is reported in 1957 by Stevens and Kolf. [4] The large interest focused presently on fluid amplification is reflected in the rising number of publications related to vortex valves, starting in 1961 with Dexter's paper. [5] Several vortex valve configurations are described by Mayer and Taplin, [6] with examples of vortex valve operations under a wide range of conditions.

Nearly all publications relating to vortex valves include both analytical and experimental research, indicating the need for experimental verification of all analytical predictions.

Vortex Valve Control Characteristics

A typical vortex valve configuration is shown in Fig. 2. The main supply flow enters the plenum behind the button at negligible velocity. The flow passes through a mixing zone in an annular sheet into the main vortex chamber. In the absence of control flow, the main flow proceeds radially toward the central outlet of the vortex chamber. In this condition, the maximum flow passes through the valve. When tangential control flow is injected, it imparts a rotational component to the main supply flow, and the combined flows pass into the vortex chamber with both tangential and radial components. The conservation of angular momentum requires that the tangential velocity increase as the flow moves inward. This velocity amplification is the basic phenomenon underlying the gain of the vortex valve.

In an ideal, lossless vortex field, the tangential velocity increases as the inverse of the radius

$$V_{ti} = V_{to} \left(\frac{r_o}{r_i} \right) .$$ (1)

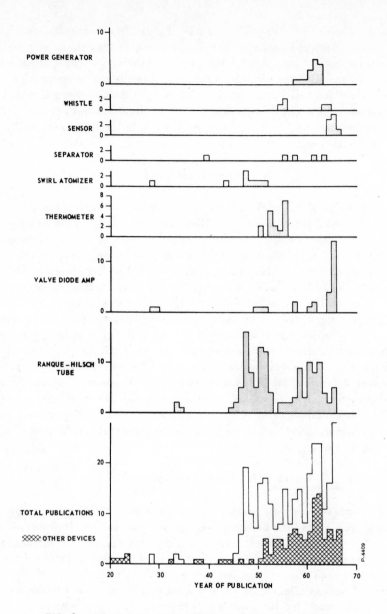

FIG. 1 – GRAPH OF PUBLICATION RATE OF VARIOUS
VORTEX FIELDS

The actual flow pattern within a vortex flow control valve is far more complex, and deviates from the prediction of equation (1). However, for small changes about an operating point, the tangential velocity pattern may be sufficiently described by the use of an empirical exponent in equation (1). The value of n in equation (2), in general, must be determined experimentally.

$$V_{ti} = V_{to} \left(\frac{r_o}{r_i} \right)^n \tag{2}$$

236

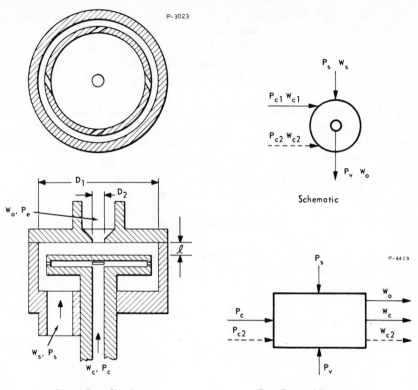

Button Type Chamber   Five Terminal Representation

FIG. 2 – SCHEMATIC OF TYPICAL VORTEX VALVE
CONFIGURATION

In an efficient vortex valve, the tangential velocity at the outer wall of the chamber varies from zero to near Mach 1 as the outlet flow is controlled from maximum to minimum. At high tangential velocities, the flow field within the vortex chamber becomes highly nonuniform. Essentially, all flow is carried from the outer wall to the center by the two boundary layers at the end walls of the vortex chamber.

Some of the details of the flow at high vorticity are shown by Savino and Keshock. [7] The report describes the results of velocity probing in a shallow (diameter – 12 inches, length – 1.25 inches) vortex chamber. The flow enters the chamber tangentially through slots between 48 flow guide vanes. A strong recirculation extends over most of the vortex chamber flow. The flow moving from the outer wall toward the central outlet is contained by the two end-wall boundary layers. A reverse flow occupies the largest portion of the vortex chamber. The boundary between the two opposing flow fields is irregular.

A second type of nonlinear velocity distribution was shown through photo-viscous flow visualization [8] at very low swirl levels in vortex valves. At low control inputs, the control jets do not impart swirl at the entire outer circumference of the vortex chamber and "pie shaped" segments of purely radial and slightly tangential flow regions alternate. This nonuniformity can be reduced by changing the configuration of the control jets.

The above two examples were cited to illustrate some of the nonuniform flow problems encountered in the operation range of the vortex valve. These, and additional nonlinearities, are not predictable to a sufficient degree on a strictly analytical basis. It is the aim of the present analysis to substitute a single experimental curve to replace the need for the exact prediction of the whole velocity distribution.

The assumption of uniform velocity distribution is useful when describing the performance of a particular valve. This approach has been described by Taplin [9] and can be applied to system design that includes known operating conditions. The following large-signal vortex analysis requires the solution of nonlinear simultaneous equations. However, the use of the $W_N(\psi)$ curve gives an accurate performance description of vortex valves over a large range of operating pressures.

Analytical Model

The major flow restriction of the vortex valve is the outlet orifice, and the zero swirl flow condition through the outlet orifice is a convenient starting point for the present analysis.

$$W_o = W_N \, C_{d2} \, A_2 \, \frac{P_s}{\left(T_s\right)^{1/2}} \, C_1 \, f_1\left(\frac{P_v}{P_s}\right) \tag{3}$$

where

$$C_1 = \left[\frac{k \, g}{R \left(\frac{k+1}{2}\right)^{\frac{k+1}{k-1}}}\right]^{1/2} \tag{4}$$

and

$$f_1\left(\frac{P_v}{P_s}\right) = \frac{\left(\frac{P_v}{P_s}\right)^{\frac{1}{k}} \left[1 - \left(\frac{P_v}{P_s}\right)^{\frac{k-1}{k}}\right]^{1/2}}{\left(\frac{2}{k+1}\right)^{\frac{1}{k-1}} \left(1 - \frac{2}{k+1}\right)^{1/2}} \tag{5}$$

$$f_1\left(\frac{P_v}{P_s}\right) = 1.00 \text{ for } \frac{P_v}{P_s} \leq \left(\frac{2}{k+1}\right)^{\frac{k}{k-1}}$$

238

Equation (3) is the familiar form presented in several textbooks, [10] with the appropriate variables substituted for the present condition. The variable W_N is the empirical variable describing the relation between outlet flow, W_o, and swirl, ψ, and will be defined later. The value of W_N is 1·0 for purely radial flow.

It is well known [11, 12] that the orifice coefficient, C_{d2}, is a function of Reynolds Number. The variation depends on the configuration of the orifice to a very large extent. In a vortex valve, the variation is in general under 10 per cent; however, changes as high as 30 per cent have been reported for shaped orifices. The value of this change may be taken into account on the basis of curves found in the literature, or can be determined for a vortex valve configuration by using available experimental data. In general, the changes in orifice coefficient occur under a Reynolds Number of 20,000. For the sake of simplicity, in the following analysis, the effect of a varying orifice coefficient will not be included.

Referring to Fig. 2, a number of relations and simplifications of the analysis can be observed:

1) The total flow through the valve is the sum of the control and supply flows.

$$W_o = W_s + W_{c1} + W_{c2} \ldots \ldots \tag{6}$$

2) The lengths of orifices do not exceed 3 diameters; thus, the basic compressible flow equations are valid, and the entrance velocities from the respective sources are also sufficiently small to be negligible.

3) The flow resistance between the supply inlet and the actual vortex chamber is small; thus, the use of P_s as the upstream pressure in equation (3) is valid.

4) The control flow is determined by the size of the control ports and the magnitude of P_c and P_s.

$$W_{c1} = Cd_{c1} \, A_{c1} \, \frac{P_{c1}}{\left(T_{c1}\right)^{1/2}} \, C_1 \, f_1 \left(\frac{P_s}{P_{c1}}\right) \tag{7}$$

where C_1 and $f_1 \, (P_s/P_{c1})$ are of the form given in equations (4) and (5). A similar equation is used to calculate the second control flow.

The swirl in the vortex chamber is defined by the vector direction of the flow at the outer wall, ψ, as shown in Fig. 3. The value of ψ can be calculated from the average radial and tangential velocities

$$\cot\left(\psi\right) = \frac{V_t}{V_r} \, . \tag{8}$$

The value of the average radial velocity is established by the flow area at the outer wall of the vortex chamber

$$V_r = \frac{W_o}{\rho A} = \frac{W_o \, R \, T_s}{\pi \, D_1 \, \ell \, P_s} \, . \tag{9}$$

239

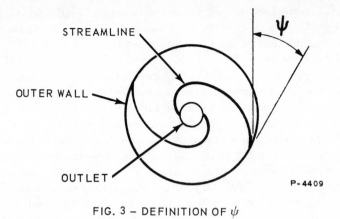

STREAMLINE

OUTER WALL

OUTLET

P-4409

FIG. 3 – DEFINITION OF ψ

The average tangential velocity is calculated on the basis of momentum transfer between the control jets and the total flow

$$V_t = \frac{1}{W_o} (W_{c1} \, V_{c1} \pm W_{c2} \, V_{c2} \, ...).$$

(10)

The individual control velocities may be approximated to a sufficient degree by calculation of the Mach Number on the basis of upstream conditions, but limiting the Mach Number to 1·0 below the critical pressure ratio.

$$V_c = \left[\left| g \, k \, R \, T_c \right| \left(\frac{2}{k-1} \right) \left[1 - \left(\frac{P_s}{P_c} \right)^{\frac{k-1}{k}} \right] \right]^{1/2}.$$

(11)

Equation (11) is a good description of the control velocity as long as the control injector is less than a few diameters in length, as is the case in a typical vortex valve.

The relationship between W_N and ψ is to be established experimentally. However, certain characteristics of this function are of interest. For pure radial flow, W_N is 1·00 and ψ is 90 degrees for any combination of operating pressures. Complete flow turndown would coincide with the point at which $W_N = 0$ and $\psi = 0$ degree on the curve. The zero outlet flow condition actually cannot be reached because the operation of the vortex valve requires the existence of tangential control flow. Thus, even when supply flow is shut off by the tangential control flow, the control flow still must pass through the chamber outlet. Vortex valves operating with a compressible gas are normally limited to a flow turndown ratio of about 12:1. Thus, a practical lower limit for W_N is about 0·08. Further consideration of the $W_N (\psi)$ curve will be given in the experimental verification section.

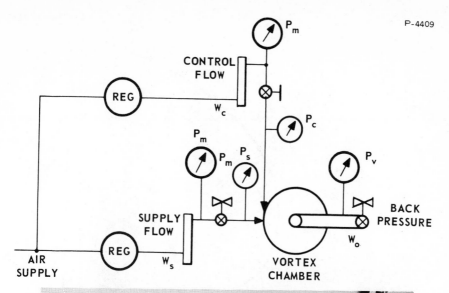

FIG. 4 – TEST SETUP

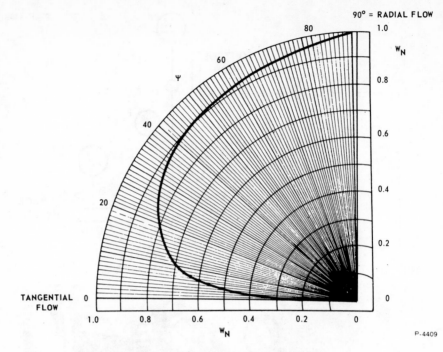

FIG. 5 – $W_N (\psi)$ CURVE, POLAR PLOT

Experimental Verification

An extensive series of experiments were conducted to verify the validity of the single $W_N (\psi)$ curve. A typical cold gas test setup is shown in Fig. 4. The supply and control weight flow were measured with variable-area rotameters. Experiments were carried out with eight vortex chamber diameters, ranging from 0.44 inch to 4.00 inches. For each chamber diameter, a number of outlet orifice sizes and vortex chamber lengths were evaluated. Tests were conducted at several vent pressures, ranging from 0.1 psia to 74.7 psia. Several control port sizes and control injector configurations were also evaluated. A large volume of experimental data was evaluated to prove the generality of the analysis. The test results indicated that a single $W_N (\psi)$ curve is a valid representation of the experimental results for changes of control pressures, P_c, supply pressure, P_s, vent pressure, P_v, and control port diameter, D_c. Other changes in vortex chamber geometry affected the $W_N (\psi)$ curve. Only typical results of the experiments are given in the following paragraphs.

A characteristic $W_N (\psi)$ curve is shown in Fig. 5. As expected, the curve starts at $W_N = 1.0$ and $\psi = 90$ degrees at the radial flow condition. Gradual increase in swirl initially affects the flow, as represented by W_N, only to a very small degree; e.g., at $W_N = 0.8$, $\psi = 20$ degrees. The curvature of the W_N curve increases until it approaches the origin tangent to the $\psi = 0$-degree line. In the general area of $\psi < 5$ degrees, small changes in ψ result in large changes in W_N.

A better resolution of the $W_N (\psi)$ curve for a second vortex valve in the low-argument zone is given in Fig. 6 by using polar logarithmic representation. Three cycles were found sufficient to represent ψ in all of the experimental results

242

obtained to the present. The lowest values of ψ observed were at about 0·1 degree. The curve drawn through the test points was selected to represent the $W_N(\psi)$ curve for the valve.

Using this single experimental curve to represent the flow conditions within the vortex valve, performance characteristics were calculated, using the equations defined above. The $W_N(\psi)$ curve shown in Fig. 6 was used in all calculations.

The effect of control port size on the negative resistance is shown in Fig. 7. Both the calculations and experiments used a 0·5 inch diameter by 0·050 inch long vortex chamber with two 0·060 inch diameter outlets. The 60 psig control pressure characteristic curves were calculated for 0·030, 0·052 and 0·062 inch control port diameters. The curves indicate that the negative resistance is more pronounced for the smaller control port dimensions. The term "negative resistance" is used to describe the negative incremental resistance particularly noticeable for the 0·030 inch diameter control port data. As the total flow increases from 8 x 10^{-4} to 18 x 10^{-4} lb/sec, a corresponding increase in supply pressure occurs. Further increasing total flow to 50 x 10^{-4} lb/sec results in a decrease of supply pressure

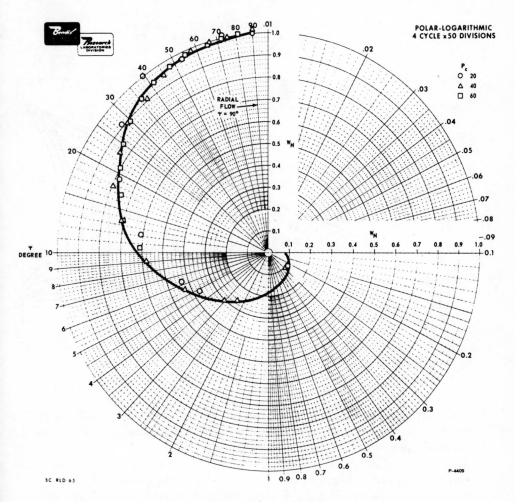

FIG. 6 – $W_N(\psi)$ CURVE

243

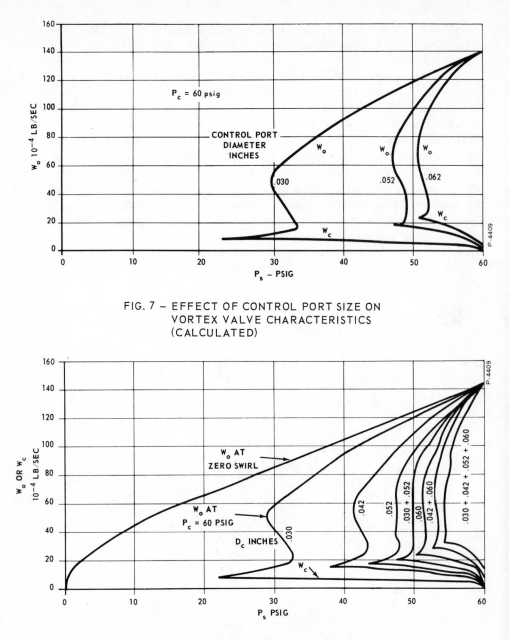

FIG. 7 – EFFECT OF CONTROL PORT SIZE ON
VORTEX VALVE CHARACTERISTICS
(CALCULATED)

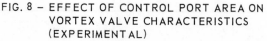

FIG. 8 – EFFECT OF CONTROL PORT AREA ON
VORTEX VALVE CHARACTERISTICS
(EXPERIMENTAL)

in this negative resistance zone. Additional increase of total flow results in the
normal increase of the supply pressure. The negative resistance zone can be used
to advantage in vortex power oscillators [6].

Test results of vortex valves having control port sizes in the range of the calculations are compiled in Fig. 8. The agreement between the calculated and the experimental curves is considered very good; the slight irregularities of the experimental curves are to be expected.

One result of the negative resistance is the generation of a hysteresis loop in the vortex valve characteristics when the unit is operated at constant supply pressure. The calculated hysteresis loop is shown in Fig. 9. The calculations also show that the hysteresis loop, for a given vortex valve configuration, is smaller at a subsonic operating condition $(P_s/P_v = 1.20)$ than at ratios greater than the critical pressure ratio $(P_s/P_v = 3.16)$, an effect observed in many previous experiments with vortex valves.

Calculated and experimental curves, similar to the examples shown in Fig. 7, 8 and 9, may be combined to describe other vortex valve performance criteria in dimensionless forms. One such criterion is the turndown ratio, defined as the ratio between the maximum total flow and the minimum total flow through the vortex valve at any given supply pressure. This ratio is relatively independent of operating pressures, such as supply or downstream vent pressures; thus, the turndown ratio may be used as a figure-of-merit to compare various vortex valve designs [6].

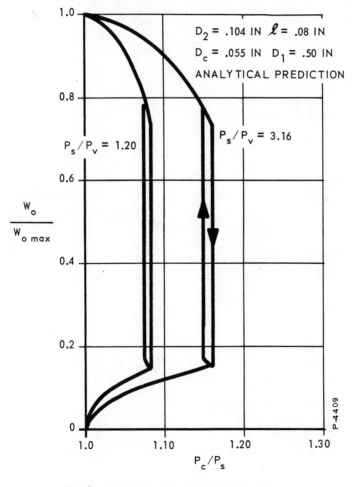

FIG. 9 – EFFECT OF VENT PRESSURE ON
TURNDOWN

The turndown ratio is affected by the size of the control port; increasing the control port size increases the control flow to the valve at a given ratio of control pressure and supply pressure. When the control flow becomes equal to the outlet flow, the turndown point of the valve is reached. For the larger control port sizes, the control flow reaches the value of the outlet flow at subsonic P_s/P_c ratios. This decreases the value of the maximum tangential velocity in equation (11) with a larger final value of ψ occurring at zero supply flow. The effect is a reduction of the turndown ratio for increasing control port sizes. Accurate analytical prediction of the relationship between the critical control pressure ratio (the exact ratio of P_c/P_s required to stop supply flow) and the turndown ratio is very important. Experimental evaluation requires the use of several vortex valves, with various sizes of control ports.

The calculated turndown ratio as a function of control port size is compared with experimental results in Fig. 10. Both the experimental and analytical results were obtained over a range of operating pressures. The critical control pressure was selected to represent the control port size. Both the analysis and the experiments indicate a rapid decay of turndown ratio for very large control port sizes, particularly sizes giving critical P_c/P_s ratios of less than 1·20.

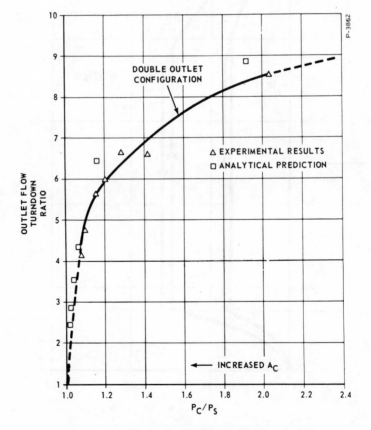

FIG. 10 – TURNDOWN RATIO VERSUS CONTROL
PORT SIZE

246

Fig. 11 presents the same information, directly as a function of control port to outlet diameter ratio. The nearly linear relation on the semilogarithmic plot indicates an exponential relationship between the control port size and the ultimate turndown ratio for the design.

The analysis offers a valuable tool to predict accurately the interaction of vortex valves with other circuit elements over a wide operating range. One simple circuit of particular interest is shown in Fig. 12. An orifice placed in series with the supply line is of interest for two reasons: first to represent the effects of finite input impedances, such as inlet holes and lines in the supply to the vortex valves; second, it allows the study of such a system when only a single pressure source is available and an orifice is used to reduce the vortex valve supply pressure below the maximum control pressure available from the pressure source.

Typical analytical results are shown in Fig. 13 for series orifice to valve outlet diameter ratios of 3, 2, 1, 0.7 and 0.5. The input pressure to the series orifice was held constant at 147.7 psia, and curves of total flow were calculated and plotted for increasing steps of control pressures on a digital computer and plotter. The

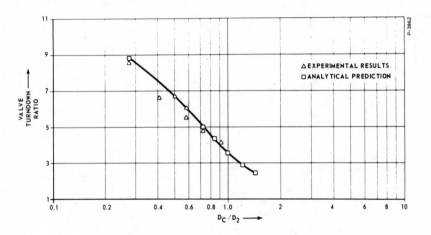

FIG. 11 – FLOW TURNDOWN AS A FUNCTION OF
RELATIVE CONTROL PORT SIZE

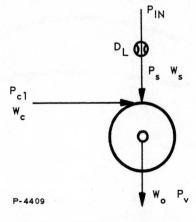

FIG. 12 – CIRCUIT SCHEMATIC

247

corresponding experimental results are shown in Fig. 14. The excellent agreement over a wide, nonlinear operating range of the orifice and vortex valve combination proves the analysis a worthwhile tool for prediction of nonlinear operating characteristics of vortex valves. An interesting effect of series impedance is the initial increase of total flow through the vortex valve as the control pressure is increased initially. This increase is due to a rise of the supply pressure, P_s, downstream as the decreasing supply flow, W_s, reduces the pressure drop across the series load orifice.

The $W_N(\psi)$ curve generated at low pressures (under 100 psia) was used successfully to predict the performance of a similar vortex unit operating at 1000 psia. The examples of applications of the $W_N(\psi)$ curve indicate that this single curve may be used to describe the performance of a vortex valve uniquely over a wide range of vent pressures, supply inlet pressures, control port sizes, and control pressures. The use of a single curve offers the advantages of the single description of vortex valve nonlinearities for comparing characteristics of different vortex valves.

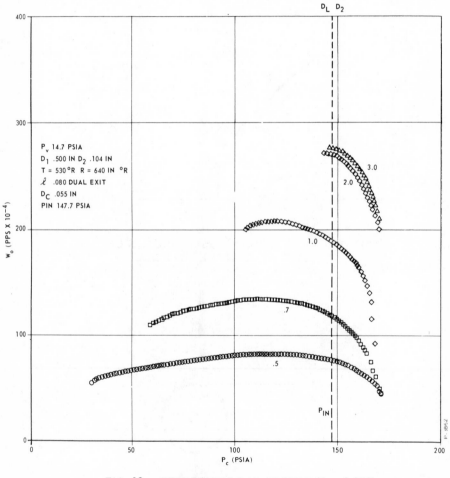

FIG. 13 – EFFECT OF LOAD ORIFICE (D_c = 0.055) –
CALCULATED

248

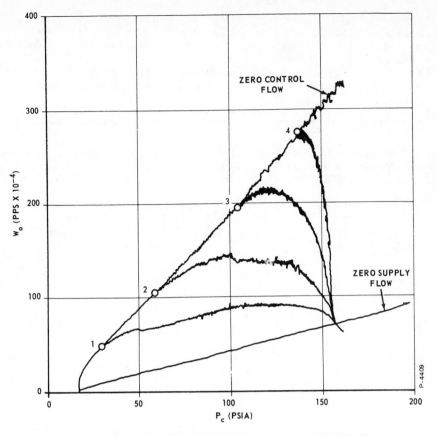

FIG. 14 – EXPERIMENTAL EVALUATION OF SERIES
ORIFICE CIRCUIT

Acknowledgement

The author wishes to thank the Research Laboratories Division of The Bendix
Corporation for assistance given in the preparation of the paper and for permission
to publish results of corporate-funded research.

References

[1] Dieter Thoma, "Fluid Lines," U.S. Patent No. 1,839,616, June 4, 1928.
[2] R. Heim, "An Investigation of the Thoma Counterflow Brake," Transaction of the
Hydraulic Institute, Munich Technical University Bulletin 3, 1929, pp. 13-28.
[3] C. S. Posey and H. C. Hsu, "How the Vortex Affects Discharge," Engineering
News Record, March, 1950, p. 30.
[4] J. C. Stevens and R. C. Kolf, "Vortex Flow Through Horizontal Orifices," Journal
of the Sanitary Engineering Division, Proceedings of the American Society of Civil Engineers, December, 1957, pp. 1461-1 to 1461-21.
[5] E. M. Dexter, "No Moving Parts — A Feature of New Valves," Society of Automotive
Engineers Journal, September, 1961, p. 102.
[6] E. A. Mayer and L. B. Taplin, "Vortex Devices," published in "Fluidics," edited
by E. F. Humphrey and D. H. Taramuto, Fluid Amplifier Associates, Boston, Massachusetts,
1964, pp. 185-200.

[7] J. M. Savino and E. G. Keshock, "Experimental Profiles of Velocity Components and Radial Pressure Distribution in a Vortex Contained in a Short Cylindrical Chamber," Proceedings of the Fluid Amplification Symposium, Harry Diamond Laboratory, Washington, D.C., October, 1965, pp. 269-299.

[8] E. A. Mayer, "Photoviscous Flow Visualization in Fluid State Devices," Proceedings of the Fluid Amplification Symposium, Harry Diamond Laboratory, Washington, D.C., October, 1965, Vol. 2, pp. 347-361.

[9] L. B. Taplin, "Phenomenology of Vortex Flow and Its Application to Signal Amplification," Summer Engineering Seminar Notes, Pennsylvania State University, July, 1965.

[10] J. F. Blackburn, G. Reethoff and J. L. Shearer, "Fluid Power Control," Technology Press of M.I.T. and J. Wiley & Sons, New York, 1960, pp. 43-89.

[11] V. L. Streeter, "Fluid Mechanics," McGraw Hill, New York, Second Edition, 1958, pp. 78-270.

[12] G. Bloom, "Errorless Orifices," Product Engineering, October 25, 1965, pp. 61-64.

A Thermistor Probe for Low Velocity Flow Measurements

R. S. Lane

Cummins Engine Company
Columbus, Indiana

R. B. Keller

University of Michigan
Ann Arbor, Michigan

Abstract

The results of an experimental study to develop an inexpensive thermistor probe for measuring steady-state and transient velocities in the 0 to 6 inch per second range are presented. Probe characteristics were determined by employing an annular water channel through which the probe was carried by a rotary arm. Steady-state results show that that thermistor probes can accurately measure low velocity flows in water. Transient response data show minimum total response times of 0.3 second for step velocity changes in water. The effects of water temperature were also examined.

Introduction

In many areas of current interest, very small liquid velocities (less than one foot per second) must be measured. At these velocities, instruments based on impact pressure cannot be used. However, experience has shown that instruments based on convection heat transfer are applicable in this range for both steady and transient flows, and various methods of flow visualization may be used in steady flows. Basic considerations in technique selection include cost, ruggedness, reliability, and accuracy.

The thermistor probe is an instrument based on convection heat transfer. Thermistors are semi-conductors with high negative temperature coefficients of resistance. If a thermistor is immersed in a still fluid and a heating current is supplied, it reaches thermal equilibrium with its environment when the internal heat generation rate is equal to the heat transfer by natural convection to the surrounding fluid. Now, if this fluid is brought to motion the thermistor temperature will drop owing to the higher heat transfer rate by forced convection — the amount of drop being related to the fluid velocity. This drop in temperature will cause a rise in the resistance of the thermistor. If the thermistor is inserted in one leg of a Wheatstone bridge and the bridge is balanced for the zero-velocity condition,

251

this rise in resistance will lead to a voltage unbalance across the bridge that is proportional to the fluid velocity.

This type of sensor is attractive from a number of standpoints. It is capable of detecting very low speeds; has a relatively fast response time allowing its use in slowly moving, transient flow fields; does not significantly alter the flow field; is very rugged; and uses inexpensive circuitry such that multiple sensors can be arranged in a grid throughout the flow field.

Some information is available relative to the use of thermistors as velocity sensors. Rasmussen [1] discussed the development of a bathythermograph and an oceanographic velocimeter, and Veprek [2] developed a thermistor flowmeter for very low flowrates. Delaunois [3] used a catheter equipped with a thermistor to measure blood flow. Lumley [4] reported the development of a constant-temperature, hot-thermistor anemometer using a thin-film thermistor. However, these applications require elaborate signal-conditioning instrumentation for their operation, whereas the present application uses readily available laboratory equipment. The velocity signal requires no amplification; the bridge circuit is powered with a simple, D.C. power supply or battery; and the probes are commercially available.

Thermistor Characteristics

An early treatment of thermistor technology was presented by Becker, Green, and Pearson [5] in 1946. Recent publications which include information of a general nature include Scarr and Setterington [6], Smith [7], and Sapoff and Oppenheim [8].

The major thermistor characteristic exploited in this application is the high negative temperature coefficient of resistance. The relationship between the resistance and the ambient temperature can be approximated by the formula:

$$R_T = R_{T_o} e^{\beta\left(\frac{1}{T} - \frac{1}{T_o}\right)}$$

where R_T is the resistance at absolute temperature T.

R_{T_o} is the resistance at a standard absolute temperature T_o, usually 298K.

β is a material constant.

Typical values of β range from 2000 to 5000K, while values of R_{T_o} vary from 1 ohm to 75 megohms. Fig. 1 shows the resistance-temperature characteristics of the three thermistor elements used in these tests.

Test Equipment and Procedure

Steady-state calibration of the thermistor probes was accomplished by moving the probes at various known velocities through quiescent water and recording the Wheatstone bridge voltage unbalance for each velocity. A schematic diagram of the test equipment is shown on Fig. 2.

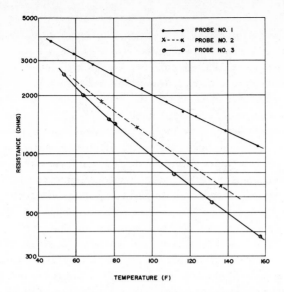

FIG. 1 RESISTANCE – TEMPERATURE CHARACTERISTICS

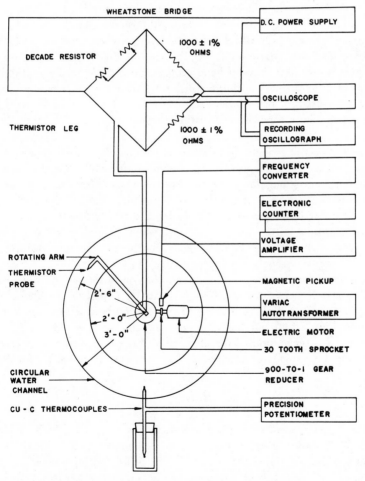

FIG. 2 SCHEMATIC DIAGRAM OF TEST EQUIPMENT

253

The thermistor probe to be studied was mounted on a rotary arm driven by an electric motor through a 900-to-1 gear reducer. A variable autotransformer was used to control motor speed. The signal from a magnetic pickup, used to measure motor speed (thermistor probe speed), was displayed on a counter and also recorded. The water channel consisted of a 4-foot inside diameter by 6-foot outside diameter channel with a water level of 3 inches.

The thermistor was inserted into one leg of a Wheatstone bridge which included two $1,000 \pm 1$ per cent ohm resistors and a decade resistor which was used to determine the resistance of the thermistor and hence its temperature at bridge balance conditions. The bridge was supplied with regulated D.C. voltage and the voltage unbalance signal was displayed on an oscilloscope and recorded on an oscillograph.

The thermistor probes consisted of a thermistor bead mounted on a short support. Probes using thermistors from three manufacturers were studied: Probe 1, a resin-encapsulated, ellipsoidal-shaped Carborundum thermistor (Cat. 32602) with an average diameter of 0.058 inches; Probe 2, a VECO thermistor probe (Cat. ZA-32A91) with the thermistor encapsulated in a glass rod of 0.020 inches maximum diameter; and Probe 3, a Fenwal glass-encapsulated thermistor (Cat. GC-32J3) 0.014 inches in diameter. Probe 2 is commercially available; Probes 1 and 3 are handcrafted. Fig. 3 illustrates these three probes.

Steam condensate was used for the test water to minimize entrained air. The water temperature was monitored at one location with a thermocouple located at the same height as the thermistor bead (approximately 3/4 in. below the surface) and displaced 1/8 in. from the thermistor path. After the water temperature was adjusted and stabilized, the velocity of the water in the channel was zero, and the thermistor probe was positioned at the thermocouple location, the bridge was balanced.

Next the probe was brought up to the desired velocity, usually in less than one revolution; and, as the probe passed the thermocouple station, the bridge voltage unbalance and the arm angular velocity were recorded. After obtaining several data, the probe was stopped at the thermocouple location, and the bridge balance again checked. After waiting until any observable residual velocity in the water channel was dissipated, the entire procedure was repeated. Water temperature was monitored frequently, and an average temperature used. The temperatures varied less than 0.5 degree throughout each test run.

Tests to determine the transient response of two of the probes were conducted. Cyclical variations were accomplished by manually adjusting the speed of the arm, while step changes were obtained by allowing the probe, initially held stationary, to be suddenly picked up and carried along with the rotating arm.

The resistance-temperature characteristics of the thermistors were experimentally determined by standard techniques (Fig. 1). See reference [9] for details.

Results

Steady-state results are shown in Figs. 4, 5, and 6. In Fig. 4, the bridge voltage unbalance is shown as a function of probe speed and bridge voltage for Probe 2. Note the typical non-linear relationship. The bridge voltage selection should be based on the maintenance of a thermistor temperature at zero-velocity condi-

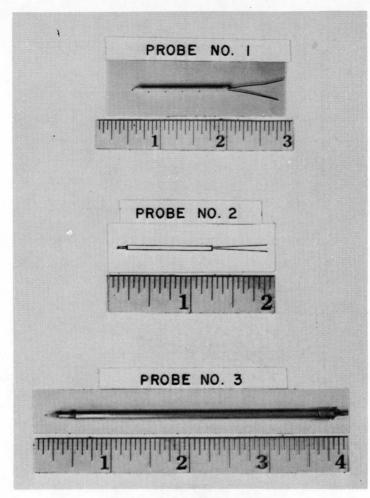

FIG. 3 THERMISTOR PROBES

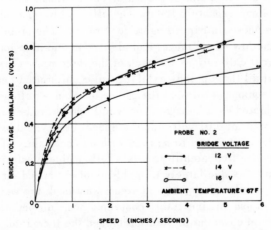

FIG. 4 SPEED CALIBRATION – VOLTAGE EFFECT

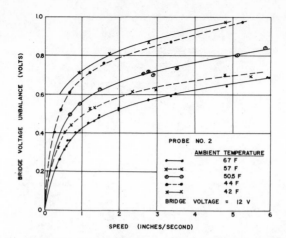

FIG. 5 SPEED CALIBRATION – TEMPERATURE EFFECT

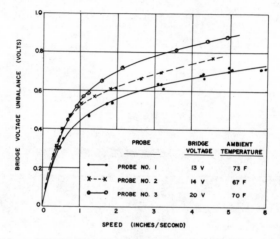

FIG. 6 SPEED CALIBRATION – PROBE COMPARISON

tions well below the boiling point of the fluid. The maximum thermistor temperature at 16 volts was approximately 160 F. The effect of water temperature on
probe calibration is shown in Fig. 5, again for Probe 2. The probe calibration is
most sensitive in the low speed range, and also most sensitive for low ambient
temperatures. Typical calibrations for each of the three probes are shown in Fig.
6, which shows that all three probes exhibit similar calibration curves.

The calibration equipment allowed the bridge unbalance voltage, which was
measured on a calibrated oscilloscope or an oscillograph, to be read with an un-
uncertainty on the order of 0.01 volt, and the speed, determined by measuring the
angular speed of the drive motor, to be read with an uncertainty of approximately
0.02 inches per second. Repeatability of data fell nominally within ± 5 per cent.
Lack of repeatability was due largely to problems of entrapped air and contamination in the water. Even though condensed steam was used, the water, with its
free surface open to room air, inevitably contained some air and dirt particles.
Tiny air bubbles would come out of solution around the thermistor bead (due to
the heating). These bubbles would tend to alter the heat transfer characteristics

256

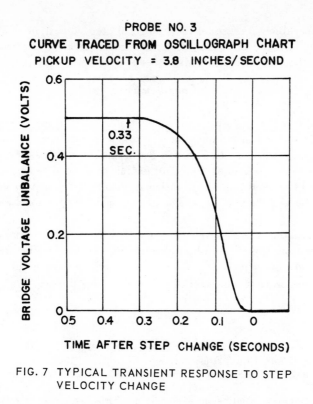

PROBE NO. 3

CURVE TRACED FROM OSCILLOGRAPH CHART

PICKUP VELOCITY = 3.8 INCHES/SECOND

FIG. 7 TYPICAL TRANSIENT RESPONSE TO STEP
VELOCITY CHANGE

of the thermistor and hence change the average temperature difference between
the water and the thermistor. Altering thermistor temperature changes the resistance of the thermistor and hence affects the bridge voltage unbalance signal.
The use of Probe 2 minimized this problem.

The importance of the water temperature measurement is indicated by Fig. 5.
At room temperature, a tolerance of ± 0.5 F is acceptable; at 42 F, a tolerance
of ± 0.1 F is required to maintain an accuracy of 1 per cent in speed measurement.

The overall accuracy level in speed measurements using this device with controlled water purity and environment should approach ± 5 per cent. Runstadler [10]
experienced repeatability difficulties with hot-film probes in water; also problems
of the same type encountered in the use of hot-wire anemometers in liquids tend
to verify the accuracy level at around 5 per cent.

Transient calibration tests were made using Probes 1 and 3. At a frequency
of 3 cycles per second, Probe 3 showed no perceptible phase shift, while Probe
1 showed a phase lag of about 50 deg. at 4 cycles per second, owing to its larger
size. The cyclical variations consisted of speed perturbations of the order of 0.1
inch per second about a mean speed of 2 inches per second. Probe 1 also responded to gradual velocity increases and decreases of the order of 2 inches per
second with imperceptible time lag.

Fig. 7 shows a typical transient response to a step velocity change of 0 to
3.8 inches per second for Probe 3. The steady-state value of the bridge voltage
unbalance was reached in 0.33 seconds; the time constant, which is defined as
the time required to each 63.2 per cent of the total signal change, was 0.11

257

seconds. These values are typical for a range of step velocities of 2 to 5 inches per second. Similar data for Probe 1 indicated nearly five times slower response, again owing to the size of the thermistor bead.

Conclusions

The thermistor probe is potentially capable of accurately measuring the speed of a slowly moving fluid in the range of 0 to 6 inches per second with inexpensive circuitry and instrumentation. A unit which includes probe, bridge, and storage battery should cost less than $50, exclusive of readily available readout equipment. Individual probe calibration is required. Sensitivity generally increases for increased Wheatstone bridge voltage and for decreased ambient temperatures.

The useful range of the meter may be extended by appropriate probe design such as the addition of a shield which decelerates the flow in the area of the thermistor. Directions as well as magnitudes may be obtained by alternate designs which incorporate two or more thermistors on one probe.

References

[1] R. A. Rasmussen, "Application of Thermistors to Measurements in Moving Fluids," *Review of Scientific Instruments*, Vol. 33, 1962, p. 38-42.

[2] J. A. Veprek, "A Thermistor Flowmeter," *Journal of Scientific Instruments*, Vol. 40, 1963, p. 66-68.

[3] A. L. Delaunois, "Continuous Measurement of Blood Flow and Cardiac Output by Means of a Cournand Catheter Equipped with Thermistors," *Archive International Pharmacodyn.*, Vol. 134, 1961, p. 245-253.

[4] J. L. Lumley, "The Constant Temperature Hot-Thermistor Anemometer," *ASME Symposium on Measurement of Unsteady Flow*, 1962, p. 75-82.

[5] J. A. Becker, C. B. Green, and G. L. Pearson, "Properties and Uses of Thermistors — Thermally Sensitive Resistors," *Transactions AIEE*, Vol. 65, 1946, p. 711-725.

[6] R. W. A. Scarr, and R. A. Setterington, "Thermistors, Their Theory, Manufacture, and Application," *Proceedings IEE*, Paper No. 3176-M, January, 1960, p. 395-405.

[7] R. W. Smith, "Thermistors — The Story of Thermally Sensitive Semi-Conductors," *Ceramic Industry*, Vol. 74, 1960, p. 79-81 (May), 84-87 (June).

[8] M. Sapoff and R. M. Oppenheim, "Theory and Application of Self-Heated Thermistors," *Proceedings IEEE*, Vol. 51, 1963, p. 1292-1305.

[9] M. L. Miller, "Considerations in Testing Thermistors," *Electrical Manufacturing*, Vol. 59, 1957, p. 102-106, 320.

[10] P. W. Runstadler, "Stable Operation of Hot-Film Probes in Water," *ASME Symposium of Measurement in Unsteady Flow*, 1962, p. 83-84.

Report on the Second Cranfield Fluidics Conference

T. Sarpkaya
University of Nebraska
Lincoln, Neb.

J. M. Kirshner
Harry Diamond Laboratories
Washington, D.C.

The second in a new series of European research conferences in Fluidics was held in Cambridge, England, on 3 through 5 January 1967. The conference was organized by the British Hydromechanics Research Association in conjunction with the Department of Production and Industrial Administration College of Aeronautics, Institution of Mechanical Engineers, and the Society of Instrument Technology. During the three day conference 49 papers were presented and 10 countries (USSR, East Germany, France, Italy, Japan, Netherlands, Switzerland, UK, USA, and West Germany) were represented. The delegates received the preprints of the papers about four weeks before the meeting. The papers of each session (there were 10 sessions) were presented by one or two rapporteurs[1] and afterwards each author was allowed three minutes for presentation of additional information relating to their papers. Subsequently, the papers were discussed from the floor. Delegates contributing to the discussion were handed record sheets at the time and were asked to submit a written discussion for inclusion in the Proceedings of the Conference.

The ten sessions were comprised of the presentation of papers on (A) Wall Attachment Properties; (B) Wall Attachment Devices; (C) Interaction Devices; (D) Miscellaneous Elements and Circuits; (E) Pneumatic Transducers; (F) Signal Conversion and Element Manufacture; (G) Moving Parts versus Non-Moving Part Elements; (H) Fluidic Modular Circuits; (K) Applications-I; and (J) Applications-II. In addition, there was a display of fluidic devices and demonstrations by their manufacturers.

Aside from temporary difficulties with the mobile microphone, the Conference ran rather smoothly and the kind hospitality of the British People, Conference Organizers, and the host institution, Cambridge University, impressed all delegates.

---

[1] The use of rapporteurs is a generally accepted continental style. It is most effective for foreign speakers with language difficulties. It's time saving value is rather questionable. Furthermore, the delegates who did not study the papers beforehand cannot intelligently follow the rapporteur let alone discuss the paper. As far as the present conference is concerned, it must, in all fairness be noted that the rapporteurs have done a marvelous job in presenting, combining, and discussing the papers and raising thought provoking questions.

Prior to a session by session description of the Conference, certain distinguishing features of the Fluidics activity in Europe and particularly in the United Kingdom must be pointed out. Most of the fluidics research in England is carried out by the educational institutions whereas in the United States Fluidics received an intense interest from industry and today about 20 or 25 corporations have major development programs for fluid amplifiers and fluidic circuits. Secondly, some of the European work appears to repeat work which has already been done. This is essentially due to the fact that much of the work in the States is essentially proprietary and therefore up-to-date, detailed information is not readily available to European researchers. Thirdly, in Europe the applications of fluidic devices appear to be confined to factory machine operations whereas in the States the applications are to a large degree space oriented. Finally, there appears to be some difference between notations used by US and European researchers in describing various parts of amplifiers, e.g., passive port is sometimes called "void exit"; active port, the "target exit"; and the vent, "bleeder."

As noted earlier the first session dealt with "Wall Attachment Properties." Of the five papers presented[2] four [1-4] were on the analysis of bubble size and switching times of turbulent amplifiers and one on the deflection of a finite jet by a curved wall. The works of Bourque and Newman [50] and others were extended or modified by describing the separation bubble growth in terms of the net flow into the bubble, taking into account the control port flow and assuming quasi-steady flow conditions [1]. At any given instant the jet centre line is assumed to be on a circular arc and the pressure in the bubble is taken to be uniform. In addition to the assumption of a classical two dimensional jet profile, the jet is assumed to divide in such a manner that the sum of momentum and pressure forces in the direction parallel to the wall round the control volume containing the attachment point is conserved. [2] Although Sawyer [2] reported good agreement between his theory and the experimental observations of attachment times and attachment behaviour of known wall shapes, the accuracy of his theoretical calculations was challenged in the discussion.

Jones et al., [3] after pointing out certain limitations in Bourque and Newman's work, devised a somewhat new model by considering the flexibility offered by a digital computer. Certain important concepts used by Bourque and Newman were, however, retained. The changes incorporated into the model consisted of the use of the free jet profile developed by Albertson [51] instead of the classical "free-jet" profile; the pressure in the bubble was assumed to vary continuously with zero transverse pressure gradient; and finally no assumptions were made concerning the conditions downstream of the reattachment point. Then the bubble was split up into several control volumes throughout its length and the equilibrium of each volume was expressed by a recurrence formula. The pressure of the successive control volumes as well as the incremental angle through which the jet turns at each station was numerically calculated. The method requires only one experimental constant and this is the one applicable to a free jet shape, which has been extensively studied. The results show that the maximum vacuum pressure locus is in good agreement with the experimental points. The predictions of the bubble length as well as the actual bubble pressure distribution are less accurate but still offer an improvement over the previous results.

---

[2] Papers presented at the Conference are listed in the References 1 through 49. The other references cited in this article are listed starting 50.

Thompson [4] discussed the switching of supersonic gas jets by atmospheric venting. Jets of air expanding through a non adapted, convergent-divergent, two-dimensional duct at pressure ratios in excess of critical, were forced to change their direction by transverse introduction of air at atmospheric pressure via critically located control ports. The transverse to main thrust gain in the order of 25 per cent was reported for a control to main flow power ratio approaching zero.

The deflection of a jet by an adjacent lateral convex wall, when the velocity profile of the jet is rather thick with respect to the radius of curvature of the wall, was discussed by Kadosch [5] and it was reported that the Reynolds number exerts an influence on both laminar and turbulent jets but the curved wall effect should disappear for the laminar case. A more detailed discussion of the curved-wall effect is given in ref. [52].

The second session dealt with wall attachment devices [6-13]. Chadwick [6] described a method of increasing the effective sensitivity of a bistable device by using a pulsed power supply. The method of operation described overcomes the difficulties encountered in the fan-out of more than four wall attachment devices and in the detection and amplification of very low level signals. But this is achieved at the expense of reduced speed of operation.

The optimal design of the control jet nozzle of a turbulence amplifier was presented by Dražan [7]. In addition, a graphical method was given for checking the predictions. Steptoe [8] described steady-state and dynamic characteristic variations of miniature OR/NOR and bistable wall-attachment elements. Results are presented in the form of histograms of input and output pressure characteristics for batches of elements manufactured by the epoxy replication process. Hart [9] presented a work on the performance of a wall-attachment device as a pressure regulator and as a switch or selector when coupled with a vortex chamber. The discussers pointed out that the flow gain of such an amplifier-vortex switch would be rather low (Fig. 1).

König [10] described a new bistable device (Fig. 2) which has no separating wedge. The jet nozzle is made like a cusp diffuser which ensures two stable jet positions on account of the Coanda effect. One receiver nozzle is placed at each jet position. The best geometrical configuration is obtained mainly by trial and error. The advantage of this configuration is that it operates over the standardized pressure range (3 to 15 psi). The author claimed that the amplifier system also responded to low signal magnitudes and substantially reduced the transmission times.

Certain changes in the geometry of a cusped, vented, and load insensitive bistable amplifier was described by Rechten [11]. The side walls and vent entrances were contoured (Fig. 3) with curves obtained from the Kutta-Joukowski equations. The speaker concluded that good pressure recovery is possible if the splitter position is chosen such that minimum amount of fluid escapes through the vent on the passive side and if the entrances to the vents are curved such that the fluid makes a sharp turn in front of the closed active port before discharging through the vent. This work is an extension of the earlier works [53,54] on vented cusped bistable fluid amplifiers.

Boucher [12] discussed the similarity and modelling of fluid logic devices in terms of the Reynolds number and the ratio of the Reynolds number to Mach number. The latter parameter is chosen in place of the Mach number alone since it remains fairly constant as the flow is changed by altering the upstream pressure.

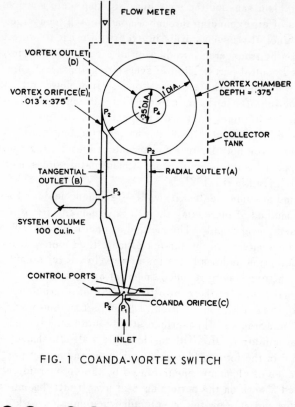

FIG. 1 COANDA-VORTEX SWITCH

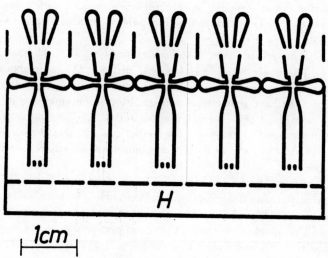

FIG. 2 SWITCH DIFFUSER "PRINTED TECHNIQUE"
UNIT

262

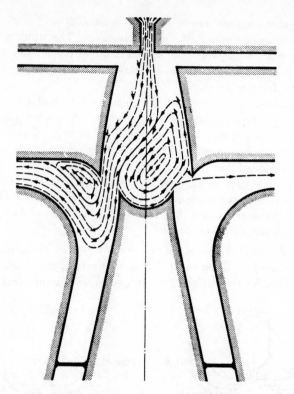

FIG. 3 BISTABLE AMPLIFIER

This ratio obviously expresses a new Reynolds number based on acoustic velocity. It is concluded that the boundary layer flows on the cover plates and the rate of spread of the jet are the major factors governing the flow gain and stability of a wall-attachment device and that both factors may vary significantly with Re and Re/M.

Glaetti [13] discussed the Mach-and Cavitation number effects in fluid dynamic elements and circuits. He assumed a constant radius of curvature for the deflected jet and ignored the spreading of the jet [compare with the conclusions of ref. 12]. It was concluded that the Mach-and Cavitation number effects manifest themselves in three different ways: 1) they set upper limits to operating pressure, power consumption, and power output; 2) they influence the general behaviour of isolated elements; and finally 3) they affect the stability of complete circuits. On the basis of these observations it was suggested that large scale models of complete circuits (not only the single elements) must be tested at the same Mach-and Reynolds numbers.

The third session was concerned with the interaction devices [14-18]. Carne [14] described the characteristics of a momentum interaction amplifier with a centre dump. It was developed essentially for use in connection with a pneumatically operated ram within a positional control system to replace the electro-pneumatic servo valve. Render [15] presented the results of tests, with high pressure jets, on the total pressure distribution and the manner with which it varies with the jet deflection. The apparatus consisted of a power nozzle and a control nozzle clamped between a base plate and a perspex top plate. A series

263

of interchangeable nozzles was made with throat widths of 0.05 or 0.12 inches. The depth of the nozzle was 0.375 in. in all cases. The width and set-back of the control nozzle were both adjustable over a range of 0.5 in. The total pressure distributions in the deflected and undeflected jet were presented in the form of "universal" performance curves.

Douglas and Neve [16] described the characteristics of a similar momentum interaction device. Experiments were conducted with a water table and also with an enlarged scale pneumatic model. In addition, an approximate theory was used for predicting the amplifier gain on the basis of momentum, mass flow, and power. The authors concluded that the jets appear to retain their integrity during interaction and are subsequently subjected to the normal viscous mixing. This interaction process is almost completed within four nozzle widths. The inviscid model is not valid at distances larger than four nozzle widths and one must once again resort to the submerged jet idea.

Parker and Jones [17] discussed the characteristics of the passive momentum Half-Adder proposed by Greenwood [55] and presented the results for both static and dynamic tests for two different configurations with side vents (Fig. 4). Due to

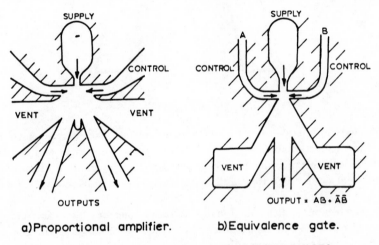

a)Proportional amplifier.   b)Equivalence gate.

FIG. 4 ACTIVE MOMENTUM INTERACTION DEVICES

difficulties in generating the EXCLUSIVE-OR function in these elements, additional investigations were confined to separate AND and EXCLUSIVE-OR logic elements. It was concluded that the AND element may be comparatively easily designed to provide good static and dynamic characteristics and the EXCLUSIVE-OR configurations tested show a substantial improvement over the Half-Adder design. It appears that a combination of wall attachment and momentum effects would be the most promising approach for future developments.

McCabe and Hughes [18] described the initial results of flow visualization in the interaction region of a submerged water operated proportional amplifier and concluded that the interactions between the power jet and one control stream produce deflections which are essentially controlled by the momentum phenomena. The mixing of the streams on impact is governed by the ratio of the control and power nozzle exit velocities, in agreement with the existing turbulent mixing theories.

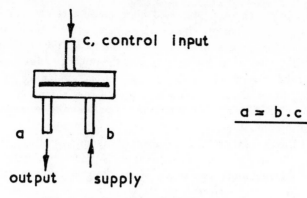

c, control input

$$a \approx b . c$$

a   b

output   supply

FIG. 5 FOIL ELEMENT AND LOGIC

The fourth session was confined to the discussion of miscellaneous elements and circuits [19-24]. The first paper by Foster and Retallick [19] dealt with some experiments carried out on a type of moving part fluid logic element called the "foil switching device." The device (Fig. 5) consists of a free moving circular foil contained in a chamber of a shape to contrain the foil so that it has only one translational degree of freedom, in a direction normal to the plane of the foil. The parts of the chamber to which the supply, input, and output connections are made determine the logic function of the element. The applications of the device to a 2-input OR hybrid element, a multiple-input OR, and a multiple-input AND were described. The device, aside from containing a moving element, has certain disadvantages and peculiarities. The authors claimed that the manufacture of the elements is no more complicated or expensive than turbulent devices and the tolerances are not as critical as with some other elements.

Davies [20] described an empirical expression for the resistance of small bore tubes to turbulent flow. An expression was developed in terms of mass flow and total head, containing an unknown non-dimensional factor which was determined experimentally. The theoretical analysis appears to have too many loop holes and the results should not be taken on faith without a careful study of the underlying assumptions. Bouteille's work [21] concerned recent developments in piston fluid logic devices (Fig. 6). By using the many logic possibilities of 3-way and 4-way valves, the author explained how few valves are needed for a given problem and how the piston valves provide a flip-flop whose state cannot be lost by a temporary loss of power. In addition several examples and miniaturization techniques were discussed.

The only paper on vortex devices was presented by Royle[3] and Hassan [22]. The authors, assuming the sink to be a cylinder of radius R_1, without any form of external torque restraint, and allowing the outer cylinder R_2 to have a peripheral velocity V_2 and hence an entry moment of momentum $V_2 R_2$ per unit mass, examined the moment of momentum flux under the influence of a tangential shear stress $\epsilon = \mu \ (\partial v / \partial r - v/r)$, Fig. 7.

---

[3] Professor Royle, at an after-dinner speech, discussed the existence of a perfect analogy between Fluidics and woman. According to him the latter like the former required a steady income or power source, had a shifty character, was at times turbulent and a bit noisy, had a weak memory and a slow response, and her performance was rather difficult to predict!

On the basis of the experimental evidence, the authors concluded that the vortex element can be either a switch with an impressive ratio of impedance or a highly sensitive pressure amplifier and that the outlet flow from the unit is in a highly unstable state under the influence of the severe radial pressure gradient. It is suggested that the radial outflow resulting from a spinning jet can be turned to good effect, particularly with liquids, to give a very sharp cut-off in pressure recovery at an axial pick-up. This technique is believed to be already used in USA by several organizations.

Bowles and Dexter [23] presented a general discussion of the components for FM and AM fluidic circuits and concluded that the continued emphasis on the development of AC techniques presently offers the greatest potential for improving analog fluidic system performance.

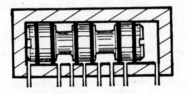

FIG. 6 PISTON FLUID LOGIC

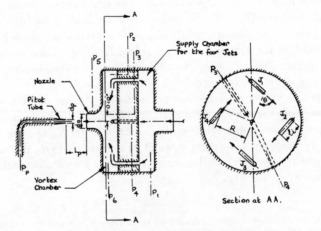

FIG. 7 EXPERIMENTAL EQUIPMENT OF THE
VORTEX DEVICE

266

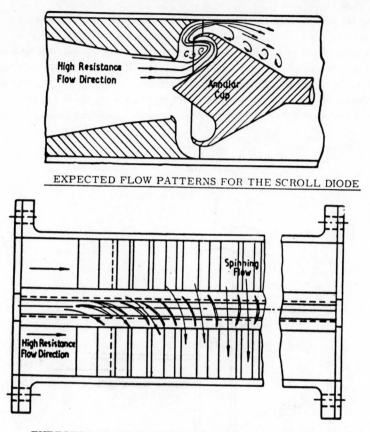

EXPECTED FLOW PATTERNS FOR THE SCROLL DIODE

EXPECTED FLOW PATH FOR THE FLUID FLOW RECTIFIER.

FIG. 8 SCROLL DIODE AND FLOW RECTIFIER

A comprehensive discussion of fluid diodes was presented by Baker [24]. Particular emphasis has been placed upon correlating the performance defined as the ratio of the pressure drop in the reverse-flow direction to the pressure drop in the forward flow direction under steady-state conditions over a range of Reynolds numbers for a vortex diode, scroll diode, and a fluid-flow rectifier (Fig. 8). Baker found that his vortex diode gave a performance ratio (defined in terms of pressure) of 12.5 to 1 (note that ratios of 50 to 1 have been previously reported), scroll diode gave a maximum ratio of 6.6 to 1, and the rectifier a ratio of 31 to 1. The rectifier, though probably more suitable geometrically for most applications, is more expensive to manufacture.

The fifth session was confined to the discussion of various types of pneumatic transducers [25-28]. Gant [25] described a fluidic digital displacement indicator, Fig. 9. The device consisted essentially of a back pressure nozzle system and a code strip. An important feature in the design of the code strips was to ensure adequate depth of slot and clearance between strips for the air expelled from the nozzles to be able to escape freely. An accuracy better than 0.001 in. was claimed for the measurement of rectilinear displacement.

A pneumatic tape reader which has been designed for use with either 5 or 8 hole standard punched paper tape at reading speeds of about 20 lines per second was described by Rosenbaum and Cant [26]. The hole sensing head was mounted underneath the tape, directly below the driving sprocket drum and consisted essentially of a chamber in the top of which row of sensing nozzles was formed which align with the hole positions on the tape, (Fig. 10). In operation, compressed air is fed to the chamber and the pressure existing in the sensing nozzles is detected via side ports which form output connections to the reader, (Fig. 11).

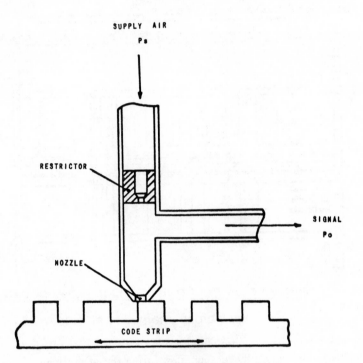

FIG. 9 NOZZLE DESIGN AND CODE STRIP

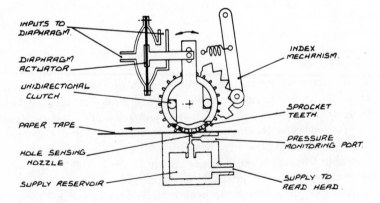

FIG. 10 DIAGRAMMATIC SKETCH OF TAPE READER

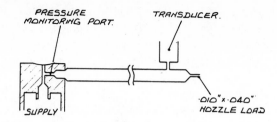

FIG. 11 ARRANGEMENT FOR RECORDING OUTPUT
SIGNALS

A fluidic measuring system capable of linear or angular indication with a resolution of 0.001 in. was described by Sharp and his associates [27]. The operating principle of the device is quite similar to that described by Gant [25]. The present device uses a simple pneumatic-mechanical system for the readout. An array of tubes containing slugs, each to open and close a window, are arranged in matrix form. The logic actuates one slug in each decade to indicate a decimal length quantity. Consideration of future application of this measuring system to closed-loop control devices will depend on its transient response.

The last paper of the session was on the design of a pure fluid shaft encoder. Ramanathan et al., [28] discussed an encoder which has been designed for application to a machine tool linear displacement in increments of 0.001 in. to a total length of 10 in. A Petherick coded multi-turn two disc encoder with 16 nozzle outputs was used. Only one set of 4 nozzles was employed to give the binary signals for each decade. Each of the 16 encoder signals were fed into one input of a 2-input NOR/OR gate. The second input of each of the four devices comprising each decade was interconnected and the signals into this input were obtained from the negated output of a counter. The authors concluded that for positional linear control systems the Gray code and for rotational positional control the Petherick code is the most suitable code.

The sixth session was allocated to the discussion of signal conversion and element manufacture [29-33]. Render [29] discussed a piezoelectric crystal bent by an electric voltage and thereby caused to cover or uncover a port resulting in the conversion of a binary electrical signal into a binary fluid signal. Good square waves were obtained at 300 Hz, but the wave shapes began to deteriorate by 400 Hz. Voltages as low as 45 volts were adequate for operation.

Verhelst [30] presented a very useful method of plotting the characteristics of a turbulence amplifier. The curves very compactly provide a great deal of information on the turbulence amplifier and help establish design criteria. The second part of the paper was devoted to a description of planar turbulence amplifiers which lend themselves better to modular construction than do the axisymmetric type.

The use of an electrical signal to switch a binary fluid amplifier by first converting the electrical signal into an acoustic signal using an earpiece was described by Hawgood [31]. Switching at 500 Hz was obtained with 0.1 watts. The author also described how a piezoelectric crystal can be used as a hole sensor for punched card reading. The pressure signal is converted into an electrical signal by the crystal. The device could also be operated at 500 Hz and gave 1 volt output per psi input.

269

Brown [32] described the pertinent dimensions of a number of fluid elements together with a brief description of the Dycril etching process and epoxy molding. Along the same lines Joklik [33] discussed a molding technique using acrylic polymers which is claimed to give units which are of considerable uniformity and low cost.

Glaettli [34] was the only speaker of the seventh session. He asked whether it is actually true that non-moving part devices are more reliable, faster, smaller, or consume more power than moving parts devices and concluded that there is still insufficient information and that one cannot make any definite statements either way and that the answer depends on the particular use of the devices under consideration.

The eighth session dealt with fluidic modular circuits [35-40]. Parker and Jones [35] compared three binary adder circuits and briefly discussed the design of a half-adder element together with its static and dynamic characteristics. Bryan [36] also discussed three binary to decimal converter circuits together with a fourth circuit which is a modification of one of the other circuits.

Hawgood and his associates [37] discussed the problems and requirements of modular and/or integrated circuits and some important questions such as the causes and/or effects of pulse stretching, variation in response time, and reflections. Some data was given on the pressure drop around 90 deg. bends of various radii.

Foster et al., [38] described the use of turbulence amplifiers, diaphragm foil amplifiers, and wall effect devices in combination for the control of a drilling sequence where the input is by means of punched cards. Turbulence amplifiers were used for the card reading, the outputs were amplified by the diaphragm foil amplifiers, and the signals interpreted and used for control by wall attachment devices.

Bantle [39] classified various types of flip flops according to whether they are wall effect, beam deflection, or turbulence devices, and then again as to whether they are asymmetrically keyed or symmetrically keyed, bistable or stable. The author described his variation of a counter element and a number of counter circuits.

Aviv et al., [40] gave a comparison circuit which operates up to 600 Hz with a signal output level of 1.00 Lbf/in.^{2} and 0.182 ft^3/min. The calculations as well as the experimental device are used to design an EXCLUSIVE-OR as shown in the paper.

The ninth and the tenth sessions were allocated to the discussion and description of various applications [41-49]. Sevcik [41] discussed the ZPA system (diaphragm type devices) in terms of the digital storage and processing of information in the optimization of control systems, i.e. for adaptive systems.

Some of the requirements of fluidic circuits used for nuclear plant control were discussed by Grant [42]. He tested and compared several types of no-moving-parts diodes. Campagnuolo and Holmes [43] described a four stage digital fluid amplifier driven by an oscillator which is caused to give a net output force proportional to a small d.c. analog signal. The last stage is supersonic.

An ingenious no-moving-parts self cleaning filter which combines a digital oscillator, vortex motion, and baffles was described and demonstrated by Floyd [44].

During the last session, Jura [45] described a driving nozzle which pushes tape along without the use of moving parts. A binary switch operated by sparks from automobile spark plugs was used in the system as well as both diaphragm and spool type devices. Brewin [46] presented a discussion of spring controlled diaphragm devices, a pneumatic "microswitch", and a pneumatic drum programmer for drilling machine operation. Abbate-Daga [47] described a no-moving-part fluid modular element called the AF-relay and a number of its applications.

Monge's [48] work was concerned with a set of no-moving-part fluid production type modular elements. These elements can be easily connected by plugging them together so that only a minimum amount of flexible tubing is necessary. The devices are being used in an inspection machine for checking the cylinder bores in the engine blocks of the FIAT-124 automobile.

The last paper of the Conference was presented by Stal and his associates [49]. They described the positioning of machine tools using turbulence amplifiers, pneumatic coding disks, and electrical readouts (lights) operated by membrane switches.

In order to familiarize the delegates with the fluidics activities of Japan, the chairman asked Mr. Harada of the Government Mechanical Laboratory of Japan, to present a brief discussion (not to be published in the Proceedings) on Fluidics in Japan. Mr. Harada described with slides the use of spool valves as universal logic elements (3, 4, or 5 mm diameter) in the operation of a gasoline dispenser and sequential control. In addition, the use of diaphragm elements in an automatic sizing grinder, pneumatic switches, and some pure fluid elements were also described.

It is obvious from the foregoing that Fluidics became an enormous international field. Many of the really challenging problems still await solution by those who are willing to take up the challenge to carry the analysis further and find imaginative applications. In this report, there has been space for only a few gentle excursions into selected papers. The hope is that the report will help to put the reader into the position where he can determine the degree of his interest in a particular paper without going through all of them as the authors did and, at the same time, get a quick overall view of the current European Fluidics research.

The authors have drawn freely on papers and comments provided by the participants of the Conference. This help is gratefully acknowledged.

References

[1] P. A. Lush, "Investigation of the switching mechanism in a large-scale model of a turbulent reattachment amplifier."

[2] R. A. Sawyer, "Analysis of time dependent jet attachment processes and comparison with experiment."

[3] K. Foster, N. S. Jones, and D. G. Mitchell, "A method of calculating the pressure distribution along a reattachment bubble."

[4] M. Kadosch, "The curved wall effect."

[5] R. V. Thompson, "The switching of supersonic gas jet by atmospheric venting."

[6] V. J. Chadwick, "A method of using wall attachment devices in an ultrasensitive mode."

[7] P. Dražan, "Optimal design of the control jet of pneumatic element."

[8] B. J. Steptoe, "Steady-state and dynamic characteristic variations in digital wall attachment devices."

[9] R. R. Hart, "Performance of Coanda device as a pressure maintainer and as a switch or selector."

[10] G. König, "Design of inputs and outputs of digital pneumatic jet components for adaption to the standardized pressure range."

[11] A. W. Rechten, "Flow stability in bi-stable fluid elements."

[12] R. F. Boucher, "Some considerations in the development and operation of fluidic devices."

[13] H. H. Glaettli, "Mach number effects in fluid elements and circuits."

[14] C. M. Carne, "Experiments using momentum interaction to produce a proportional fluid amplifier."

[15] A. B. Render, "The design of jet-interaction amplifiers using supercritical pressure ratios."

[16] J. F. Douglas and R. S. Neve, "Investigation into the behaviour of a jet interaction proportional amplifier."

[17] G. A. Parker and B. Jones, "Experiments with AND and EXCLUSIVE OR passive elements."

[18] D. L. Hughes and A. McCabe, "Static and dynamic characteristics of fluid jet amplifiers."

[19] K. Foster and D. A. Retallick, "Some experiments on a free foil switching device."

[20] G. E. Davies, "An empirical expression for the resistance of small bore tubes to turbulent flow."

[21] D. Bouteille, "Recent developments in Piston Fluid Logic and Applications in general automation."

[22] J. K. Royle, "Operational characteristics of a Vortex Amplifier."

[23] R. E. Bowles, "Components for FM and AM Fluidic Circuits."

[24] P. Baker, "Comparison of Fluid Diodes."

[25] G. C. Gant, "A fluidic digital displacement indicator."

[26] J. Cant and H. M. Rosenbaum, "A pneumatic tape reader."

[27] R. Sharp, R. Maclean and A. McClintock, "A fluidic absolute measuring system."

[28] S. Ramanathan, R. E. Bidgood and I. Aviv, "The design of a pure fluid shaft encoder."

[29] A. B. Render, "Electrical control of fluid logic elements."

[30] H. A. M. Verhelst, "On the design, characteristics and fabrication of turbulence amplifiers."

[31] D. Hawgood, "Electrical transducers for fluidic systems."

[32] C. C. Brown, "Design and manufacture of pure fluid elements."

[33] Prof. O. F. Joklik, "Industrial scale manufacture of pure fluid devices from acrylic material by a special casing process."

[34] H. H. Glaettli, "Moving parts versus non-moving part elements."

[35] G. A. Parker and B. Jones, "A fluidic subtractor for digital control systems."

[36] B. Bryan, "A pure fluid binary to decimal converter."

[37] D. Hawgood, W. C. Morton, B. J. Steptoe and S. Ties, "Design procedures for a multi-element fluidic plate using wall-attachment devices."

[38] K. Foster, D. G. Mitchell and D. A. Retallick, "Fluidic circuits used in a drilling sequence control."

[39] K. Bantle, "Counters with bi-stable fluid elements."

[40] I. Aviv, R. E. Bidgood and S. Ramanathan, "The design and construction of a pure fluid four bit binary comparator."

[41] M. Sevcik, "Pneumatic digital optimizing device."

[42] J. Grant, "Potential application of fluidics in nuclear plant."

[43] C. Campagnuolo and A. B. Holmes, "Experimental analysis of digital flueric amplifiers for proportional thrust control."

[44] G. M. Montgomerie and T. J. Floyd, "Heavy Current Fluidic Devices."

[45] S. Jura, "Some applications of fluid logic element in devices for driving recording tape."

[46] G. M. Brewin, "Application of spring controlled NOR units to machine switching operations."

272

[47] A. Abbate-Daga, "The AF-relay: some applications to automatic control systems."

[48] M. Monge, "Some industrial applications of the MODUFLOG system."

[49] H. P. Stal and J. Bulk, "The application of fluidics in numerical control of machine tools."

[50] C. Bourque and B. G. Newman, "Reattachment of a two-dimensional incompressible jet to an adjacent flat plate," Aero. Quarterly, Vol. II, 1960, p. 201.

[51] M. L. Albertson, Y. B. Dai, R. A. Jensen and H. Rouse, "Diffusion of Submerged Jets," Proc. ASCE, Vol. 74, 1948.

[52] R. Wille and H. Fernholz, "Report on the first European Mechanics Colloquium, on the Coanda effect," Jour. Fluid Mechanics, No. 23, 1965, pp. 801-819.

[53] T. Sarpkaya, "Steady and Transient Behavior of a Bistable Amplifier with a Latching Vortex," HDL Fluid Amplification Symposium, October, 1965.

[54] T. Sarpkaya, "Characteristics of Vented and Unvented, Cusped, Bistable Amplifiers," HDL Internal Report, NU-TS Hydro-Report No. 26, 1966.

[55] J. R. Greenwood and F. D. Ezekiel, "Hydraulics Half-Add Binary Numbers," Control Engineering, Vol. 8, No. 2, February, 1961, p. 145.

Vortex Valve Performance Power Index

Vernon D. Gebben
Lewis Research Center
Cleveland, Ohio

Introduction

A performance index for confined vortex flows is proposed as a figure of merit for evaluating vortex valves. The conventional vortex valve illustrated in Fig. 1 is a short cylindrical chamber with two inlets — a radial inlet and a tangential nozzle. The fluid leaves the chamber through the outlet orifice located at the center of one or both end walls. The total flow leaving the vortex chamber is controlled by the amount of swirl imparted to the fluid inside the chamber. Typical outlet mass flow characteristics for a constant radial supply pressure are shown in Fig. 2. The maximum outlet flow (point R) occurs when the tangential nozzle flow is zero; a condition of no swirl in the chamber. The minimum outlet flow (point T) occurs when the vortex conditions prevent radial inlet flow.

One objective is to optimize the performance at conditions R and T. Performance at R is generally gauged by comparing the actual flow rate to the theoretical flow rate that would result if the outlet orifice was the only flow restriction and its discharge coefficient was unity. A figure of merit for condition T, however, is more difficult to represent because a practical, realistic model that characterizes the three-dimensional flow in the chamber has not been developed. Mathematical models of confined vortices are complicated by compressible and viscous effects that influence the amount of inflow along the end walls, the mixing efficiency of the radial and tangential inlet flows, velocity limits, turbulence, secondary vortices, and the three-dimensional sink flow [1-7]. Consequently, reported methods for analyzing the vortex valve are based on empirical models derived from measurements external to the valve [8-14].

A performance index for evaluating the power supplied to the tangential nozzle at operating condition T is proposed in this paper. The quantity that is used to normalize the actual power supplied at condition T is the theoretical maximum power computed from the flow rate that would result at condition R if the outlet orifice was the only flow restriction and its discharge coefficient was unity. By using the theoretical instead of the measured flow at condition R, the normalizing quantity is independent of the outlet orifice discharge coefficient and the

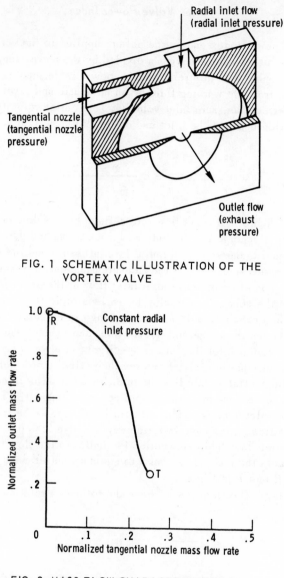

FIG. 1 SCHEMATIC ILLUSTRATION OF THE
VORTEX VALVE

FIG. 2 MASS FLOW CHARACTERISTICS OF A
TYPICAL VORTEX VALVE

index can be used for evaluating vortex elements similar to the vortex diode that
have no radial inlet. Since the proposed index is a ratio between the theoretical
maximum power at condition R and the actual power at T, the index represents
the potential power turndown ratio of the valve. To illustrate the characteristics
and applications for the index, the results from an experimental investigation are
presented.

275

Vortex Valve Power Index

The proposed power index equals the power supplied to the vortex valve when the outlet flow is a theoretical maximum divided by the power supplied when the outlet flow is minimum. For this relationship, power is defined as the maximum power extractible from the working fluid by an adiabatic and reversible machine operating with perfect gas, zero inlet velocity, zero outlet velocity, and zero difference in elevation between the inlet and outlet. Mathematically, the power index is expressed

$$\text{Power Index} = \frac{(\dot{m}_r')(\Delta h_r)}{(\dot{m}_t)(\Delta h_t)} \qquad (1)$$

where $\dot{m}_r'$ is the theoretical mass flow rate defined by the flow through the outlet orifice with unity discharge coefficient and for upstream and downstream stagnation pressures equal to the specified radial inlet pressure and the specified exhaust pressure, respectively; $\dot{m}_t$ is the measured tangential nozzle mass flow rate for the operating condition of zero radial inlet flow at the specified radial inlet pressure; Δh_r is the change in enthalpy for an isentropic flow process between the radial inlet and exhaust; and Δh_t is the change in enthalpy for an isentropic flow process between the tangential nozzle inlet and exhaust during the operating condition of zero radial inlet flow at the specified radial inlet pressure.

The numerator of equation (1) defines the theoretical power delivered to the valve when the tangential nozzle flow is zero. Its function is to normalize the denominator that represents the power supplied to the tangential nozzle for maintaining the radial inlet shutoff condition, point T of Fig. 2. An increase in the power index signifies an increase in efficiency because less power is required to stop the radial inlet flow. This convention is similar to the flow turndown quantity [10] that equals the ratio of maximum to minimum outlet mass flow rates as given by points R and T in Fig. 2.

For the isentropic flow process we have the following relationship

$$\Delta h = \frac{RT_1}{\alpha} \left[1 - (P_2/P_1)^\alpha \right] \qquad (2)$$

where R is the gas constant, T is temperature, P is pressure, α equals $(k-1)/k$, and k is the ratio of specific heats. Subscripts 1 and 2 refer to the upstream and downstream conditions, respectively.

Generally, the same gas at equal temperature is supplied to both the radial inlet and the tangential nozzle. Therefore, for these conditions the power index can be defined

$$\text{Power Index} = \frac{\left[\dot{m}_r'/\dot{m}_t \right] \left[1 - (P_e/P_r)^\alpha \right]}{1 - \left[\dfrac{1}{\left(\dfrac{P_t - P_e}{P_r - P_e} \right)\left(\dfrac{P_r}{P_e} - 1 \right) + 1} \right]^\alpha} \qquad (3)$$

276

where P_e is the specified exhaust pressure, P_r is the specified radial inlet supply pressure, and P_t is the tangential nozzle supply pressure.

Experimental Investigation

The effects of varying tangential nozzle area were investigated with the vortex chamber shown in Fig. 3. The vortex chamber was constructed from two adjacent plates with semi-circular open sections that formed both the cylindrical wall of the chamber and two adjustable tangential nozzles. The chamber diameter was 2.54 cm (1 in.) and the distance between the end walls was 0.30 cm (0.12 in.). The end walls were flat and had a smooth surface of approximately 16 microinch finish. The tangential nozzles, located at the chamber periphery, had rectangular cross sections that extended between the end walls. The nozzle area was adjusted by the position of the two plates that formed the cylindrical wall. Because the unit contained no radial inlet, the pressure at the chamber periphery was used to represent the radial inlet pressure during the condition of zero radial inlet flow. This peripherial pressure measurement was obtained from a pressure tap located in the cylindrical wall 90 degrees downstream from a tangential nozzle. The outlet, located in one of the end walls, was an orifice with diameter of 0.358 cm (0.141 in.) and length of 0.05 cm (0.02 in.) followed by an axisymmetric 60 degrees conical diffuser.

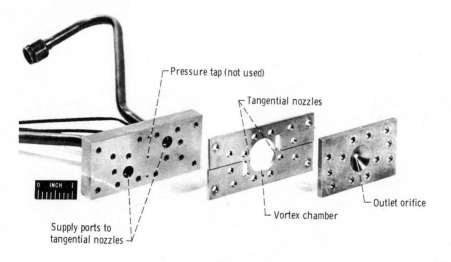

FIG. 3 VORTEX CHAMBER DISPLAY

The supply media was air that varied in temperature between 77 and 81 F. Variations in the supply temperature were recorded but not used in the flow calculations. The outlet flow exhausted to the atmosphere. Pressures were measured with the following gages: 0 to 10 N/cm² gage (15 psig), 0 to 52 N/cm² gage (75 psig), 0 to 69 N/cm² gage (100 psig), and 0 to 3 N/cm² (4.5 psi) differential for pressures less than 10 N/cm² gage (15 psig). These were precision gages with errors less than 0.1 per cent of full scale. Except for the differential gage, the tangential nozzle supply pressure and the peripherial (radial inlet) pressure were measured with the same gage to eliminate errors due to small differences

277

between gages. A calibrated rotameter in the supply line measured mass flow rate with erros estimated to be less than 1.5 per cent of the actual value. The barometric pressure was recorded and used in computing the power index and the flow turndown index.

Test data shown in Figs. 4 and 5 are given in terms of dimensionless quantities; where

$$\text{Flow turndown index} \quad = \dot{m}'_r / \dot{m}_t$$

$$\text{Supply pressure ratio} \quad = P_r/P_e$$

$$\text{Control pressure ratio} = (P_t - P_e)/(P_r - P_e)$$

Power index is defined by equation (3)

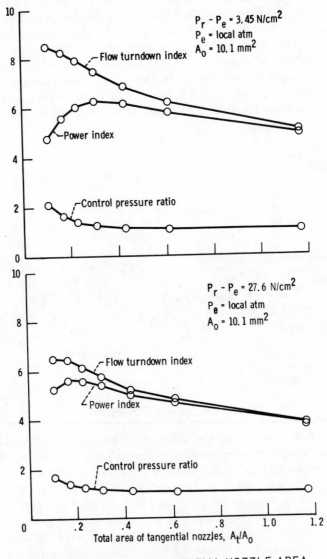

FIG. 4 EFFECTS OF TANGENTIAL NOZZLE AREA

Fig. 4 shows the effects of tangential nozzle area for a radial inlet pressure of 3.45 N/cm² gage (5 psig) in the upper plot and for 27.6 N/cm² gage (40 psig) in the lower plot. For the largest nozzle area tested, the pressure drop across the tangential nozzle $(P_t - P_r)$ was very small, resulting in a control pressure ratio near unity. Consequently, the power index and flow turndown index for the largest nozzle area were nearly equal as indicated by equation (3). For the area range tested, a decrease in nozzle size resulted in an increase in both the flow turndown index and the control pressure ratio. The power index also increased as the nozzle size was reduced but it reached a maximum and then decreased when the nozzle area ratio (nozzle area/outlet area) was reduced below 0.3 in the upper plot or below 0.2 in the lower plot. The decrease in power index for the

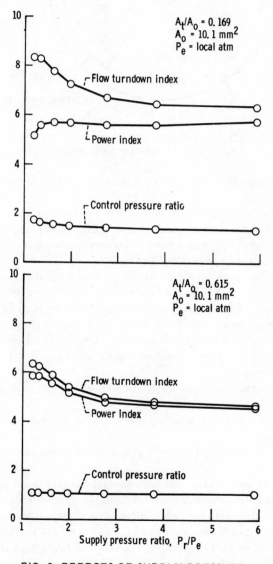

FIG. 5 EFFECTS OF SUPPLY PRESSURE

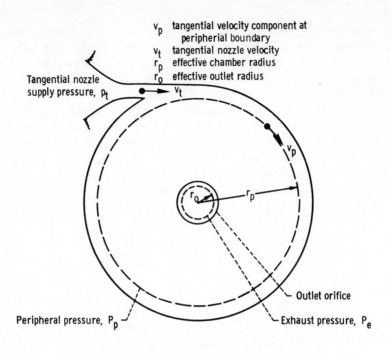

v_p tangential velocity component at peripherial boundary
v_t tangential nozzle velocity
r_p effective chamber radius
r_o effective outlet radius

Tangential nozzle supply pressure, p_t

v_t

v_p

r_o r_p

Outlet orifice

Peripheral pressure, P_p

Exhaust pressure, P_e

FIG. 6 SCHEMATIC ILLUSTRATION OF THE
THEORETICAL MODEL GEOMETRY

smaller nozzles was probably caused by mixing losses in the chamber and viscous losses in the nozzle.

The configuration with the maximum power index is considered as the most efficient vortex valve. For the unit tested, the maximum power index occurred for a tangential nozzle geometry that had a control pressure ratio less than 1.5; a geometry within the range of conventional designs.

Fig. 5 shows the effects of supply pressure. The upper plot was obtained from an element with a tangential to outlet area ratio of 0.169. Characteristics for a larger nozzle (area ratio of 0.615) are presented in the lower plot. In both cases flow turndown ratio increased appreciably for reduced pressures.

The characteristics shown in Figs. 4 and 5 are appreciably different from those predicted by an inviscid isentropic two-dimensional vortex model (Fig. 6) that has the following characteristics:

a) Control pressure ratio is essentially independent of the tangential nozzle area;

b) flow turndown index is essentially inversely proportional to the tangential nozzle area; and

c) power index is essentially inversely proportional to the tangential nozzle area.

In Fig. 4 the control pressure ratio was not constant but increased appreciably when the tangential nozzle area decreased. The flow turndown index also deviated from the theoretical model; for example, an area change from 0.2 to 0.6 caused the flow turndown index to decrease by a factor of 1.3 instead of 3 in the theoretical case. The slope of the power index curve changed sign in Fig. 4, thus, displaying no correlation to the inviscid model. These large differences between

280

theoretical and physical characteristics were considered to be caused by secondary flows not represented in the model.

Conclusion

The vortex valve power index defined in the report provides a useful and effective approach for comparing efficiencies of various vortex valves. This index is considered to be an important parameter which should be examined during the design of an optimized vortex valve. It was concluded that the three normalized quantities representing pressure, flow, and power are all necessary in optimizing the steady state performance of vortex valves.

References

[1] O. L. Anderson, "Theoretical Solutions for the Secondary Flow on the End Wall of a Vortex Tube," United Aircraft Corp., Report No. R-2494-1, November, 1961.

[2] A. C. Pinchak and R. Poplawski, "On the Attainment of Extremely High Rotational Velocities in a Confined Vortex Flow," AIAA Paper No. 65-400, July, 1965.

[3] R. Poplawski and A. C. Pinchak, "Aerodynamic Performance of Reversed Flow Vortex Chambers," Report No. ARL-65-219, AD-625405, United States Air Force, October, 1965.

[4] D. H. Ross, "An Experimental Study of Secondary Flow in Jet-Driven Vortex Chambers," Report No. ATN-64(9227)−1, AD-433052, Aerospace Corporation, January 27, 1964.

[5] J. M. Savino and E. G. Keshock, "Experimental Profiles of Velocity Components and Radial Pressure Distributions in a Vortex Contained in a Short Cylindrical Chamber," NASA Technical Note D-3072, October, 1965.

[6] C. D. Donaldson and G. G. Williamson, "An Experimental Study of Turbulence in a Driven Vortex," Technical Memo. 64-2, AD-609460, Aeronautical Research Associates of Princeton, Inc., July, 1964.

[7] J. R. Weske and T. M. Rankin, "Production of Secondary Vortices in the Field of a Primary Vortex," Technical Note BN-244, AFOSR-623, University of Maryland, April, 1961.

[8] E. A. Mayer and P. Maker, "Control Characteristics of Vortex Valves," Proceedings of Second Fluid Amplification Symposium, Harry Diamond Laboratories, May 26-28, 1964, Volume 2, pp. 61-84. (DDC No. AD-602001.)

[9] L. B. Taplin, "Phenomenology of Vortex Flow and Its Application to Signal Amplification," Report No. RLDP 65-14, Rev. 1, Bendix Research Laboratories, October 1, 1965.

[10] E. A. Mayer and L. B. Taplin, "Vortex Devices," Fluidics, E. F. Humphrey, ed., Fluid Amplifier Associates, Boston, Massachusetts, 1965, pp. 185-200.

[11] L. B. Taplin, "Small Signal Analysis of Vortex Amplifiers," Bendix Research Lab. Report included in the 2.73 course Notes, Department of Mechanical Engineering, Massachusetts Institute of Technology, July 1, 1966.

[12] I. Greber, P. E. Koerper and C. K. Taft, "Fluid Vortex Amplifier Optimization," Proceedings of Third Fluid Amplification Symposium, Harry Diamond Laboratories, October 26-28, 1965, Vol. 2, pp. 223-243. (DDC No. AD-623456).

[13] A. C. Bell, "Optimization of Vortex Valve," S. M. Thesis, Department of Mechanical Engineering, Massachusetts Institute of Technology, December, 1965.

[14] D. N. Wormley, "Static Characteristics of Vortex Valve Pure Fluid Modulators," 2.73 course notes, Department of Mechanical Engineering, Massachusetts Institute of Technology, July, 1966.

A Jet Driven Flueric Oscillator

Albertus E. Schmidlin
Edward L. Rakowsky

General Precision, Inc.
Aerospace Research Center
Little Falls, New Jersey

Abstract

This paper presents the results of an analytical and experimental study of a flueric resonant cavity. An analysis is given of the resonant modes of the cavity treated as a mechanical wave guide. An experimental program conducted to determine the applicability of the analysis showed agreement between the basic frequencies in the device and the calculated frequencies of the wave guide analysis. The phase relationship between the standing waves at several points in the cavity agreed with the analytic predictions.

Nomenclature

b	= radius of the cylindrical cavity
B	= constant appearing in the Bessel equation
c	= acoustic speed
C	= constant appearing in the Bessel equation
D	= diameter of water table cylinder model
f	= frequency
h_o	= head of water employed in the water table evaluation
J	= Bessel function of the first kind
n	= order of the Bessel equation
N	= Bessel function of the second kind
M	= constant appearing in the Bessel equation
p	= static pressure
P	= dimensionless pressure amplitude

r	=	radial coordinate
u_r	=	radial displacement
u_θ	=	circumferential displacement
u_z	=	axial displacement
t	=	time
z	=	axial coordinate
θ	=	circumferential angular coordinate
λ	=	eigenvalue parameter
ρ	=	density
ϕ	=	displacement potential function
ω	=	angular wave velocity

Subscripts

r, θ, z	=	coordinate directions
n	=	integer
m	=	integer

Introduction

Flueric systems perform many of the functions of conventional electronics. Hence, there is a continual interest in the fluid analogs of the electronic elements. This is true in the case of flueric oscillators as indicated by the literature [1, 2, 3].

Flueric oscillators can perform the normal functions of clocks and timers. Some oscillators are sensitive to the fluid properties and therefore can be used as sensors. For example, the sensitivity to pressure, or temperature, may be employed in a system where that variable is to be measured. Hence, there are two distinct areas of application for flueric oscillators; first, as substitutes for their electronic counter parts and, secondly, as transducers because of their sensitivity to a specific property of the flow.

Many flueric oscillators are sensitive to more than one flow variable. Some oscillators are sensitive to both pressure and temperature as well as other properties of the gas. Some oscillators lend themselves to analytical description while others require an extensive empirical approach as a means for defining their characteristics.

In the present case, a jet driven flueric oscillator was investigated and the frequency spectrum of this device was found to agree with the analysis treating the device as a mechanical wave guide. For this reason, the jet driven flueric oscillator was of further interest owing to the analytic feasibility to design and scale the device for specific frequencies.

The flueric oscillator studied was a shallow, cylindrical cavity shown in Fig. 1. The gas is supplied to the oscillator through a nozzle which enters at

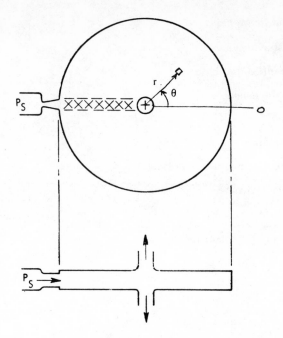

FIG. 1 – FLUERIC OSCILLATOR SCHEMATIC

the outer periphery of the cylindrical shape; this gas fills the cavity and also drives it. Gas exits from the oscillator through an orifice located on the axis of the cylinder. Several devices were constructed in sizes varying from ½ in. to 8 in. in diameter and were operated at supply pressures up to 150 psi.

Theoretical Analysis

The natural modes of the cylindrical resonant cavity were determined from a model representing the device as a mechanical wave guide. The configuration was as shown in Fig. 1. The problem requires a solution of the wave equation:

$$\nabla^2 \varphi = \frac{1}{c^2} \frac{\partial^2 \varphi}{\partial t^2} \tag{1}$$

subject to the boundary condition $r = b$, $u_r = 0$, $\dot{u}_r = 0$, $u_z = 0$ and of period 2π in θ. The components of displacement are

u_r, u_θ, and u_z in r, θ, and z directions respectively

defined by

$$u_r = \frac{\partial \varphi}{\partial r} \quad , \quad u_\theta = \frac{1}{r} \frac{\partial \varphi}{\partial \theta} \quad , \quad u_z = \frac{\partial \varphi}{\partial z}$$

A two-dimensional acoustic field was assumed so that $\dfrac{\partial}{\partial z} = 0$. Hence the independent variables were r and θ as shown in Fig. 1.

This equation was solved by separation of variables. The solution for the potential function is as follows:

$$\varphi = \{C \epsilon^{i n \theta}\} \times [J_n (\lambda r) + B N_n (\lambda r)] \epsilon^{i \omega t}$$

where n must be an integer since the solution must be periodic with period 2π in θ.

The pressure at any point in the cavity is given by

$$p = -\rho \frac{\partial^2 \varphi}{\partial t^2} = \rho \sum_{n,m} \omega^2_{nm} \varphi_{nm}$$

$$= \sum_{n,m} \epsilon^{i n \theta} P_{nm}(r) \epsilon^{i \omega_{nm} t}$$

where

$$P_{nm}(r) = C_{nm} \rho \, \omega^2_{nm} J_n \left(\frac{\omega_{nm}}{c} r \right) .$$

The dimensionless pressures given by

$$P_{nm} = \frac{P_{nm}(r)}{C_{nm} \rho \, \omega^2_{nm}} = J_n \left(\frac{\omega_{nm}}{c} r \right) .$$

are qualitatively represented in Fig. 2.

Note that the pressure at any point is given by the sum of an infinite number of terms, each term having a different cyclic frequency. The influence of each term on the instantaneous static pressure in the oscillator is pictured in the graphs of Figs. 2 and 3. In Fig. 2 the spatial distribution of each term is shown. The graph shows P_{11} versus r/b where P_{11} is the dimensionless amplitude and the graph is plotted for a constant θ corresponding to the greatest amplitudes.

The results are also shown in the Chladni figures of Fig. 3. The shades zones show pressure changes opposite to the unshaded [4].

285

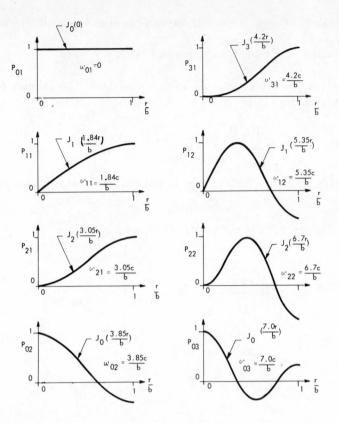

FIG. 2 – DIMENSIONLESS PRESSURE DISTRIBUTION
PREDICTED BY THE WAVE ANALYSIS

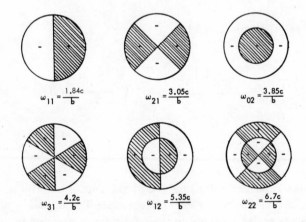

FIG. 3 – CHLADNI FIGURES CORRESPONDING TO THE
PRESSURE DISTRIBUTIONS OF FIG. 2

286

Note that for some modes the pressures on opposite sides of the nodal diameter were 180 degrees out of phase with each other, for example, the case of ω_{11}, while in another case such as ω_{12} there was a double reversal of phase relationship. The complete solution of the wave equation for a cylindrical resonant cavity is presented in the Appendix.

Experimental Program

The primary objective of the experimental program was to corroborate the theoretical analysis. This was done by measuring the pressure distribution within a pneumatic cavity and the resonant frequencies. Several sizes of the pneumatic oscillator were fabricated to accomplish this objective. In each case, the oscillator was supplied with compressed air at various pressures. The instantaneous pressures on the walls of the devices were recorded using Kistler Model 601A piezoelectric pressure transducers, flush mounted on the walls.

Results using an 8 in. diameter oscillator with a converging nozzle are shown in Figs. 4 through 9. These are typical of all the tests with other sizes. Fig. 4 shows a trace of the pressures recorded at two points located symmetrically with respect to the axis of the incoming jet. For this case the supply pressure was 2.5 psig and the resonant frequency determined from this trace was 1000 Hz. The other pertinent data are given in the figure. It was apparent that the two standing waves were 180 degrees out of phase. This agreed with the analysis for a pressure term having a spatial dependency of $\sin \theta$ (see eq. (5) Appendix). The magnitude of the pressure oscillation was approximately 0.25 psi peak to peak. Fig. 5 shows the same configuration at a higher supply pressure. The phase relationship again was 180 degrees out of phase and the amplitude had increased to between .9 and 1 psi peak to peak. The frequency was 1000 Hz. In Fig. 6 an oscillation at 2950 Hz is shown at a supply pressure of 27 psig. The phase relationship exhibited here corroborated again a component of the $\sin \theta$ variety. The pressure waves were approximately 180 degrees out of phase, and the peak to peak pressures were of the order of 1 psi. In each of the above cases, the pressure transducers were mounted as shown in the sketches located symmetrically with respect to the axis of the incoming jet and at a radius of 2 in.

Additional experiments were conducted with the pressure transducers both mounted on the same side of the axis located at radii of 2 and 3½ in., respectively. Typical results for this case are shown in Fig. 7 which illustrates a 2900 Hz oscillation. Although the oscilloscope traces showed a strong evidence of noise it was evident that the 2900 Hz oscillations were approximately 180 degrees out of phase. This result is in agreement with the analysis of the wave guide for the oscillatory mode designated by ω_{12} (see Fig. 2).

Discharge conditions were adjusted in a similar experiment to obtain 1000 Hz operating condition and the results are as shown in Fig. 8. Note here that the pressure oscillations for this frequency are in phase at these two locations. This result correlates with the mode ω_{11}.

Fig. 9 presents typical results for the case in which the pressure transducers were mounted on opposite sides of the axis of the driving jet. It was apparent, however, that at 1000 Hz the waves were 180 degrees out of phase, while at 2900 Hz they were in phase. Again, the results agreed with the oscillatory modes predicted by the analysis of the cylindrical oscillator.

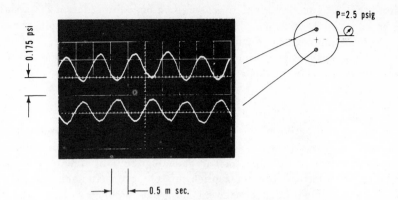

FIG. 4 – PRESSURE OSCILLOGRAMS, 8 IN. OSCILLATOR,
FREQUENCY – 1000 Hz, SUPPLY PRESSURE 2.5
PSIG, TRANSDUCERS LOCATED SYMMETRICALLY

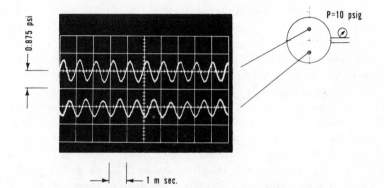

FIG. 5 – PRESSURE OSCILLOGRAMS, 8 IN. OSCILLATOR,
FREQUENCY – 1000 Hz, SUPPLY PRESSURE 10
PSIG, TRANSDUCERS LOCATED SYMMETRICALLY

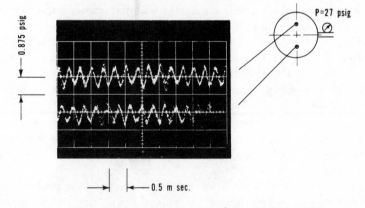

FIG. 6 – PRESSURE OSCILLOGRAMS, 8 IN. OSCILLATOR,
FREQUENCY – 2950 Hz, SUPPLY PRESSURE 27
PSIG, TRANSDUCERS LOCATED SYMMETRICALLY

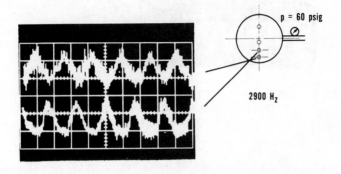

FIG. 7 – PRESSURE OSCILLOGRAMS, 8 IN. OSCILLATOR,
FREQUENCY 2900 Hz, SUPPLY PRESSURE OF 60
PSIG, TRANSDUCERS LOCATED ASYMMETRICALLY

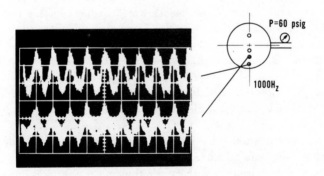

FIG. 8 – PRESSURE OSCILLOGRAMS, 8 IN. OSCILLATOR,
FREQUENCY 1000 Hz, SUPPLY PRESSURE OF 60
PSIG, TRANSDUCERS LOCATED ASYMMETRICALLY

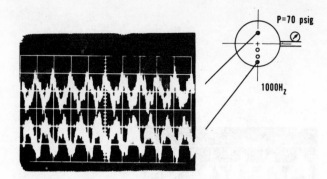

FIG. 9 – PRESSURE OSCILLOGRAM TRACES, 8 IN. OSCILLATOR,
FREQUENCY 1000 Hz, SUPPLY PRESSURE OF 70 PSIG,
TRANSDUCERS LOCATED SYMMETRICALLY

There was a considerable amount of noise shown in the oscilloscope pressure transducer traces for the high nozzle inlet pressure conditions. This high noise level may be attributed to several effects. First, and possibly the most predominant, was the noise spectrum associated with the driving jets especially for sonic and supersonic flow conditions. Noise spectra of the jet flow between two parallel disks with no cylinder wall appeared to substantiate this hypothesis. Other possible sources of noise were higher transverse (z direction) oscillatory frequencies produced in the cavity and viscous effects in the boundary layer flow over the flush mounted transducer elements. Frequency spectra were obtained from the piezoelectric transducer signal using a General Radio spectrum analyzer and recorder. Typical results are shown in Figs. 10 and 11. Each oscillatory component occurred at a frequency predicted by the analysis.

In order to develop an understanding of the coupling of the driving jet with the standing waves in the cavity, experiments were conducted using the hydraulic analog. A circular water table was employed as shown in Fig. 12. The reservoir for the water table consisted of an annular volume filled to a height h_0, with the diameter of the resonant cavity designated at D. At a specific point in the periphery a water jet was used to simulate the inlet jet of the oscillator. The water entered in a radial direction at velocities corresponding to Mach 2. The water exited from the device through a circular drain at the center of the cylindrical section.

Experiments on the water table demonstrated that the oscillations were of two principle modes. The pulsing mode consisted of standing waves in the test section which were in synchronism with cyclic pluming of the incoming jet. This pluming was symmetrical with respect to a radial line. It was typical of the cycling pattern which occurs on the water table when a supersonic jet is subjected to a cycling exit pressure.

The other mode was a lateral flip. It consisted of a cyclic lateral deflection of the jet. This mode produced wave emanations from the jet which travel in a circular fashion around the acoustic cavity.

The frequency of the oscillations on the water table were in approximate agreement with the mode ω_{11}. The diameter D was 16 in. and the mean water depth was approximately ¼ in. The frequency was 1/3 cycles per second.

290

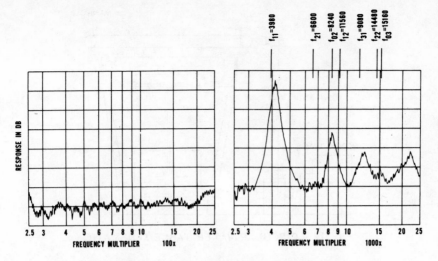

FIG. 10 – EXPERIMENTAL FREQUENCY SPECTRUM OF THE
2 IN. OSCILLATOR COMPARED WITH THE
THEORETICALLY PREDICTED MODES.

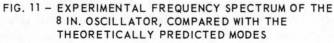

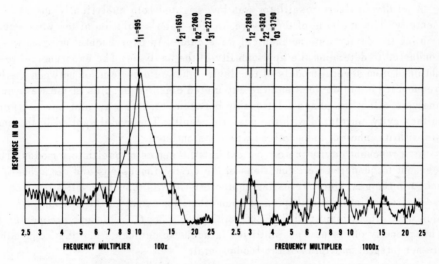

FIG. 11 – EXPERIMENTAL FREQUENCY SPECTRUM OF THE
8 IN. OSCILLATOR, COMPARED WITH THE
THEORETICALLY PREDICTED MODES

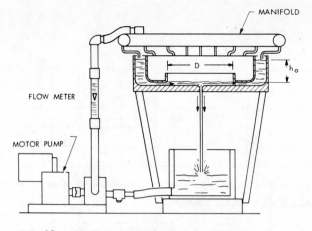

FIG. 12 – CIRCULAR WATER TABLE SCHEMATIC

Concluding Remarks

A jet driven flueric oscillator was investigated both analytically and experimentally. The analysis of the device was based on a solution of the wave equation treating the device as a mechanical wave guide. An experimental program was conducted to determine the applicability of the analysis. The experimental results obtained from several models of the device showed a correlation between the basic frequencies in the devices and the calculated eigenfrequencies of the wave guide analysis. Also, the phase relationship between standing waves at several points in the cavity correlated with the analytic results. The model applied in the analysis with its inherent assumptions was substantiated.

As a resonant cavity the device exhibited a series of oscillatory modes. The resonant frequencies were functions of the cavity dimensions and the acoustic speed in the gas. One interesting characteristic was that the oscillatory frequencies were not integral multiples of each other; for example, the resonant frequencies were proportional to 1.84, 3.05, 3.85, 4.2, 5.35, 6.7, 7.0, etc., respectively. This property offers new possibilities in acoustic devices since the frequencies are not integral multiples of the fundamental.

The complex coupling mechanism at the jet which drives the cavity requires additional study. A hydraulic analog used in an attempt to explain this phenomena showed two possible mechanisms. The first consisted of a periodic pluming of the inlet jet along with a standing wave pattern which was symmetric with respect to the jet axis. The second mechanism consisted of a periodic lateral deflection of the inlet jet along with a standing wave pattern which was non-symmetric with respect to the jet axis.

Preliminary attempts were made to view the pneumatic device using high speed shadowgraph photography. Some cyclic motion of the main body of the jet was discernible although conclusive results were not available at this writing.

Appendix

Treated as a mechanical wave guide the wave equation to be solved is

$$\nabla^2 \varphi = \frac{1}{c^2} \frac{\partial^2 \varphi}{\partial t^2}$$

where components of displacements are

u_r, u_θ, and u_z in r, θ, and z directions

$$u_r = \frac{\partial \phi}{\partial r}, \quad u_\theta = \frac{1}{r} \frac{\partial \phi}{\partial \theta}, \quad u_z = \frac{\partial \phi}{\partial z}$$

subject to the boundary condition $r = b$, $u_r = 0$, $\dot{u}_r = 0$, $u_z = 0$ and with period 2π in θ and the functions must be finite within the domain.

Assume a product solution, then $\phi = R(r) \cdot \Theta(\theta) \cdot T(t)$ for a 2 dimensional configuration since $u_z = \dfrac{\partial \phi}{\partial z} = 0$.

$$\nabla^2 \varphi = \frac{1}{r} \frac{\partial}{\partial r} \left(r \frac{\partial \varphi}{\partial r} \right) + \frac{1}{r^2} \frac{\partial^2 \varphi}{\partial \theta^2} = \frac{1}{c^2} \frac{\partial^2 \varphi}{\partial t^2}$$

then

$$\frac{1}{R} \frac{\partial^2 R}{\partial r^2} + \frac{1}{rR} \frac{\partial R}{\partial r} + \frac{1}{r^2 \Theta} \frac{\partial^2 \Theta}{\partial \theta^2} = \frac{1}{c^2 T} \frac{\partial^2 T}{\partial t^2} \qquad (1)$$

Hence, the variables are separable and the equations are

$$r^2 \frac{\partial^2 R}{\partial r^2} + r \frac{\partial R}{\partial r} + \left[\frac{r^2 \omega^2}{c^2} - n^2 \right] R = 0 \qquad (2)$$

Bessels equation, order n, parameter $\lambda = \dfrac{\omega}{c}$

$$\frac{\partial^2 \Theta}{\partial \theta^2} + n^2 \Theta = 0 \quad [\text{periodicity as } f(\theta)] \qquad (3)$$

$$\frac{\partial^2 T}{\partial t^2} + \omega^2 T = 0 \quad [\text{periodicity as } f(t)] \qquad (4)$$

General Solution

$$\varphi = \{ C \epsilon^{in\theta} \} \times [J_n(\lambda r) + BN_n(\lambda r)] \epsilon^{i\omega t} \qquad (5)$$

293

where n must be an integer since solution must be periodic with period 2π in θ.

Consider the radial displacement $R(r)$; assuming that the displacements are finite inside the cylinder $B \equiv 0$.

Thus

$$\varphi = C \epsilon^{i n \theta} \, J_n (\lambda r) \, \epsilon^{i \omega t} \tag{6}$$

Furthermore

$$u_r = C \epsilon^{i n \theta} \, \frac{\partial}{\partial r} \, J_n(\lambda r) \, \epsilon^{i \omega t}$$

On the wall of the cylinder $r = b$ and $u_r = 0$, so that

$$C \epsilon^{i n \theta} \frac{\partial}{\partial r} J_n (\lambda r) \quad \epsilon^{i \omega t} = 0$$

$$r = b$$

and we obtain the equation

$$[- \frac{n}{b} \, J_n(\lambda b) + \lambda J_{n-1}(\lambda b)] = 0 \tag{7}$$

for the eigenvalues λ_{nm}. The corresponding eigenfrequencies are given by

$$\omega_{nm} = \lambda_{nm} c$$

For $n = 0$ we obtain

$$\lambda J_{-1} (\lambda b) = 0 \,, \quad \lambda b = 0 \,, 3.85 \,, 7.0 \,, 10.2 \,, \dots \,,$$

giving

$$\omega_{01} = 0$$

$$\omega_{02} = \frac{3.85\,c}{b}$$

$$\omega_{03} = \frac{7.0\,c}{b}$$

$$\omega_{04} = \frac{10.2\,c}{b}$$

etc.

The eigenvalue ω_{01} is meaningless since $\lambda_{01} = 0$ and $u_r = 0$.

For $n = 1$ the equation $J_1\,(\lambda b) = \lambda b\,J_0\,(\lambda b)$,

and

$$\lambda b = 1.84,\, 5.35,\, 8.55$$

So that

$$\omega_{11} = \frac{1.84\,c}{b}$$

$$\omega_{12} = \frac{5.35\,c}{b}$$

$$\omega_{13} = \frac{8.55\,c}{b}$$

For $n = 2$

$$-\frac{2}{b}\,J_2(\lambda b) + \lambda J_1(\lambda b) = 0 \quad \text{or} \quad J_2(\lambda b) = \frac{\lambda b}{2}\,J_1(\lambda b)$$

$$\therefore \lambda b = 3.05,\, 6.7,\, 9.95$$

$$\omega_{21} = \frac{3.05\,c}{b}$$

$$\omega_{23} = \frac{9.95\,c}{b}$$

For $n = 3$

$$-\frac{3}{b} J_3 (\lambda b) + \lambda J_2 (\lambda b) = 0 \quad \text{or} \quad J_3 (\lambda b) = \frac{\lambda b}{3} J_2 (\lambda b)$$

$$\therefore \lambda b = 4.2, 8.0, 11.4$$

$$\omega_{31} = \frac{4.2c}{b}$$

$$\omega_{32} = \frac{8.0c}{b}$$

$$\omega_{33} = \frac{11.4c}{b}$$

Hence, resonant modes of oscillation are expected to occur at the following frequencies:

$$\omega_{nm} = M_{nm} \left(\frac{c}{b} \right) = \frac{c}{b} M_{nm}$$

where

$$M_{nm} = 1.84, 3.05, 3.85, 4.2, 5.35, 6.7, 7.0, \ldots$$

Note that

$$\varphi_{nm} = C_{nm} \, \epsilon^{i n \theta} J_n \left(\frac{\omega_{nm}}{c} r \right) \epsilon^{i \omega_{nm} t}$$

and

$$\varphi = \sum \varphi_{nm}$$

The pressure at any point in the cavity is expressed by

$$p = -\rho \frac{\partial^2 \varphi}{\partial t^2} = \rho \sum_{n,m} \omega_{nm}^2 \, \varphi_{nm}$$

$$= \sum_{n,m} \epsilon^{i n \theta} P_{nm} (r) \epsilon^{i \omega_{nm} t}$$

296

where

$$P_{nm}(r) = C_{nm} \rho \, \omega^2_{nm} \, J_n \left(\frac{\omega_{nm}}{c} \, r \right)$$

Fig. 2 is a plot of the nondimensional pressures

$$P_{nm} = \frac{P_{nm}(r)}{C_{nm} \rho \, \omega^2_{nm}} = J_n \left(\frac{\omega_{nm}}{c} \, r \right)$$

Each mode creates pressure pulsations phased as shown in Fig. 3. The magnitude of each modal pulsation depends upon the value of C_{nm} which in turn is dependent upon the input excitation and the dissipation of energy. This analysis is limited to conservative system (no dissipation).

Acknowledgment

The work described in this paper was conducted in the Fluidics Department of the Aerospace Research Center, General Precision, Inc., Little Falls, New Jersey, as part of a company independent research and development program.

References

[1] "Proceedings of the Fluid Amplification Symposium Diamond Ordnance Fuze Laboratory," Washington, D.C., October 1962.

[2] "Proceedings of the Fluid Amplification Symposium," Harry Diamond Laboratories, Washington, D.C., May 1964.

[3] "Proceedings of the Fluid Amplification Symposium," Harry Diamond Laboratories, Washington, D.C., October 1965.

[4] C. A. Coulson, "Waves," Interscience Publishers 1958.

[5] M. Redwood, "Mechanical Waveguides," Pergamon Press 1960.

A Pressure Insensitive
Fluidic Temperature Sensor

Carl R. Halbach
Ben A. Otsap
Richard A. Thomas

The Marquardt Corporation
Van Nuys, California

Abstract

A fluidic temperature sensor is described which has been demonstrated with heated air. The sensor uses the frequency beating technique and a detector network to generate an analog pressure signal proportional to a difference in frequencies. The frequency difference in turn is proportional to the square root of the gas temperature. An oscillator, used as the temperature sensitive element, generates a frequency signal from the coupling of two resonance tubes. Frequency is converted into an analog pressure signal using a pulse modulation technique.

Data are presented and discussed for heated air test conditions which simulate a typical metal vapor application. These data, for temperatures from 530 to 751 R, demonstrate a temperature measurement error of ± 0.3 percent.

Introduction

This paper discusses the results of the first phase of a two-phase program for the development of a fluidic temperature sensing system for high temperature application in nuclear environments [1]. One use of this application is for temperature measurements in metal vapor nuclear power systems.

Various concepts utilizing pneumatic oscillators in temperature sensing systems have been previously reported (Refs. [2] through [6]). In the work of Refs. [3] through [6], the oscillators operate on the principle of acoustic coupling of edgetone frequencies with cavity resonance frequencies. Another technique, discussed in [7], [8] and [9], utilizes the sonic delay time in negative feedback loops of bistable amplifiers to generate the frequency signal.

The oscillator presented in this paper differs from those previously reported in that two resonant tube frequencies, one open and the other effectively closed, are coupled in the oscillator. The open tube also provides feedback to enhance self-excitation and improve the signal strength of the oscillator. This technique results in an oscillator which is theoretically insensitive to the pressure of the resonant fluid.

FLUIDIC TEMPERATURE SENSOR CONCEPT

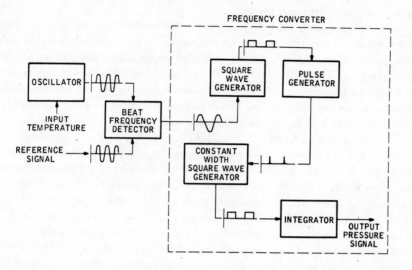

FIG. 1 – FLUIDIC TEMPERATURE SENSOR CONCEPT

The temperature sensing system reported in [2] makes use of phase shifts with a phase discriminator network to convert the oscillator frequency into a useful analog output pressure. The present system utilizes a signal differentiation and constant pulse integration technique to effect the digital to analog conversion. While similar in some respects to the approach used by Gottron and Gaylord [3], the frequency converter described in this paper developes a high gain signal without power staging over a frequency range of 90 cps.

System Concept

The fluidic temperature sensor concept is shown in Fig. 1. The temperature sensitive element which senses the fluid temperature is the acoustic resonator or oscillator. The oscillator output frequency signal is compared to a reference frequency signal by a beat frequency detector. The output of the beat frequency detector is a large amplitude difference frequency with a superimposed small amplitude sum frequency. In addition, small amplitudes of the oscillator and reference frequencies can result when the amplitudes of the detector input signals are mismatched. These low amplitude signals, considered noise, are at a higher frequency than the difference frequency and are removed by a low pass filter.

Following the detector is a frequency converter network. Fig. 1 shows the elements of the converter in which the filtered detector output signal is converted to an analog output pressure signal. The operation of the converter is as follows. The detector output sine-like wave is converted to a square wave with a bistable amplifer and the square wave in turn is differentiated producing a pulse (spike) in the second bistable amplifier. The pulse is employed in a third digital amplifer with fixed time-constant to generate a constant width square wave. Finally, the constant width square waves are integrated to produce the analog output pressure

299

signal. Employing a differentiating stage in the converter circuit produces an output signal (spike) which is independent of the input level of the square wave. This effectively de-couples the constant width square wave generator resulting in optimum square wave amplitude.

The beat frequency technique is used to improve the resolution of the temperature sensor system. Improvement in temperature measurement resolution results from an optimization of the frequency coverter performance when using the beat frequency signal. The pulse modulation frequency converter has a useful frequency ranging from zero to its saturation frequency. Saturation occurs when the frequency, in cps, is equal to the inverse of the effective width, in seconds, of the constant width square waves. As a numerical example, consider a case where the oscillator ranges in frequency from 1000 to 1200 cps. If a single oscillator (no reference) is to be used, a frequency converter capable of operating from 0 to 1200 cps will be required and will be used over one-fifth of its maximum range. On the other hand, if a 1000 cps constant reference frequency is used for frequency beating, a frequency converter capable of operating from 0 to 200 cps will be required and will be utilized over its full range. Thus, a factor of 5 improvement in resolution is afforded by the beat frequency approach.

Another advantage of beating two frequencies lies in the flexibility of temperature measurement range offered with respect to limited frequency converter capabilities. Reference frequencies can be used with sensitivities ranging from zero, as for the system discussed in this paper, to a theoretical sensitivity of 0.5 as used by Kelly [2]. Sensitivity is taken as the percent change in frequency relative to a percentage change in temperature. Consider the relationship given by

$$f = kT^n \tag{1}$$

where f is frequency, k is a constant of proportionality, T is the temperature, and n is the sensitivity. For the theoretical acoustic resonator the sensitivity is 0.5. For actual oscillators, sensitivity may vary from the theoretical value depending on the type of resonator and the proportions of the critical geometries.

The following numerical example will demonstrate the flexibility possible with frequency beating given a frequency converter characteristic. Consider a beat frequency ranging from 20 to 100 cps and a constant reference frequency (sensitivity of zero) of 500 cps. A temperature ratio of 1.33 is possible and could correspond to a temperature range of from 1000 to 1330 R. On the other hand, a temperature ratio of 25 is possible by beating two oscillators both having theoretical sensitivites of 0.5. This would correspond to a temperature range of from 200 to 5000 R. In this case, the proportionality constants of the oscillators would be chosen such that a 20 cps difference frequency would result at 200 R.

Operating Fluid Consideration

Fig. 2 depicts a typical application of the fluidic temperature sensor. The sensor is shown as it would be installed in the vapor inlet line to a power system turbine. Vapor bled from the inlet line and returned to the exhaust line is used to operate the sensor in this application.

System design criteria were established on the basis of temperature sensing in a turbine inlet line as depicted in Fig. 2. Conditions typical of a potassium vapor

Rankine-cycle space power system were considered. These design criteria included a temperature ratio of 1.4 corresponding to potassium vapor temperatures from 1660 to 2310 R and inlet pressure from 20 to 100 psia.

The effect of potassium vapor properties on the temperature sensor system performance were considered analytically. Two properties of potassium vapor, the sonic velocity and the enthalpy, affect the temperature sensor design. For a non-perfect gas, sonic velocity is a function of pressure as well as temperature. Since the frequency of the oscillator is proportional to the potassium vapor sonic velocity, it is thus somewhat dependent on inlet pressure as well as temperature.

A second pressure effect which will affect temperature sensor performance with potassium vapor occurs as a result of the expansion process through the oscillator inlet nozzle. The fluid to be sensed is expanded through the nozzle into the resonance chambers. The resonance chambers respond to the expanded fluid rather than the fluid external to the temperature sensor.

Total enthalpy is constant during the expansion process through the oscillator inlet nozzle. For a perfect gas, such an expansion results in a decrease in pressure inside the oscillator, but does not affect the gas total temperature. This follows from the perfect gas specific heat being constant. The total enthalphy change is found from the integral

$$H_2 - H_1 = \int_1^2 C_p \, dT \qquad (2)$$

where stations 1 and 2 represent the stagnation conditions upstream and downstream of the inlet nozzle, respectively. For H_2 equal to H_1 in Equation (2) and

FLUIDIC TEMPERATURE SENSOR APPLICATION

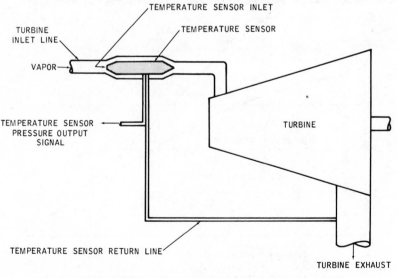

FIG. 2 – FLUIDIC TEMPERATURE SENSOR APPLICATION

a constant and finite value of the specific heat C_p, dT must be zero and total temperature is constant. With potassium vapor, the constant pressure specific heat is not a constant, rather

$$C_p = C_p \ (P, T) \tag{3}$$

A constant total enthalpy expansion of potassium vapor across the oscillator inlet nozzle results in a total temperature drop. The sonic velocity within the oscillator is thus affected by the inlet nozzle expansion. This effect is minimized by operating the oscillator at a high internal to inlet pressure recovery. A trade-off occurs here since the oscillator frequency signal amplitude decreases as the oscillator internal to inlet pressure recovery increases.

An analysis was conducted to determine the extent of these pressure effects on oscillator frequency. Due to the frequency corresponding to potassium vapor properties internal to the oscillator, the temperature sensed by the fluidic temperature sensor would be in error relative to the true temperature external to the oscillator. The solid curve in Fig. 3 indicates the magnitude of this error for an inlet pressure variation from 20 to 100 psia. The error is systematic and is seen to depend on the oscillator internal to inlet pressure recovery.

Another factor to be considered in examining the effects of potassium vapor properties on temperature sensor performance is heat transfer. Since total temperature internal to the oscillator is lower than the external total temperature, a gradient for heat transfer into the oscillator from the external fluid environment exists. The dashed curve in Fig. 3 shows the combined effects of a variation in inlet pressure on the systematic error using potassium vapor as a working fluid and typical heat transfer conditions.

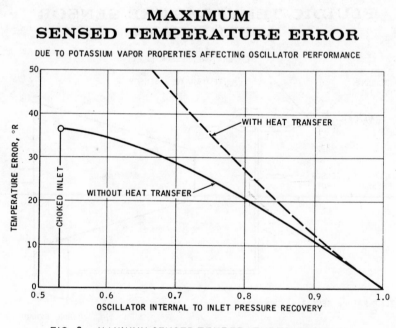

MAXIMUM
SENSED TEMPERATURE ERROR

DUE TO POTASSIUM VAPOR PROPERTIES AFFECTING OSCILLATOR PERFORMANCE

FIG. 3 – MAXIMUM SENSED TEMPERATURE ERROR

Fig. 3 shows that the oscillator should be sized for high internal pressure recovery operation when used with potassium vapor. For example, with an oscillator pressure recovery of 90 percent, the error in sensed temperature due to uncompensated pressure effects (20 to 100 psia) is 12 R. At a potassium vapor temperature of 2000 R, this is a systematic error of 0.6 percent.

The fluidic temperature sensor can be operated directly in gases and vapors; however, by employing a secondary fluid (gaseous or vaporous) and a heat exchanger, the sensor can be used in solids and liquids. The sensor can be embedded in the medium whose temperature is to be sensed. A heat exchanger forming an integral part of the temperature sensor package would heat the secondary fluid (air for instance) to the temperature of the surrounding medium. The temperature of the secondary fluid would in turn be measured by the temperature sensor.

Components Description

The oscillator used in this investigation and depicted by Fig. 4 is self excited and pressure insensitive. Flow from the inlet ports is expanded through the inlet nozzle toward the knife edge. The flow is divided by the knife edge and flows through a feedback resonance channel and an output resonance channel. Either the output resonance channel flow or flow tapped from the feedback resonance channel can be used as a signal as shown in Fig. 4.

With proper proportioning of the output and feedback resonance channels, a stable oscillation in pressure occurs within the oscillator as well as in output flow from the oscillator. This oscillation is harmonic with a frequency corresponding essentially to the natural frequency of the coupled resonance channels. The oscillator will operate stably over a considerable (±50 percent) variation in the proportions of the output and feedback resonance channel lengths, however, optimum performance occurs when the feedback channel length is about twice the output channel length. The output nozzle opening is small compared to the output

SELF EXCITED, PRESSURE INSENSITIVE, FLUIDIC OSCILLATOR

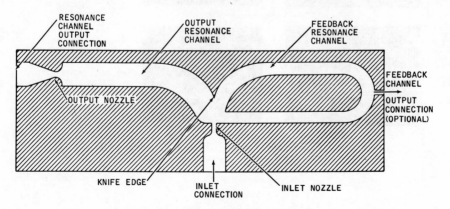

FIG. 4 – SELF EXCITED, PRESSURE INSENSITIVE, FLUIDIC OSCILLATOR

PRESSURE INSENSITIVE OSCILLATOR

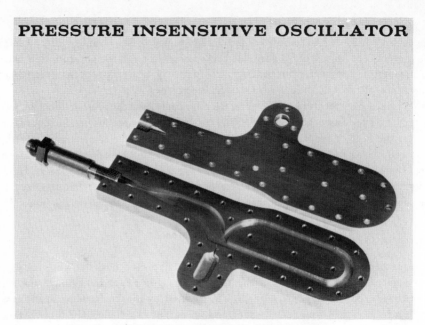

FIG. 5 – PRESSURE INSENSITIVE OSCILLATOR

FREQUENCY BEATING WITH
PNEUMATIC SIGNALS

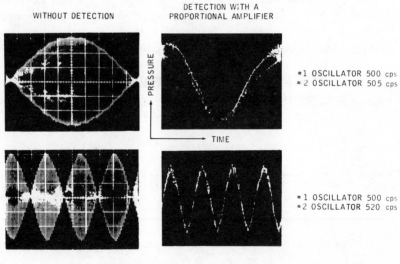

WITHOUT DETECTION

DETECTION WITH A
PROPORTIONAL AMPLIFIER

PRESSURE

TIME

#1 OSCILLATOR 500 cps
2 OSCILLATOR 505 cps

#1 OSCILLATOR 500 cps
#2 OSCILLATOR 520 cps

FIG. 6 – FREQUENCY BEATING WITH PNEUMATIC
SIGNALS

channel cross section; the output resonance channel thus behaves acoustically like a closed resonance tube. On the other hand, the feedback channel is open at both ends and would appear acoustically to be an open resonance tube. These tubes are coupled with their nodes, one for the output channel and two for the feedback channel, coincident in the region of the inlet nozzle and knife edge. The signal outputs are taken at the corresponding antinodes.

A prototype oscillator is shown in Fig. 5. This oscillator has a feedback resonance channel length of 9.5 in. and an output resonance channel length of 6.1 in. The resonance channel cross section changes from two dimensional to axisymmetric. In an integrated fluidic system, the oscillator channels would be everywhere two dimensional. Size reduction is possible by coiling the output and feedback channels. Since signal frequency is inversely proportional to the oscillator size, operation at a maximum frequency minimizes size.

Since the frequency signal of the oscillator is that of the coupled resonances, it is relatively insensitive to inlet pressure. The oscillator can be operated with the output nozzle flow subsonic or sonic. Sensitivity of signal frequency to inlet pressure is a minimum with a sonic (choked) output nozzle, however.

A beam deflection proportional amplifier was used for the beat frequency detector. Two oscillator signals (one a reference) can be combined on one side of the detector and opposed by a constant bias, or they can be applied to the detector in an opposing manner. While both methods are effective, the latter is acoustically simpler. Fig. 6 shows data for two typical beat frequency cases. These are photographs of oscilloscope traces with detector output pressure on the ordinate versus time on the abcissa. Pressure amplitude is 0.67 psi/cm. The envelopes on the left hand side occur when the two oscillator signals are combined without a beat frequency detector. The right hand traces show the detector output corresponding to the same oscillator condition.

The frequency converter consisted of 3 bistable Corning units as shown in Fig. 7. The first unit converts the beat frequency into a variable width square wave at the same frequency. The second unit acts as a differentiator to obtain a pulse for every positive half cycle of the square wave. The final unit acts as a constant width square wave generator. Integration of the constant width square wave yields an analog pressure proportional to the beat frequency.

Breadboard Description

The breadboard fluidic temperature sensor system is shown in Fig. 8. The feedback resonance channel of the oscillator was tapped for impedance matching to a beam deflection proportional amplifier. This amplifier, which serves as the beat frequency detector, is seen in the lower left hand corner of Fig. 8 with the vent region enclosed (canned) for an intermediate vent pressure. On the far left hand side is the reference frequency input connection.

The remaining elements are 2X size Corning elements vented to ambient. These include the three bistable amplifiers represented in Fig. 7 plus one proportional amplifier to interface the beat frequency detector with the frequency converter.

Fig. 9 is a silhouette of the temperature sensor system similar to the breadboard but including second generation improvements. Four levels of fluidic elements are shown which would be stacked and spaced with other levels (not shown)

FREQUENCY CONVERTER
TEST SETUP

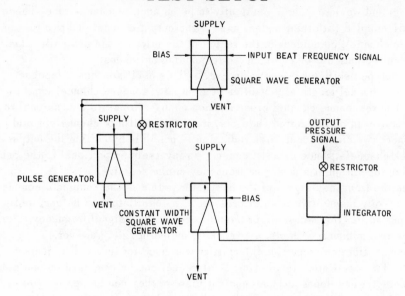

FIG. 7 – FREQUENCY CONVERTER TEST SETUP

FLUIDIC TEMPERATURE SENSOR
SYSTEM BREADBOARD

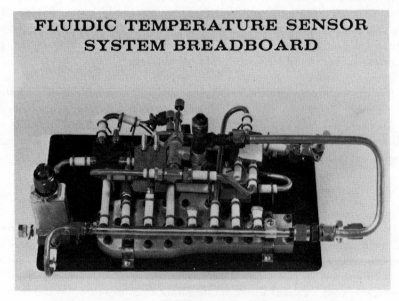

FIG. 8 – FLUIDIC TEMPERATURES SENSOR SYSTEM
BREADBOARD

FLUIDIC TEMPERATURE SENSOR
SILHOUETTE

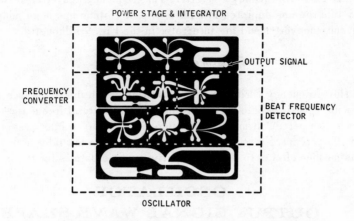

POWER STAGE & INTEGRATOR

OUTPUT SIGNAL

FREQUENCY
CONVERTER

BEAT FREQUENCY
DETECTOR

OSCILLATOR

FIG. 9 – FLUIDIC TEMPERATURE SENSOR SILHOUETTE

OSCILLATOR PERFORMANCE
COLD FLOW FREQUENCY

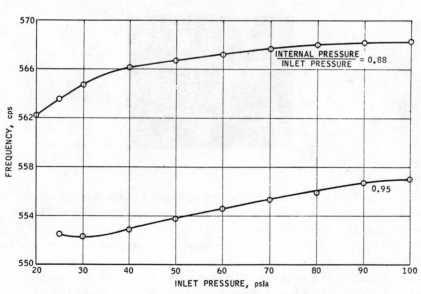

$\dfrac{\text{INTERNAL PRESSURE}}{\text{INLET PRESSURE}} = 0.88$

0.95

FREQUENCY, cps

INLET PRESSURE, psia

FIG. 10 – OSCILLATOR PERFORMANCE

containing supplies, vents and interconnecting channels. The output nozzle of the oscillator is used for a signal and connects to one side of a centered receiver proportional amplifier which performs the beat frequency detection. The beat frequency detection network includes a second amplifier stage and a signal conditioner stage for the frequency converter. The frequency converter network is essentially like the one depicted in Fig. 7. A power stage has been added between the frequency converter and the integrator in the Fig. 9 silhouette.

Experimental Performance

Cold flow frequency variation of the oscillator with inlet pressure is shown in Fig. 10 with a partial scale on the ordinate. Sensitivity of frequency to inlet pressure is one percent from 20 to 100 psia for internal to inlet pressure recoveries of 88 and 95 percent. No attempt was made to optimize the inlet and output nozzle Reynolds number effects to reduce sensitivity. This data is for the oscillator

OSCILLATOR
OUTPUT SIGNAL WAVE SHAPE

INLET PRESSURE = 60 psia
FREQUENCY = 526 cps
SIGNAL TO INLET PRESSURE RECOVERY = 0.94
SIGNAL AMPLITUDE = ± 2.6 psia
WORKING FLUID - AIR

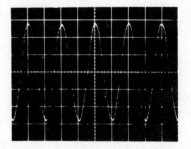

FIG. 11 – OSCILLATOR OUTPUT SIGNAL WAVE SHAPE

shown in Fig. 5 with a feedback to output resonance channel length ratio of 1.56. The oscillator was also operated with an optimum resonance channel length corresponding to a feedback channel twice as long as the output channel. Sensitivity of frequency to inlet pressure for the optimum geometry was one percent for inlet pressure from 10 to over 100 psia.

The output signal from the oscillator is shown in Fig. 11. This is a photograph of an oscilloscope trace from a pressure transducer flush mounted in the output resonance channel close to the output nozzle. The output pressure signal on the ordinate versus time along the abcissa in Fig. 11 is seen to be sinusoidal with a high signal to noise ratio.

The frequency-temperature relationship of the oscillator depends on the geometry. In particular, it depends on the proportions of the resonance channels and the location and impedance of the output signal connection. For the oscillator shown in Fig. 5 with an output signal tap in the feedback channel (as shown in Fig. 4), frequency was found to be proportional to temperature to the 0.45 power. Thus Equation (1) becomes,

$$f = 31.31 \ T^{0.45} \tag{4}$$

The output signal strength of the oscillator depends on the oscillator internal to inlet pressure recovery. For example, the ratio of a.c. signal amplitude to inlet pressure varies from 0.04 to 0.06 ±psi/psia for pressure recoveries of 0.95 and 0.88, respectively.

During the development of the oscillator, noise was introduced at the oscillator inlet connection to determine if the oscillator could be forced into overtones. Noise consisting of an a.c. pressure variation was superimposed onto the inlet pressure using an electrodynamic driver. Frequencies of from 50 to 5000 cps were introduced into an oscillator operating at 500 cps. The amplitude of the simulated noise varied from 10 to 30 percent of the oscillator a.c. output signal amplitude. This simulated noise did not cause an eigenfrequency shift. At most, the frequency shift was less than 0.2 percent. The two worst cases corresponded to noise frequency at one-half and three times the oscillator output frequency.

A subsystem demonstration was performed on the frequency converter with a constant amplitude, constant d.c. level, variable input frequency signal. The data recorded are shown in Fig. 12 and include operation at three different temperatures with air as the working fluid. While the effect of temperature on the frequency converter is about 20 percent of the output signal it is not detrimental to the temperature sensor system steady state performance. A transient error could result, however, if the oscillator response differs from the response of the fre-

FREQUENCY CONVERTER CHARACTERISTIC

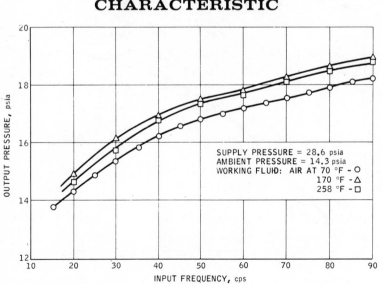

FIG. 12 – FREQUENCY CONVERTER CHARACTERISTIC

309

quency converter during thermal changes. This effect may be minimized by integrating the entire temperature sensor into one package immersed in the substance whose temperature is being measured. Referring to the Fig. 2 application, the temperature sensor shown includes the oscillator, the beat frequency detector and the frequency converter networks. The vapor flow is around the sensor package and serves to increase the thermal response of the temperature sensor package. Frequency converter temperature sensitivity is then absorbed into the temperature sensor system calibration. Fortunately, the temperature sensitivity of the frequency converter introduces an additive effect which results in increased overall system temperature sensitivity.

The fluidic temperature sensor system performance is shown in Fig. 13. These data are for runs made on three consecutive days to demonstrate the temperature measurement repeatability of the sensor. The temperature sensor was operated with air from 530 to 751 R corresponding to a temperature ratio of 1.4. This temperature ratio corresponds to the typical space power system application mentioned previously. Inlet pressure was held constant at 28.6 psia and the inlet to exhaust pressure ratio was 2.0.

The scatter in the data of Fig. 13 is within ±2 R or within ±0.5 percent. The error in the measurement of the output pressure was ±0.1 percent and measured thermocouple temperature error was ±0.25 percent. Combining these statistically, it appears that the temperature measurement error of the fluidic temperature sensor is less than ±0.3 percent.

The data in Fig. 13 was obtained with the breadboard sensor (Fig. 8). No power stages were used after the constant width square wave generator. The integrator was passive and consisted of a resistive filter and a capacitance. Yet the output signal is seen in Fig. 13 to span more than 5 psi over the range of oper-

FLUIDIC TEMPERATURE SENSOR
SYSTEM PERFORMANCE

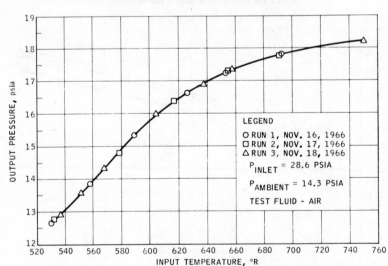

FIG. 13 – FLUIDIC TEMPERATURE SENSOR SYSTEM
PERFORMANCE

ation of the sensor. The data of Fig. 13 cover a beat frequency from 17.3 cps at 530 R to 106.5 cps at 751 R. The average output signal gain is high at 0.06 psi/cps. Thus, the pulse modulation frequency converter signal gain and accuracy is exceptionally high for such a simple fluidic network.

System Accuracy

The temperature sensor system demonstration with a perfect working fluid (air) and a constant inlet pressure indicated an error of ± 0.3 percent for a sensed temperature ratio of 1.42. Effectively, this error includes the statistical sum of the random errors of the oscillator and frequency converter. There is no error associated with the beat frequency detector since the beat frequency is exactly the difference frequency between the oscillator signal and reference signal frequency.

Considering operation with a pressure variable over a 4 to 1 range, additional estimated sensed temperature errors include the following:

1) 0.5 percent (systematic) due to oscillator pressure sensitivity.
2) 0.5 percent (systematic) due to frequency converter pressure sensitivity.
3) ± 0.3 percent (random) due to inlet to exhaust pressure ratio variations.

Combining the above values statistically, the estimated error for a temperature sensor using a perfect working fluid with a variable inlet pressure becomes 1.0 percent systematic plus or minus 0.4 percent random. The systematic portion of the error is an inlet pressure effect. Considering potassium vapor as the working fluid with an oscillator internal to inlet pressure recovery of 0.90, an estimated additional systematic error of 0.6 percent results. For this case the system error in sensed temperature becomes 1.6 percent systematic plus or minus 0.4 percent random.

Conclusions

A simple pressure insensitive fluidic temperature sensor has been demonstrated which is suitable for direct temperature measurement in gases and vapors. By using a secondary fluid, temperature sensing can be extended to liquids and to solid substances.

The sensor utilizes a pressure insensitive oscillator which generates a stable sinusoidal pressure signal from the coupling of two resonance tubes. The oscillator can be operated at high internal to inlet pressure recoveries to minimize the non-perfect gas effects encountered with potassium vapor. A pulse modulation type of frequency converter is employed in the sensor system which uses three bistable amplifiers and generates a high gain output pressure signal.

A breadboard temperature sensor system using air from 530 to 751 R at constant inlet pressure demonstrated a temperature measurement error of ± 0.3 percent.

References

[1] Halbach, C. R., Otsap, B. A. and Thomas, R. A., "Fluidic (Pure Fluid) Temperature Sensor," AEC Research and Development Report SAN 639-7 January 1967, prepared under AEC Contract AT(04-3)-639.

[2] Kelly, L. R., "A Fluidic Temperature Control Using Frequency Modulation and Phase Discrimination," Joint Automatic Control Conference, 123-131, Seattle, Washington, August 1966.

[3] Gottron, R. N. and Gaylord, W., "A Temperature Control System Using Flueric Components," Proceeding of the Third Harry Diamond Laboratories Fluid Amplification Symposium, Vol. III, 244-265, October 1965.

[4] Erickson, D. S., et al, "Feasibility Studies of Advanced Pneumatic Techniques for Control of Turbojet Engine," AFAPL TR 65-27, May 1965 (CONFIDENTIAL Report).

[5] Gottron, R. N. and Gaylord, W., "A Temperature Sensing Pneumatic Oscillator," Harry Diamond Laboratories Report No. TR 1244, May 4, 1964, (CONFIDENTIAL Report).

[6] Gottron, R. N. and Gaylord, W., "Design Considerations of the HDL Pneumatic Temperature Sensor," Harry Diamond Laboratories Report No. TR-1273, February 19, 1965 (CONFIDENTIAL Report).

[7] Spyropoulos, C. E., "A Sonic Oscillator," Proceedings of the Second Harry Diamond Laboratories Fluid Amplification Symposium, Vol. II, 27-52, May 1964.

[8] Warren, R. W., "Negative Feedback Oscillator," U.S. Patent No. 3,158,166, November 24, 1964.

[9] Reeves, D., Inglis, M.E. and Airey, L., "The Fluid Oscillator as a Temperature Sensor," Proceedings of the First International Conference on Fluid Logic and Amplification, Cranfield, England, September 1965.

Acknowledgment

This study was sponsored by the United States Atomic Energy Commission and technically administered by the Division of Reactor Development and Technology, located at Germantown, Maryland under Contract No. AT(04-3)-639.

Pneumatic Diaphragm Logic

D. F. Jensen
H. R. Mueller
R. R. Schaffer

IBM Corporation
System Development Division
Endicott, New York

Abstract

This paper presents the basic concepts of a diaphragm element developed to meet the digital logic requirements of data processing equipment. The functions of the device and its switching phenomena are discussed in relationship with pneumatic logic and circuit requirements. Several logic functions and integrated logic circuits are discussed in depth to show how these elements are combined to produce monolithic integrated pneumatic logic circuitry.

Nomenclature

A	= Total Diaphragm Area
A_1	= Upstream Diaphragm Area
D	= Delay Element, Delay Time
P_A	= Atmospheric Pressure
P_c	= Control Pressure
P_h	= High Pressure Pulse
P_k	= Input Pulse from Strobe Circuit, Fig. 17
$P\ell$	= Low Pressure Pulse
P_o	= Output Pressure
P_s	= Supply Pressure
$P_1, (P_2)$	= Pressure Upstream (Downstream) of Ridge
P_{s1}, P_{s2}	= System Timing Pulses (Figs. 17, 18)
R	= Impedance

313

$R_1, (R_2)$ = Up-(downstream) Impedance (Fig. 1)

T_H, T_L = Switching Times, T_H for High Control Input, T_L for Low Control Input

Introduction

Since the birth of the data processing industry, electronics has enjoyed an un-challenged position in the fields of logic, sensing, and control. Pneumatics has been used mainly for cooling the electronics or supplying power amplification at the mechanical interface. Within the past few years, however, a new technology has been developed that allows the design of entire digital pneumatic systems employing low-pressure air to perform the logic, sensing, and control functions.

Conventional pneumatic devices such as spool valves have been used suc-cessfully in specific control applications [1], [2] at low speeds for a number of years. However, the rather recent upsurge of interest in this area was triggered by work being done on the pure fluid amplifier [3], [4] at the Harry Diamond Lab-oratories in Washington, D.C. Although the general fluid phenomena of stream interaction and wall attachment were observed as early as 1932 by Coanda [5], the addition of control jets to modulate or deflect a main jet stream to achieve amplification or "on-off" control and its application to logic were not seriously considered until 1960. One of the motivations behind the development of the pure fluid amplifier was its potential ability to overcome deficiencies of existing energy systems operating in extreme temperature, radiation, shock, and vibration environments. Special purpose jet devices and circuits were developed to perform a limited amount of logic for these critical applications. As the work on this de-vice matured, it became apparent that although the wall attachment amplifier ap-pears to be a simple device, its performance depends on a wide range of inter-dependent geometric parameters and complex fluid flow phenomena.

The lack of suitable analytical techniques to predict their performance, coupled with dynamic interaction of these components, hampered applications to general digital circuitry. When an effort was made to extend these principles to meet the economic objectives and general purpose logic criteria for commercial data processing equipment, the additional considerations of reproducibility, pack-aging, logic capability, and air consumption of the jet amplifier overwhelmed its former advantages of insensitivity to environment and no moving parts. However, the fluid amplifier was responsible for a technological breakthrough that stimu-lated the development of a wide array of fluid devices and pointed the way to new and exciting possibilities of fluid systems.

This paper presents the basic concepts of a new diaphragm element that was developed to meet the digital logic requirements of commercial data processing equipment. The requirements of a family of logic functions and considerations for combining these functions to implement digital circuitry formed the guidelines for the development of the diaphragm element. Several logic functions and circuits will be discussed in depth to show how these elements are combined to perform specific logical operations.

314

The Diaphragm Element

The logic device developed from this work (Fig. 1) utilizes a thin flexible membrane to control the flow of air over a ridge. Air under pressure flows through the device by deflecting the diaphragm upward, thereby allowing a passage area between the diaphragm and the ridge. This flow, however, can be blocked by the presence of air pressure in the control chamber above the diaphragm, causing a downward deflection that closes the passage. Therefore, air flow through the diaphragm-type pneumatic logic device is controlled in a manner analogous to the control of electrical current through a triode by a grid voltage, thus permitting circuits to be built up of diaphragm devices that duplicate many electronic logic circuits.

The element is designed such that elastic forces, due to displacement of the diaphragm, are small compared to the pressure forces acting on the diaphragm. Thus, the switching behavior of the device depends on the relative pressure across the diaphragm rather than the absolute supply pressure. This "pure pressure control" mode of switching, coupled with natural isolation of the control ports by the diaphragm, serves to enhance the interconnection capability, fan-in/fan-out, and minimize power consumption, thereby making feasible the implementation of low-cost general purpose pneumatic logic circuitry. Furthermore, these considerations imply that the Reynolds number, close control of geometric parameters, and fluid properties such as viscosity and density have only a secondary effect on the operation of the element.

Introducing restrictions up and downstream of the ridge permits the basic element to be used as either an amplifier or an inverter depending on whether the output is taken up or downstream of the ridge. With the condition being considered in which the diaphragm above the ridge is open, the impedance to flow over the ridge is designed to be small compared with the restrictors R_1 or R_2 so that the outputs P_1 and P_2 are substantially equal and depend only on the relative values of R_1 and R_2. As P_c increases, thereby blocking the flow across the ridge, P_1 increases to P_s (amplified output) and P_2 decreases to atmospheric pressure (inverted output).

Inverter Function

When the basic element is used in the inverter mode (Fig. 2), the downstream restrictor R_2 is generally made larger than R_1 so that the output P_o is greater than $1/2 \, P_s$. In order for switching to occur, the force exerted by P_c above the diaphragm must become equal to the total upward force of P_1 and P_o on A_1 and A_2 respectively. Thus, since P_1 and P_o are substantially equal, the switching occurs when

$$P_c = P_o = \frac{R_2}{R_1 + R_2} \, P_s \tag{1}$$

(on the 45 degree line in Fig. 2).

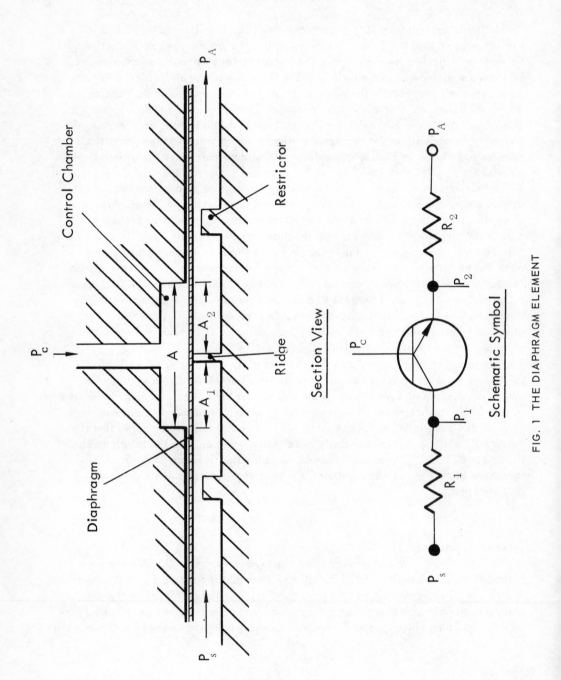

Control Chamber

Restrictor

P_C

P_S

P_A

A

A_2

A_1

Ridge

Diaphragm

Section View

P_S — R_1 — P_1 — P_C — P_2 — R_2 — P_A

Schematic Symbol

FIG. 1 THE DIAPHRAGM ELEMENT

316

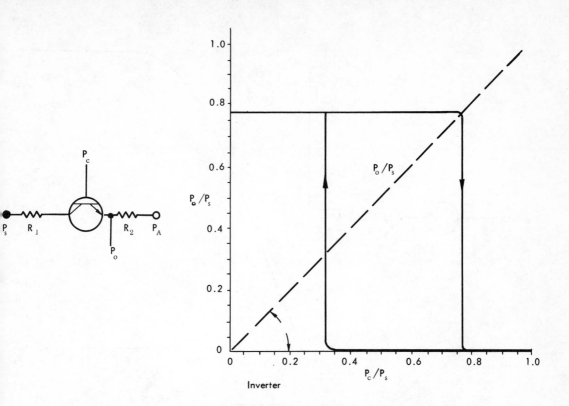

FIG. 2 INVERTER ELEMENT

Hence, the basic inverter has no gain. Once the diaphragm is seated against the ridge, there is no flow so that the switch open point depends only on the relative areas A_1 and A_2. The control pressure P_c must decrease until

$$P_c A = P_s A_1$$

or

$$P_c = P_s \left(\frac{A_1}{A} \right) \qquad (2)$$

Fig. 2 shows a hysteresis loop in the switching curve. For hysteresis to occur the switch closed point must be greater than the switch open point, or

$$\frac{R_2}{R_1 + R_2} > \frac{A_1}{A} \qquad (3)$$

The effective area ratio, A_1 / A for this element was about 0.3 and the restrictor ratio $R_2 / R_1 + R_2$ was 0.8.

Thus, the output is digital, only high or low, and the switching between states is a "snap action." The trace shows a slight rounding of P_o prior to the switch closed and switch open points. This rounding off in the switch closed point is due to the fact that as P_c nears the equilibrium value, the net upward force on the diaphragm, while still positive, has decreased so that the deflection over the ridge is less, thereby slightly increasing the ridge impedance. At the switch open point, as P_c decreases, the sealing force decreases and some flow begins to leak into the output.

317

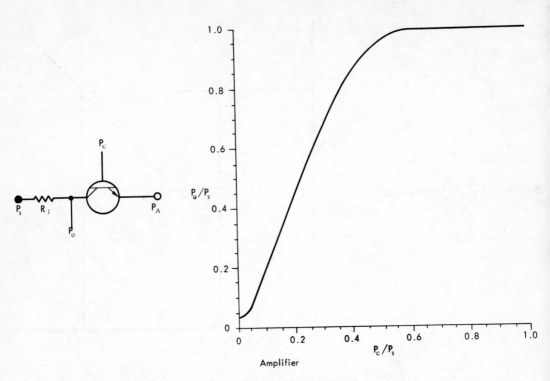

FIG. 3 AMPLIFIER ELEMENT

Amplifier Function

In the amplifier mode (Fig. 3) the restrictor R_2 is small compared with R_1 so that the pressure drop from P_s to atmospheric pressure occurs primarily across R_1, and when no control pressure is applied, the output is nearly zero. With the assumption of negligible elastic forces, the diaphragm will deflect to maintain a balance between the forces $P_c A$ and $P_o A_1$. Thus,

$$P_o \sim P_c \frac{A}{A_1} \tag{4}$$

The output P_o is therefore, nearly linearly related to the input P_c with an amplification factor A/A_1. The output of such a device, with an effective area ratio A/A_1 of 2.2 is also shown in Fig. 3. The nonlinearity at the low pressure is due to the fact that when the pressure forces are very low, the elastic forces of the diaphragm are no longer negligible. A more rigorous treatment of the static operating characteristics of the diaphragm element is given by Jensen [6].

Push Pull Function

In the inverter and amplifier described above, the restrictors R_1 and R_2 tend to limit the power transfer capability. In addition, these devices are sensitive to the impedance of the load. While this may be acceptable for integrated logic circuits where fan-out is limited and the loads are high impedance, in general it is advan-

318

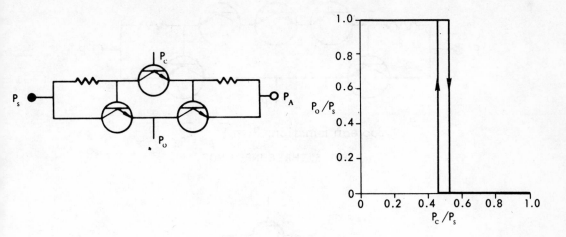

FIG. 4 PUSH-PULL INVERTER

tageous to have a device with low output impedance (good drive capability) which is insensitive to the loading conditions. To achieve such characteristics, a push-pull amplifying stage (shown in Fig. 4) was added to the basic element. In this case, the restrictors R_1 and R_2 were made equal so that $P_1 = P_2 = 1/2 \ P_s$ with the diaphragm open. The upstream push-pull ridge was made with an area ratio (A_1/A) of about 0.8 and the downstream ridge has an area ratio of about 0.2. Thus, with $P_c = 0$, the upstream ridge is open and the downstream ridge is closed and the output P_o is connected directly to P_s. When P_c is greater than $1/2 \ P_s$ the control diaphragm closes, thereby raising P_1 to P_s and dropping P_2 to zero. Now the upstream diaphragm closes and the downstream diaphragm opens connecting the output to the atmosphere. It should be noted that there are no restrictors in the push-pull stage and the output is completely isolated from the control stage. In addition, no stand-by power is consumed by the push-pull stage since one of the two ridges is closed at all times except during switching.

In order to provide the logical NOR function (Fig. 5) several ridge elements are connected in series in the control stage with the push-pull stage retained as in the inverter. There is a limitation on the number of series ridges that can be used in the push-pull configuration since the pressure drop through the combination of ridges must remain small, compared with the drop through restrictors R_1 and R_2. NOR circuits with fan-in of four have been operated successfully. The NAND function (Fig. 6) is provided by a parallel arrangement of ridge elements in the control stage. A large number of inputs can be provided in the NAND without affecting its static performance; however, the use of a large number of inputs increases the volumes to be charged (internal capacitance) so that switch times may be affected. NAND circuits with fan-in of up to six have been constructed with no significant increase in switch times.

An obvious extension of the NAND and NOR push-pull circuits is the use of hybrid logic in which mixed parallel and series arrangements of ridge elements are used in the control stage of a push-pull circuit. These hybrid circuits can be designed for a specific application and have significant economic and speed ad-

319

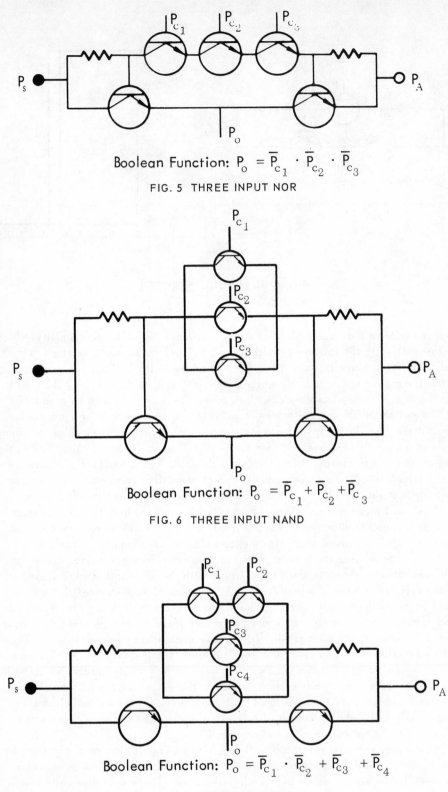

Boolean Function: $P_o = \bar{P}_{c_1} \cdot \bar{P}_{c_2} \cdot \bar{P}_{c_3}$

FIG. 5 THREE INPUT NOR

Boolean Function: $P_o = \bar{P}_{c_1} + \bar{P}_{c_2} + \bar{P}_{c_3}$

FIG. 6 THREE INPUT NAND

Boolean Function: $P_o = \bar{P}_{c_1} \cdot \bar{P}_{c_2} + \bar{P}_{c_3} + \bar{P}_{c_4}$

FIG. 7 HYBRID CIRCUIT

320

vantages over the use of pure NAND-NOR circuitry since one hybrid circuit can perform the function of several NAND or NOR circuits. An example of such a hybrid circuit is shown in Fig. 7.

Latch Function

With the ability to perform the NAND or NOR functions, a latch or memory element may be constructed by suitable interconnection. If push-pull NANDs or NORs are used, the memory will have the characteristics of the push-pull circuits described above. In cases where fan-out is limited and the low output impedance of the push-pull is not required, a simple memory element (Fig. 8) is used. This memory consists of a ridge element which is designed with a large hysteresis zone. The switch closed point is 0.8 to 0.9 P_s and the switch open point is 0.2 to 0.3 P_s. Hence, two stable outputs exist at a control pressure of 0.5 P_s. In order to construct a memory element, a control stage is added with equal up and downstream restrictors so that $P_1 = 0.5\ P_s$. The latch is controlled by placing ridge elements between the upstream restrictor and P_1 and between P_1 and the downstream restrictor. When P_{SET} is raised above $1/2\ P_s$, P_1 drops to zero and opens the output of the latch element to 0.8 P_s (state I in Fig. 8); the latch remains open after P_{SET} is returned to zero. If P_{RESET} is raised $1/2\ P_s$, P_1 will rise to P_s, the latch will close (state II), and P_o will go to zero and remain there after P_{RESET} is dropped. The controlling ridge elements may be replaced with series or parallel arrangements of ridges to provide multiple or gated set and reset features. This hysteresis latch has the particular advantage that no significant output will occur when an input of insufficient duration is used to set the latch; whereas in a feedback latch, such as a NAND or NOR latch, self-sustained oscillation can occur if the input is shorter than the feedback delay time.

Power Consumption

An important advantage obtained in the use of diaphragm devices is their relatively low power consumption. In a push-pull element the flow is determined by the size of the restrictors in the intermediate stage. In the steady-state case, when the control pressure is low, the flow rate is approximately 700 cc/min at 1 psi supply pressure, which leads to a power consumption of 0.075 watt called stand-by power (Fig. 9). When control pressure varies between zero and supply pressure, the power consumption changes due to the dynamic flow delivered at the output stage. This flow is consumed at the output stage by the compressibility of the air in the lines and the displacement of the control diaphragm at the end of the transmission line. Since the upper push-pull diaphragm cannot close until the lower one has opened, flow is momentarily discharged to the atmosphere. Also, when the control pressure is high, the air in the output stage is discharged through the lower push-pull element. Therefore, the output power consumption of the control stage drops to a value close to 1/2 the stand-by power, because the flow is interrupted about half the time. Fig. 9 shows the power consumption as a function of frequency of a typical push-pull element with a 3/16 in. ridge and a fan-out of 1. From this curve it is possible to estimate the maximum power consumption of a system with reasonable accuracy when the duty cycle of the various logic blocks are known.

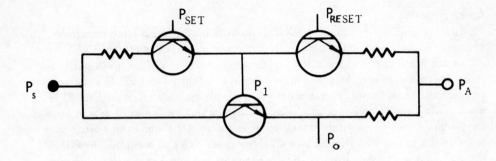

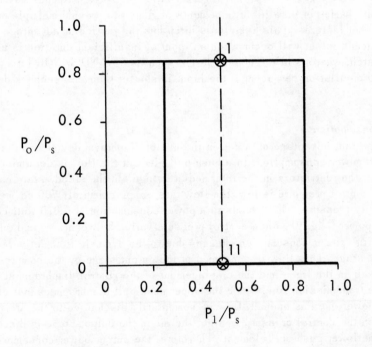

FIG. 8 HYSTERESIS LATCH

322

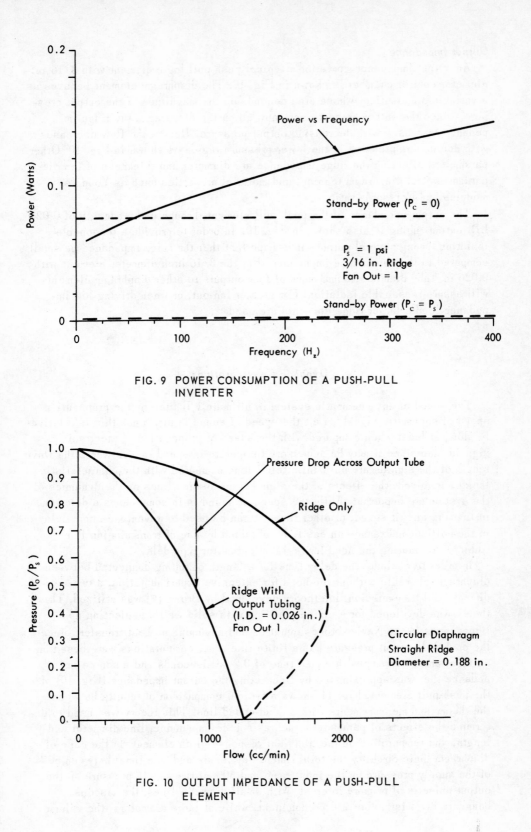

FIG. 9 POWER CONSUMPTION OF A PUSH-PULL
INVERTER

FIG. 10 OUTPUT IMPEDANCE OF A PUSH-PULL
ELEMENT

323

Output Impedance

An output impedance curve for a typical push-pull logic element with 3/16 in. diameter control chamber is shown in Fig. 10. The diaphragm element behaves as a variable area orifice, whose area depends on the magnitude of the output pressure. Since the output pressure acts upward on the diaphragm, the ridge impedance increases with decreasing output pressure. Hence, the flow decreases with decreasing pressure in the lower pressure region as shown in Fig. 10. Other parameters affecting the ridge impedance are diameter and thickness of the diaphragm, initial diaphragm tension, and material properties such as Young's modulus and Poisson's ratio.

The output impedance of the push-pull element through a short length of 0.026 I.D. output tubing is also shown in Fig. 10. In order to provide a reasonable isolation among several outputs it is important that the ridge impedance be small compared to the output tube impedance. For the 3/16 inch diameter element with 0.026 in. tube diameter, a maximum of four outputs to other diaphragm elements will assure reasonable isolation. For greater fan-out, or when driving low impedance loads, larger ridge elements are used.

Dynamic Considerations

The speed of any pneumatic system is ultimately limited by the propagation speed of pneumatic signals, i.e., the speed of sound in air. Since this is relatively slow, at least when compared with the speed of propagation of electronic signals, and since it may be necessary to operate in speed ranges where the wave length of the signals are not "infinitely" long compared with the characteristic lengths involved, the effects of the signal transmission lines on the dynamics of the system are important. While the speed of sound is in some cases a deterrent in limiting circuit speed, at other times it can be used to advantage since delays in the millisecond range can easily be obtained by use of transmission lines (tubing) eliminating the need for resistor/capacitor type delays.

In order to evaluate the delay time for a length of tubing connected between diaphragm elements without the need for extensive experimentation, a two-dimensional transmission line theory developed by Brown [7] was utilized. This theory was developed for a cylindrical line with solid walls, neglecting non-linear terms in the Navier-Stokes equation and assuming no heat transfer. Since the push-pull output pressure has a finite rise time, computations were based on an input pressure ramp with a rise time of 0.2 milliseconds and a source impedance that was approximated by linearizing the output impedance (Fig. 10) of the push-pull element. Fig. 11 shows a typical comparison of results between the theory and measurements with a dead-ended line. This theory was used to determine the effects of parameters such as source impedance, line diameter and length, and temperature on the transient response of an element. In the case of diaphragm logic circuitry the total time delay (sonic and rise time) between 50% of the supply pressure on the input ramp and 50% of the supply pressure on the output pulse is of primary interest. With small diameter lines, the viscous boundary layer terms become predominant, while at large diameters, the volume

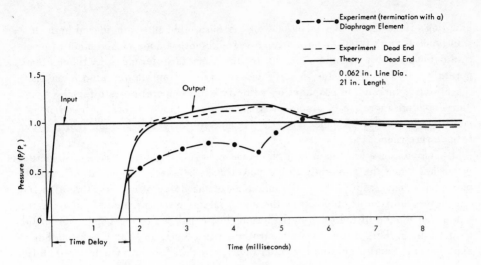

● ● ● Experiment (termination with a) Diaphragm Element

– – – Experiment   Dead End
——— Theory   Dead End

0.062 in. Line Dia.
21 in. Length

FIG. 11   PRESSURE PULSES IN PNEUMATIC
TRANSMISSION LINE

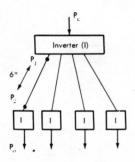

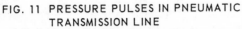

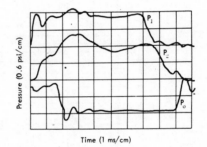

· 3/16 in. Ridge
Tube Diameter 0.026 in.

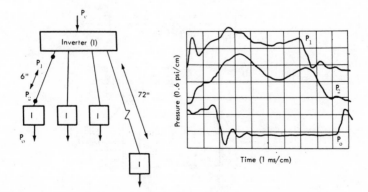

FIG. 12   INVERTER – TRANSMISSION LINE RESPONSE

charging effect of the line is large. For the logic elements considered here, it was found that an 0.035 in. diameter line represents a good compromise to obtain minimum delay and insensitivity to line diameter tolerances. Although temperature influences both the density and viscosity of air, it was also found that the effect of increasing propagation velocity with temperature is offset by a corresponding increase in viscosity with the result that the total delay time as measured by 60% of the pulse rise time remains relatively constant over a wide temperature range.

If many outputs are taken from the same element, the delay times will increase somewhat since the push-pull output power must be shared among all of the outputs. This undesirable effect, the changing of the delay of one transmission line due to the addition of others from the same output, was minimized by making the output impedance of the push-pull element low compared to the impedance of the output tubing. This effect is demonstrated quite clearly in Fig. 12 which shows experimental results obtained from an inverter with a fan-out of four six-inch lines

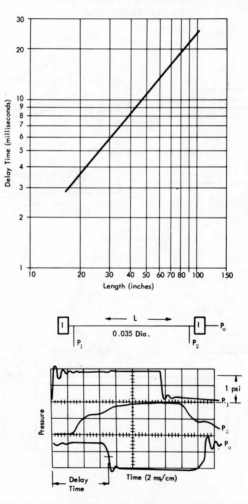

FIG. 13 EXPERIMENTAL TRANSMISSION DELAY TIME

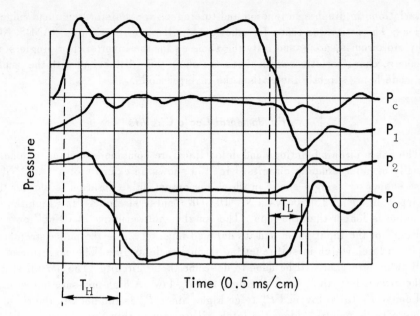

FIG. 14 SWITCHING TIME FOR PUSH-PULL ELEMENT

compared with a case where one of the lines is considerably longer (72 in.). It is obvious that the influence of the 72-inch line on the transient response of the six-inch line is negligible and the outputs are quite independent.

The above results were obtained for a pneumatic transmission line terminated by a dead end. If the termination is at the control chamber of another diaphragm element, the transient behavior of the line is affected. The effect of a diaphragm termination compared with a dead end is also shown in Fig. 11. The dip in the pressure is caused by the sudden motion of the diaphragm when the critical switch pressure is reached. The two curves start to deviate before the snap action starts due to the slight motion of the diaphragm under increasing control pressure. Calculations as well as experiments have shown that the control volume at the end of a transmission line can be increased several times before the rise time is considerably affected since the change in flow caused by the diaphragm motion is much greater than the compressibility of the air in the control volume.

Since nonlinear termination introduces considerable complexity into the transmission line analysis, a numerical analysis of the transmission and source/ termination effect is required before a complete analytical model is available. Fig. 13 shows an experimental curve which gives the delay time as a function of tube length. This curve is most useful in the design of pneumatic circuits.

An oscillogram showing the dynamic switching of a push-pull inverter circuit is shown in Fig. 14. With switching time defined as the time interval between $0.5\,P_s$ on the control pressure and $0.5\,P_s$ at the output, the characteristic switch times are 1.3 millisecond for high going control input (T_H), and 1.0 millisecond for low going control input (T_L). Variations of ±20 per cent can be expected due

327

to variations in diaphragm tension and tolerances for resistor sizes and ridge locations. The switching times for other push-pull circuits, such as NANDS, NORS, or hybrid circuits, are essentially the same as for the inverter. For single stage elements, characteristic switch times are about 0.5 millisecond with the amplifier mode being slightly faster than the inverter mode.

Fundamental Logic Circuits

The basic circuit functions and delay lines are combined together to generate a family of pulse-shaping circuits. Fig. 15a shows an example of a NAND/NOR pulse shaper or "single shot" in which the output pulse duration is shorter than the input, and Fig. 15b shows a NAND/NOR "pulse stretcher" in which the output pulse is longer than the input. The single shots employ "ANDing" or "ORing" of the input pulse and its delayed inverse, while the pulse stretchers employ a latch which is self-resetting through a delay line. The operation of the NOR pulse stretcher will be used to describe these circuits. The normal state of the circuit is with P_c low, P_1 high, and P_o low. A high-pressure pulse at P_c will cause P_1 to go low and P_o to go high. Since P_o is fed back to the ridge in series with the control ridge, the latch will remain in this "set" condition (after the pressure pulse at P_c is completed) until P_o reaches the input to the second stage through the delay line and resets the latch. Hence, a short input pulse results in an output pulse, the duration of which is determined by the delay D. A NAND or NOR latch can now be obtained by removing the delay line D from the pulse stretcher. The set input is now at P_c while the reset input is at the second stage. To obtain a gated latch, additional control ridges are added in series or parallel with the setting ridge (Fig. 15c). In some applications it is necessary to obtain an output pulse during both the rise and fall of an input signal such as "double-ended" single shot as shown in Fig. 15d. The input and its delayed inverse are used as the inputs to an EXCLUSIVE OR circuit whose conditions are satisfied during the delay time interval D after both the rise and the fall of the input, and the circuit gives outputs during these times. These simple logic circuits demonstrate the technique of circuit implementation using diaphragm-type pneumatic logic devices. It will be shown in the next section how complex functional circuits were designed which contain many of these fundamental circuits on a single chip.

Integrated Logic Functions

In applications where the modes of operation are reasonably well-defined, it is advantageous to integrate the logic into functional chips to minimize the number and length of interconnections and realize the maximum logic circuit speed. To further reduce interconnections, the push-pull stage is omitted and replaced by an amplifier where the fan-out is low (three or less, depending on speed requirements) and the interconnection line is short. Push-pull elements are generally used when the fan-out is greater than one or with delay lines to ensure that the output lines will remain uncoupled. In some cases where large fan-out (greater than four) is needed, the normal 3/16-in. ridge of the push-pull element

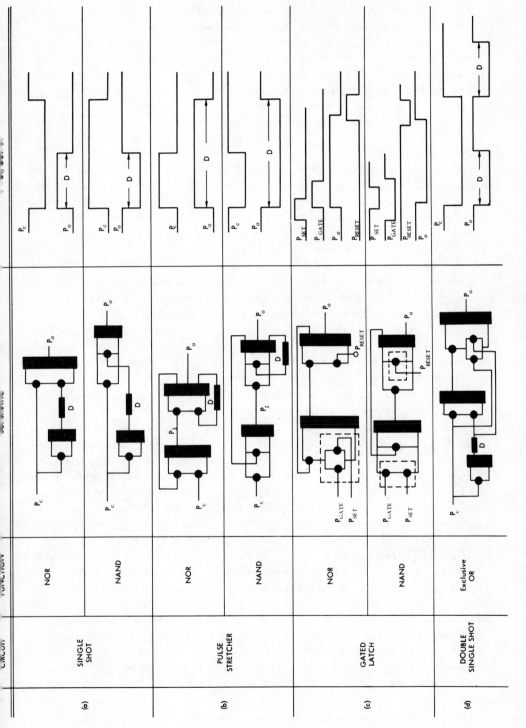

FIG. 15 BASIC LOGIC CIRCUITS

329

is replaced by a 4/16-in. ridge to further reduce the drive impedance. Also, where the fan-out from a latch is limited and interconnection occurs on the same chip, the hysteresis latch is used because of its small size and fast switching time. Whenever both the "0" and "1" outputs are needed from the latch or large fun-out is important, a NAND or a NOR latch is used. These considerations coupled with element performance and transmission line effects form the basis for development of integrated pneumatic logic circuitry. The following sections contain a description of some examples of combinational and sequential logic circuits that have been constructed with diaphragm elements.

Synchronizer Circuit

The synchronizer circuit is a good example to illustrate the combining of basic logical functions as well as the timing of a circuit where the switching times of elements are an important consideration. The fundamental problem considered is to accept an input signal at random time and to produce a corresponding output in a fixed time relationship with a system timing pulse, i.e., to bring an asynchronous input into synchronism with a machine cycle. The logic required to provide this operation includes a device for storing the input until the output is given (memory circuit described in next section), and a decision-making circuit that will determine in which machine cycle the output will be given (synchronizer circuit). For example, if the input comes too late to produce an output in the present cycle, then it must produce an output in the next cycle; however, two outputs must never be produced from a single input. It is necessary, of course, that the system cycle rate be higher than the maximum rate of the incoming information to guarantee at least one system pulse for each input pulse.

A schematic diagram of the synchronizer circuit is shown in Fig. 16. The input pulse is denoted by P_k while system timing pulses are denoted by P_{s1} and P_{s2} (see Fig. 18). For each input P_k, the circuit must produce an output P_o that is in a fixed time relationship with the system pulse P_{s2}. In this circuit, a hysteresis latch is used to decide whether an input comes early enough to produce an output in the present cycle. This is done by gating input P_k to the latch with P_{s1}. If P_k and P_{s1} coincide long enough to set the hysteresis latch, an output will occur which will set the NAND latch and hold the information until it is gated out of the NOR pulse stretcher by P_{s2}. If the overlap of P_{s1} and P_k is insufficient to set the hysteresis latch, the NAND latch is set through D_2, #1 NAND, and D_3. The sum of the delays through D_2, #1 NAND and D_3 is sufficient to ensure that the NAND latch is not set before the P_{s2} pulse is completed. Therefore, the output P_o will not occur until the P_{s2} pulse occurs in the next cycle. #1 NAND is gated by the hysteresis latch output so that if the hysteresis latch is set, the branch through #1 NAND becomes ineffective. In both cases the NAND latch is reset by the output of #2 NAND through delay D_6. Additions to the basic circuit described above are a NOR pulse stretcher at the input to allow the processing of short input pulses, and a hybrid NOR circuit that provides an output to reset the latches in the memory circuit after the information has been processed.

This circuit was designed to operate up to 125 cycles per second with a maximum strobe input cycle rate of 110 cps. Since these rates are comparatively high for a pneumatic logic circuit, the switching times of the individual elements are

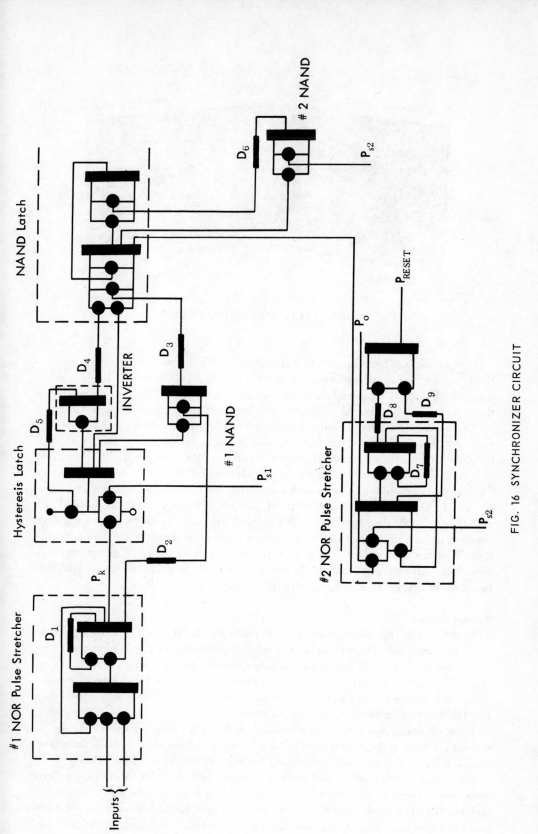

FIG. 16 SYNCHRONIZER CIRCUIT

331

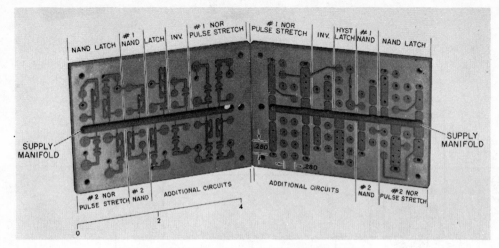

FIG. 17 INTEGRATE SYNCHRONIZER CHIP

very important and become an integral part of the circuit design. It was conserva-
tively assumed that the switching time for a push-pull element was 1.2–1.5 ms
with a high control input and 1 ms with a low control input. The switching time of
the hysteresis latch (fan-out of three) was assumed to be approximately 1.5 ms.

The actual functional circuit chip design is obtained by drawing the diaphragm
elements, shown in schematic form in Fig. 16, on a grid structure so that all of
the input and output connections are on one side of the chip (Fig. 17). Provision
is also made to externally connect coiled "spaghetti" lines for delay elements.
Then a "master" block is machined containing the control cavities, ridges, supply manifolds, and interconnection lines from which replica chips are molded or
cast (Fig. 17). A diaphragm is bonded to each half and the two halves are joined
together to form the integrated synchronizer logic chip. Therefore, by means of
this technique, a relatively cheap injection mold can be used to mass produce a
monolithic integrated logic chip. This chip can be "wired" by means of spaghetti
in a manner similar to electronic circuit components.

Memory Circuit

In order to accept information asynchronously, a buffer facility must be provided to temporarily store or delay the input information for the synchronizer circuit. This section describes a double-stage memory circuit using the hysteresis
latch (Fig. 18). A double-stage memory is used to allow the input rate to be as
close as possible to the machine cycle rate since a second input may appear before the processing of the first input is complete.

Each incoming character to the memory produces a strobe pulse, which conditions the first stage of the memory to accept the information, and also sends a
strobe pulse to the synchronizer circuit for processing. When the synchronizer
output is completed, the second memory is reset, and the information in the first-
stage memory can be transferred to the second stage as soon as a new strobe has
arrived. Both the strobe and the reset pulse set up a latch. When both are set the
transfer pulse is initiated. A pulse stretcher is used at the output of the second

332

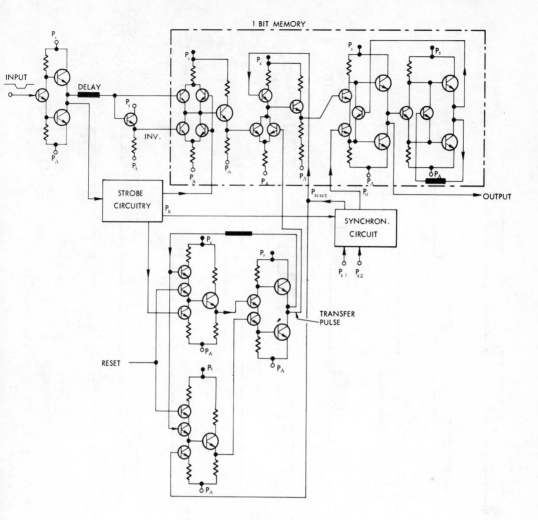

FIG. 18 MEMORY CIRCUIT

stage to keep the sync input pulse as short as possible (minimum pulse length is determined by the switching time of the latch single shot). The transfer of new information into the second stage can thus be executed before the output pulse to the processor ends. This feature is essential for high input speeds, due to the delay between an incoming pulse and the synchronizer output pulse. The timing diagram shown in Fig. 19 illustrates the timing relationship of the memory circuit coupled to the synchronizer circuit.

Binary Counter

The use of hybrid logic elements for performing the latching function results in a relatively simple up and down binary counter. By using an input pulse of fixed time duration, only one latch per stage is required, and the second memory is replaced by delay lines which store information during the counting interval.

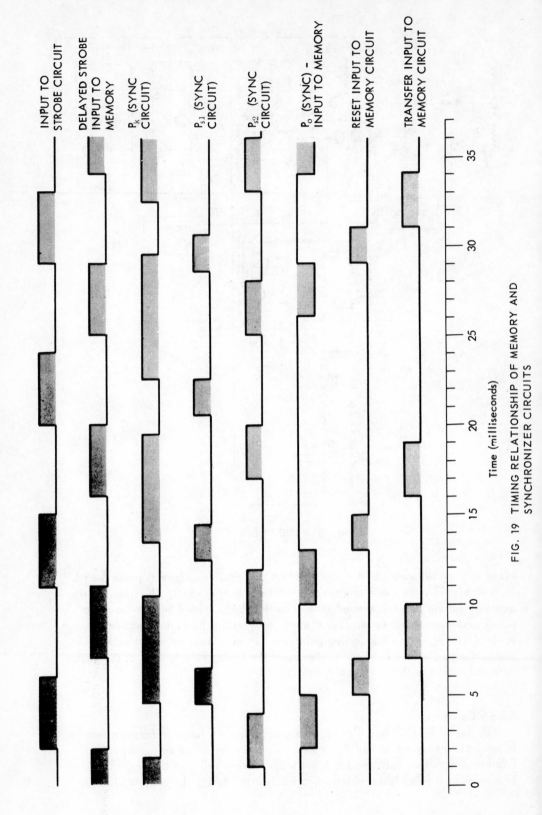

FIG. 19 TIMING RELATIONSHIP OF MEMORY AND
SYNCHRONIZER CIRCUITS

334

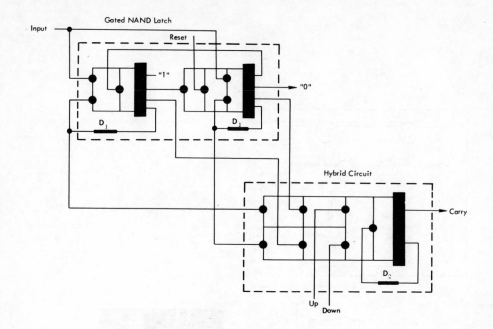

FIG. 20 BINARY UP/DOWN COUNTER

In the counter circuit shown in Fig. 20 the input line is connected to both sides of a gated NAND latch. The "1" output gates the reset pulse while the "0" output gates the set pulse; hence, each input pulse causes the first stage to change state. Delays D_1 are used to hold the previous information at the gating elements until the input pulse is complete. The hybrid logic element produces an input pulse to the second stage when a carry is required in up-counting or when a borrow is required in down-counting. This element contains a single shot to produce a fixed length input pulse to the next stage.

The binary counter circuit may be modified to provide an adding/subtracting accumulator for serial addition or subtraction of binary numbers or for use in binary multiplication. These modifications consist of providing additional inputs in parallel with the normal inputs at each stage and delaying the borrow or carry pulses until after completion of the input pulse.

Character Recognition Circuit

Frequently it is necessary to detect significant characters in data processing to perform certain programming operations. The character recognition circuit shown in Fig. 21 demonstrates the advantageous combination of simple elements in which the push-pull stage has been omitted, resulting in a reduction in size and an increase in circuit speed. The low-pressure control inputs P_ℓ are ANDed in a NOR element and the high-pressure inputs P_h are ANDed in a NAND element. One push-pull element is used in the NOR single shot to obtain good fan-out and drive capability.

335

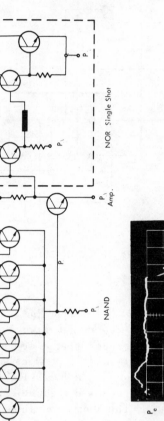
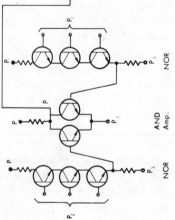

Input/Output Oscillogram   Time: 2 ms/cm

FIG. 21 CHARACTER RECOGNITION CIRCUIT

Reliability Considerations

Considerations of the reliability of a pneumatic system for commercial data processing applications must include component life, ability to function in prescribed environments, and the ability to mass produce with high yield rates. Since the diaphragm logic element utilizes the flexing of an elastic diaphragm, the fatigue life of the material must be considered. Extensive life testing of hundreds of elements has shown that life exceeding hundreds of millions of operations can easily be achieved.

The environmental insensitivity of the diaphragm device can certainly not be expected to approach that of pure fluid devices. On the other hand, extensive testing has shown that the diaphragm element can function properly over the range of temperature, humidity, vibration, and shock required of commercial data processing equipment. The problem of particulate matter contamination is no more severe than for pure fluid devices since the smallest passages, the orifice restrictions, are of the order of 0.020 in. which is comparable to the nozzle sizes proposed for fluid jet amplifiers. Experience has shown that filtration adequate for reliable operation for many thousands of hours can easily be obtained at reasonable cost.

It is in the area of reproducibility in production that the diaphragm element has a significant advantage over pure fluid devices. The operation of the diaphragm device depends on no complex flow phenomena so that Reynolds number, close control of geometric parameters and fluid properties are of secondary importance. Indeed, dimensional tolerances are of the order than can easily be obtained by inexpensive production methods such as injection molding. In addition, the desirable characteristics of low output and high input impedances enhance interconnection and fan-out capability thereby increasing the reliability of complex pneumatic systems since impedance matching considerations are minimized.

Summary

The basic concepts of the diaphragm device have been discussed with particular emphasis on its use as a digital logic element. It was shown that the inherent characteristics of high input and low output impedance simplify interconnection problems and allow the design of complex integrated circuitry. Also, the versatility and logic capability of the diaphragm device were demonstrated by the wide array of logic and circuit combinations attainable with this element. Furthermore, the ability to overcome both the speed limitations of traditional moving-part devices as well as the power consumption of pure fluid amplifiers, greatly enchance the potential applications of the diaphragm element in the commercial data processing field. Finally, the relatively simple injection-molded chip and diaphragm assembly provide a reliable, low-cost logic package that can be conveniently coupled into pneumatic systems.

Acknowledgments

The authors wish to acknowledge the contributions of M. R. Noll and Dr. R. E. Norwood to the diaphragm technology. The excellent technical work of E. F. Helinski and D. H. Rickenbach in assembling and testing the circuits is also gratefully acknowledged.

References

[1] E. L. Holbrook, "Pneumatic Logic I-IV," *Control Engineering*, August 1961.

[2] H. H. Glättli, "Hydraulic Logic," *Control Engineering*, May 1961

[3] R. E. Bowles, *et al*, "Fluid Amplification Without Moving Parts," National Academy of Sciences, 1960.

[4] F. T. Brown, Symposium on "Fluid Jet Control Devices," ASME, 1962.

[5] H. Coanda, "Procédé et dispositif pour faire devier, une veine fluide penetrant autre fluides," Patent No. 788, 140 (France, 1934).

[6] D. F. Jensen, "Static Operating Characteristics of Diaphragm Pneumatic Logic Devices," to be presented at the Fourth Fluidics Symposium, Chicago, Ill., May 8-10, 1967.

[7] F. T. Brown, "The Transient Response of Fluid Lines," *Journal of Basic Engineering*, Transactions ASME, series D, Vol. 84, 1962.

Static Operating Characteristics of Diaphragm Pneumatic Logic Devices

D. F. Jensen

IBM Systems Development Division
Endicott, N. Y.

Abstract

An analytical technique for predicting the static operating characteristics of the diaphragm pneumatic logic element is presented. Three common geometries are treated in detail and design curves are included. The technique is easily applied in the design of diaphragm elements for any desired characteristic within the limitations of the device.

Nomenclature

A	= flow area over ridge
A_1 , A_2	= flow area through restriction 1, 2
a	= radius of circular control chamber, length of rectangular control chamber
b	= width of rectangular control chamber
C	= orifice discharge coefficient for ridge
C_1 , C_2	= orifice discharge coefficient for restriction 1, 2
N_o	= diaphragm tension
P_1	= output pressure upstream of ridge
P_2	= output pressure downstream of ridge
P_c	= control pressure
P_s	= supply pressure
$\overline{P}$	= normalized pressure P/P_s
$(\overline{P}_1)_o , (\overline{P}_2)_o$	= values of normalized output pressures $\overline{P}_1 , \overline{P}_2$ for $\overline{P}_c = 0$

339

$\overline{P}_c^*$ = value of normalized control pressure at theoretical switch-open point

R = ridge impedance = $\dfrac{1}{CA}\sqrt{\dfrac{\rho}{2}}$

R_o = ridge impedance for $P_1 = P_2 = P_s$, and $P_c = 0$

$R_{1,2}$ = restriction 1, 2 impedance = $\dfrac{1}{C_{1,2}\,A_{1,2}}\sqrt{\dfrac{\rho}{2}}$

r = radial coordinate for cylindrical coordinate system

W = deflection of diaphragm above support plane

W_o = deflection of diaphragm at center point

X, Y = Cartesian coordinate axes

α = parameter denoting ridge position

ρ = air density

θ = angular coordinate for cylindrical coordinate system

Introduction

The diaphragm pneumatic logic element (Fig. 1) utilizes a thin, flexible diaphragm to control the flow of air over a ridge. Air under pressure can flow through the device by deflecting the diaphragm upward, thereby allowing a passage area between the diaphragm and the ridge. This flow, however, can be blocked by the presence of air pressure in the control chamber over the diaphragm, causing a downward deflection and closing the passage. Various series and parallel networks of these diaphragm elements may be utilized to perform logic and control functions [1].

A simple explanation of the effect of the diaphragm force balance on the operation of the device has been given by Jensen, Mueller, and Schaffer. [1] The purpose of this paper is to treat the mechanics problem of the pressure-loaded diaphragm with sufficient rigor to adequately describe the static operating characteristics of the diaphragm element.

It is found that, for most diaphragm elements, the static operating characteristics can be adequately described by the up and downstream restrictor ratio (R_1/R_2) and a single geometric parameter, $\overline{P}_c^*$. The physical interpretation of this parameter is the value of the normalized control pressure at the switch-open point.

The diaphragm analyses are performed under the assumption of constant and uniform diaphragm tension. This small deflection theory is justified since the parameter $\overline{P}_c^*$ is determined under the conditions of small deflection, indeed, zero deflection over the ridge.

Pneumatic diaphragm elements have been designed with various geometric configurations. Three of the more common are treated in this paper. These are: the circular ridge with concentrically circular control chamber (Fig. 2A), the straight ridge with rectangular control chamber (Fig. 2B), and the straight ridge with circular control chamber (Fig. 2C).

340

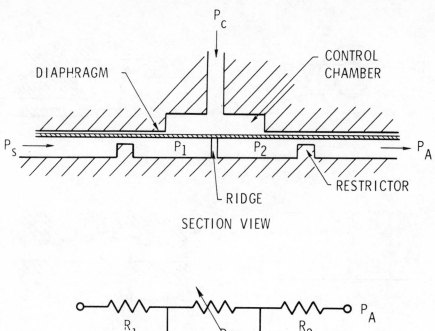

SECTION VIEW

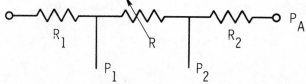

RESISTOR NETWORK

FIG. 1 THE DIAPHRAGM ELEMENT

Analysis of Static Operating Characteristics

Without becoming concerned with the details of any particular geometry, two basic equations may be stated. First assuming orifice type restrictions and incompressibility, which will be sufficiently accurate for pressures of the order 1 psi gage, conservation of flow through the element requires that

$$\frac{1}{R_1} \sqrt{P_s - P_1} = \frac{1}{R} \sqrt{P_1 - P_2} = \frac{1}{R_2} \sqrt{P_2} \qquad (1)$$

Second, the equilibrium equation [2] for the diaphragm, assuming constant and uniform tension is

$$\nabla^2 W = -\frac{P}{N_o} \qquad (2)$$

Where boundary and loading conditions must be prescribed for each particular geometry.

341

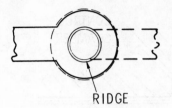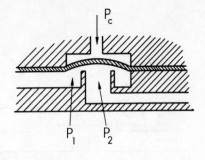

A

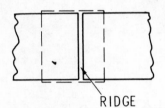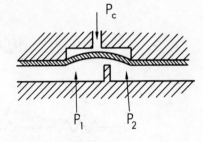

B

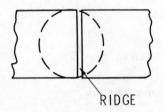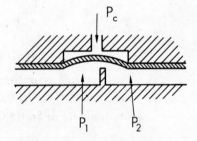

C

FIG. 2 A. CIRCULAR RIDGE, CIRCULAR CONTROL CHAMBER
B. STRAIGHT RIDGE, RECTANGULAR CONTROL CHAMBER
C. STRAIGHT RIDGE, CIRCULAR CONTROL CHAMBER

The value of the ridge impedance R required for Equation (1) is

$$R = \frac{1}{CA} \sqrt{\frac{\rho}{2}} \tag{3}$$

where

$$A = \int W ds \tag{4}$$

the integration being performed along the ridge.

Circular Control Chamber with Concentric Circular Ridge — Flow Inward

Equation (2) expressed in cylindrical coordinates may be written

$$\frac{\partial^2 W}{\partial r^2} + \frac{1}{r}\frac{\partial W}{\partial r} + \frac{1}{r^2}\frac{\partial^2 W}{\partial \theta^2} = -\frac{P(r,\theta)}{N_o} \tag{5}$$

Which, under the condition of axial symmetry, may be reduced to

$$\frac{d^2 W}{dr^2} + \frac{1}{r}\frac{dW}{dr} = -\frac{P(r)}{N_o} \tag{6}$$

In order to facilitate the solution of (6) the diaphragm will be divided into two regions: an inner region bounded by the circular ridge, and an annular region bounded on the inside by the ridge and on the outside by the control chamber. Then the net pressure load in the inner region is $(P_2 - P_c)$ and in the annular region is $(P_1 - P_c)$, and is constant in each region.

With P taken as constant the solution of equation (6) is

$$W = C_1 \ln r - \frac{1}{4}\frac{Pr^2}{N_o} + C_2 \tag{7}$$

with the boundary conditions:

Inner Region   Annular Region

$$\frac{dW_i}{dr}(0) = 0 \qquad\qquad W_o(a) = 0$$

$$W_i(\alpha) = W_o(\alpha) \qquad\qquad W_o(\alpha) = W_i(\alpha) \tag{8}$$

$$\frac{dW_i}{dr}(\alpha) = \frac{dW_o}{dr}(\alpha) \qquad\qquad \frac{dW_o}{dr}(\alpha) = \frac{dW_i}{dr}(\alpha)\ .$$

Use of (8) in (7) gives the solution for the diaphragm deflection.

$$W_i = \frac{P_s \alpha^2}{N_o}\left[\frac{\overline{P_2} - \overline{P_c}}{4}\left(1 - \frac{r^2}{\alpha^2}\right) + \frac{\overline{P_1} - \overline{P_c}}{4}\left(\frac{a^2}{\alpha^2} - 1\right) - \frac{\overline{P_1} - \overline{P_2}}{2}\ln\frac{a}{\alpha}\right]$$

$$W_o = \frac{P_s \alpha^2}{N_o}\left[\frac{\overline{P_1} - \overline{P_c}}{4}\left(\frac{a^2 - r^2}{\alpha^2}\right) - \frac{\overline{P_1} - \overline{P_2}}{2}\ln\frac{a}{r}\right]$$

$$\tag{9}$$

To determine the flow area A over the ridge, Equation (9) is evaluated at the ridge $(r = \alpha)$ and multiplied by the ridge circumference $(2\pi\alpha)$. Hence,

$$A = 2\pi\alpha W(\alpha) = \frac{\pi\alpha^3 P_s}{N_o}\left[\frac{1}{2}\left(\overline{P}_1 - \overline{P}_c\right)\left(\frac{a^2}{\alpha^2} - 1\right) - \left(\overline{P}_1 - \overline{P}_2\right)\ln\frac{a}{\alpha}\right],$$

and

$$R = \frac{N_o}{\pi\alpha^3 P_s C\left[\frac{1}{2}\left(\overline{P}_1 - \overline{P}_c\right)\left(\frac{a^2}{\alpha^2} - 1\right) - \left(\overline{P}_1 - \overline{P}_2\right)\ln\frac{a}{\alpha}\right]}\sqrt{\frac{\rho}{2}}$$

$$(10)$$

Equation (10) may now be used in (1) which may be conveniently solved for $\overline{P}_c$ to obtain

$$\overline{P}_c = \overline{P}_1 - \frac{2\ln\frac{a}{\alpha}}{\frac{a^2}{\alpha^2} - 1}\left(\overline{P}_1 - \overline{P}_2\right) - \frac{2 C_1 A_1 N_o}{\pi\alpha^3\left[\left(\frac{a^2}{\alpha^2}\right) - 1\right]P_s C}\sqrt{\frac{1 - \overline{P}_1}{\overline{P}_1 - \overline{P}_2}}$$

$$(11)$$

The equation relating the normalized control pressure $(\overline{P}_c)$ with the pressure upstream of the ridge $(\overline{P}_1)$ is obtained by using equation (1) to eliminate $\overline{P}_2$ from Eq. (11).

$$\overline{P}_c = \overline{P}_1 - \frac{2\ln\frac{a}{\alpha}}{\frac{a^2}{\alpha^2} - 1}\left(\frac{C_1 A_1}{C_2 A_2}\right)^2\left\{\left[1 + \left(\frac{C_2 A_2}{C_1 A_1}\right)^2\right]\overline{P}_1 - 1\right\}$$

$$- \frac{2 C_1 A_1 N_o}{\pi\alpha^3\left[\left(\frac{a}{\alpha}\right)^2 - 1\right]P_s C}\sqrt{\frac{1 - \overline{P}_1}{\overline{P}_1 - \left(\frac{C_1 A_1}{C_2 A_2}\right)^2\left(1 - \overline{P}_1\right)}}$$

$$(12)$$

For the downstream pressure $(\overline{P}_2)$, $\overline{P}_1$ is eliminated from (11) resulting in

$$\overline{P}_c = 1 - \left(\frac{C_2 A_2}{C_1 A_1}\right)^2\overline{P}_2 + \frac{2\ln\frac{a}{\alpha}}{\left(\frac{a}{\alpha}\right)^2 - 1}\left\{\left[1 + \left(\frac{C_2 A_2}{C_1 A_1}\right)^2\right]\overline{P}_2 - 1\right\}$$

$$- \frac{2 C_2 A_2 N_o}{\pi\alpha^3\left[\left(\frac{a}{\alpha}\right)^2 - 1\right]P_s C}\sqrt{\frac{\overline{P}_2}{1 - \left[1 + \left(\frac{C_2 A_2}{C_1 A_1}\right)^2\right]\overline{P}_2}}$$

$$(13)$$

344

To simplify these equations, two parameters will be introduced. Let R_o be the minimum ridge impedance, i.e., the impedance over the ridge under the conditions $P_c = 0$, $P_1 = P_2 = P_s$. Then from Equation (10)

$$R_o = \frac{2 N_o}{\pi \alpha^3 \left(\dfrac{a^2}{\alpha^2} - 1\right) P_s C} \sqrt{\frac{\rho}{2}} \qquad (14)$$

Next let $\bar{P}_c^*$ be that value of the normalized control pressure $\bar{P}_c$ that produces a deflection over the ridge $W(\alpha)$ of zero when $\bar{P}_1 = 1$ and $\bar{P}_2 = 0$. Equivalently, if the diaphragm is on the ridge blocking flow (so that $\bar{P}_1 = 1$, and $\bar{P}_2 = 0$), then $\bar{P}_c^*$ is the value to which $\bar{P}_c$ must decrease until the diaphragm just becomes free of the ridge. Thus, from Equation (9)

$$\bar{P}_c^* = 1 - \frac{2 \ln \dfrac{a}{\alpha}}{\dfrac{a^2}{\alpha^2} - 1} \qquad (15)$$

Now introducing R_o and $\bar{P}_c^*$ into (12) and (13) results in

$$\bar{P}_c = \bar{P}_1 \bar{P}_c^* + \frac{R_2^2}{R_1^2}\left(1 - \bar{P}_1\right)\left(1 - \bar{P}_c^*\right) - \frac{R_o}{R_1}\sqrt{\frac{1 - \bar{P}_1}{\bar{P}_1 - \dfrac{R_2^2}{R_1^2}\left(1 - \bar{P}_1\right)}} \qquad (16)$$

$$\bar{P}_c = \bar{P}_2\left(1 - \bar{P}_c^*\right) + \bar{P}_c^*\left(1 - \frac{R_1^2}{R_2^2}\bar{P}_2\right) - \frac{R_o}{R_2}\sqrt{\frac{\bar{P}_2}{1 - \left(1 - \dfrac{R_1^2}{R_2^2}\bar{P}_2\right)}} \qquad (17)$$

These equations contain no geometrical parameters other than $\bar{P}_c^*$ and R_o. For the other geometries the same equations will apply; it will be necessary only to evaluate these two parameters for each geometry.

Fig. 3 is a plot of Equation (17). For the case where the ratio R_o/R_2 is negligibly small, the initial output pressures $(P_1)_o$ and $(P_2)_o$, are equal, and from Equation (1)

$$(\bar{P}_1)_o = (\bar{P}_2)_o = \frac{1}{1 + \left(\dfrac{R_1}{R_2}\right)^2} . \qquad (18)$$

Also the control pressure required for closing is equal to the initial output pressures. The control pressure at the switch-open point is $\bar{P}_c^*$. A portion of the equilibrium curve is unstable, as indicated by the broken line, which results in the snap-action switching and the hysteresis region shown.

345

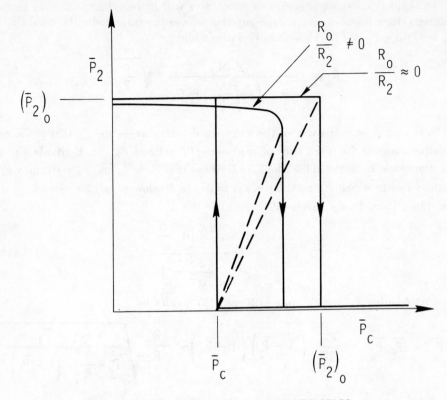

FIG. 3 STATIC OPERATING CHARACTERISTICS

The effect of a non-negligible (R_o/R_2) ratio is also illustrated in Fig. 3. The output pressure $\bar{P}_2$ decreases slightly as the control pressure increases, and there is a shift to the left of the switch point.

Diaphragm pneumatic logic devices are generally designed so that the ratios (R_o/R_1) or (R_o/R_2) are negligibly small. Thus, the straight-line characteristic curve of Fig. 3 may be used. This greatly simplifies the analysis, since the straight-line curve may be produced by knowing only the value of the parameter $\bar{P}_c^*$ and the restrictor ratio R_1/R_2.

It should be noted that the straight-line approximation is generally not applicable to the diaphragm amplifier [1] in which the restriction R_2 is made negligibly small. With this device, the output with no control pressure results from a balance between the elastic forces in the diaphragm and the output pressure force. This is contrary to the assumption of negligible elastic forces. The appropriate equation for the amplifier characteristics, determined from (16) with $R_2/R_1 = 0$ is

$$\bar{P}_c = \bar{P}_1 \; \bar{P}_c^* \; - \; \frac{R_o}{R_1} \sqrt{\frac{1 - \bar{P}_1}{\bar{P}_1}} \tag{19}$$

346

Equations (16), (17), and (19) give the static operating characteristics for diaphragm pneumatic logic devices and are generally applicable for any geometry provided R_o and $\overline{P}_c^*$ are evaluated for the particular geometry considered. Following sections will be devoted to the evaluation of these two parameters for other geometries.

Circular Control Chamber with Concentric Circular Ridge — Flow Outward

This case is geometrically similar to that treated above, the only difference being that the pressure load in the inner region of the diaphragm is now $(P_1 - P_c)$ and the load on the annular region is now $(P_2 - P_c)$.

Introducing these changes into the above analysis results in

$$\overline{P}_c^* = \frac{2 \ln \dfrac{a}{\alpha}}{\dfrac{a^2}{\alpha^2} - 1} \tag{20}$$

$$R_o = \frac{2 N_o}{\pi \alpha^3 \left(\dfrac{a^2}{\alpha^2} - 1 \right) P_s C} \sqrt{\frac{\rho}{2}} \tag{21}$$

Rectangular Control Chamber with Straight Ridge

Equation (2) expressed in Cartesian coordinates is

$$\frac{\partial^2 W}{\partial X^2} + \frac{\partial^2 W}{\partial Y^2} = - \frac{P(X, Y)}{N_o} \tag{22}$$

Equation (22) may be solved by expressing the load function $P(X, Y)$ by the series

$$P(X, Y) = \sum_m \sum_n b_{mn} \phi_{mn} \tag{23}$$

Then, with the function ϕ_{mn} suitably chosen, the deflection shape will be of the form

$$W(X, Y) = \sum_m \sum_n a_{mn} \phi_{mn} \tag{24}$$

The proper form for the functions ϕ_{mn} is determined from the solution of the eigenvalue equation

$$\frac{\partial^2 \phi}{\partial X^2} + \frac{\partial^2 \phi}{\partial Y^2} = - \lambda \phi \tag{25}$$

347

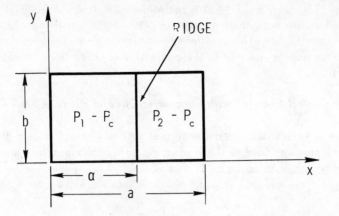

FIG. 4 COORDINATE SYSTEM FOR STRAIGHT RIDGE,
RECTANGULAR CONTROL CHAMBER

with boundary conditions (Fig. 4) $\phi(0, Y) = \phi(a, Y) = \phi(X, 0) = \phi(X, b) = 0$. Solution of (25) leads to the eigenfunctions

$$\phi_{mn} = \sin \frac{m\pi X}{a} \sin \frac{n\pi Y}{b} \qquad (26)$$

Using (23), (24), (26), in (22) and evaluating for the mn^{th} term leads to the relation

$$a_{mn} = \frac{b_{mn}}{\pi^2 N_o \left(\dfrac{m^2}{a^2} + \dfrac{n^2}{b^2} \right)} \qquad (27)$$

where [3]

$$b_{mn} = \frac{4}{ab} \int_0^a \int_0^b P(X, Y) \sin \frac{m\pi X}{a} \sin \frac{n\pi Y}{b} \, dX dY \qquad (28)$$

and

$$P(X, Y) = \begin{cases} (\bar{P}_1 - \bar{P}_c) \, P_s \,, & 0 \le X < \alpha \\[2mm] (\bar{P}_2 - \bar{P}_c) \, P_s \,, & \alpha \le X < a \end{cases} \qquad (29)$$

348

Using (29) in (28)

$$b_{mn} = \frac{4P_s}{ab} \int_0^\alpha (\bar{P}_1 - \bar{P}_c) \sin \frac{m\pi X}{a} dX \int_0^b \sin \frac{n\pi Y}{b} dY$$

$$+ \frac{4P_s}{ab} \int_\alpha^a (\bar{P}_2 - \bar{P}_c) \sin \frac{m\pi X}{a} dX \int_0^b \sin \frac{n\pi Y}{b} dY \qquad (30)$$

Evaluation of (30) results in

$$b_{mn} = \frac{8P_s}{mn\pi^2} \left[(\bar{P}_1 - \bar{P}_c) \left(1 - \cos \frac{m\pi\alpha}{a} \right) \right.$$

$$\left. - (\bar{P}_2 - \bar{P}_c) \left(\cos m\pi - \cos \frac{m\pi\alpha}{a} \right) \right] \qquad (31)$$

where $m = 1, 2, 3, \ldots$

$n = 1, 3, 5, \ldots$

and from (27)

$$a_{mn} = \frac{8P_s}{\pi^4 N_o mn \left(\dfrac{m^2}{a^2} + \dfrac{n^2}{b^2} \right)} \left[(\bar{P}_1 - \bar{P}_c) \left(1 - \cos \frac{m\pi\alpha}{a} \right) \right.$$

$$\left. - (\bar{P}_2 - \bar{P}_c) \left(\cos m\pi - \cos \frac{m\pi\alpha}{a} \right) \right] \qquad (32)$$

where $m = 1, 2, 3, \ldots$

$n = 1, 3, 5, \ldots$

Using (32) and (26) in (24) the deflection expression is

$$W = \frac{8P_s}{\pi^4 N_o} \sum_{m=1}^\infty \sum_{n_{odd}} \frac{1}{mn \left(\dfrac{m^2}{a^2} + \dfrac{n^2}{b^2} \right)} \left[(\bar{P}_1 - \bar{P}_c) \left(1 - \cos \frac{m\pi\alpha}{a} \right) \right.$$

$$\left. - (\bar{P}_2 - \bar{P}_c) \left(\cos m\pi - \cos \frac{m\pi\alpha}{a} \right) \right] \sin \frac{m\pi X}{a} \sin \frac{n\pi Y}{b} \qquad (33)$$

To determine the parameter $\bar{P}_c^*$, Equation (33) is solved for $\bar{P}_c$ with $P_1 = 1$, $\bar{P}_2 = 0$, and the deflection over the center of the ridge, $W(\alpha, b/2)$ equal to zero. Hence,

$$\bar{P}_c^* = \frac{\displaystyle\sum_{m=1}^{\infty}\sum_{n_{odd}} \frac{(-1)^{(n-1)/2}}{mn\left(\dfrac{m^2}{a^2}+\dfrac{n^2}{b^2}\right)}\left(1-\cos\frac{m\pi\alpha}{a}\right)\sin\frac{m\pi\alpha}{a}}{\displaystyle\sum_{m=1}^{\infty}\sum_{n_{odd}} \frac{(-1)^{(n-1)/2}}{mn\left(\dfrac{m^2}{a^2}+\dfrac{n^2}{b^2}\right)}\left(1-\cos m\pi\right)\sin\frac{m\pi\alpha}{a}}$$

(34)

Equation (34) has been evaluated for a/b ratios of $1/2$, 1, 2, and for α/a from 0 to 1. The results are shown graphically in Fig. 5. The parameter R_o is determined by evaluating the flow area over the ridge when $\bar{P}_1 = \bar{P}_2 = 1$, and $\bar{P}_c = 0$.

From Equation (33) the flow area is

$$A = \int_0^b W(\alpha, Y)\, dY$$

(35)

and

$$A = \frac{32 b\, P_s}{\pi^5 N_o} \sum_{m_{odd}}\sum_{n_{odd}} \frac{1}{mn^2\left(\dfrac{m^2}{a^2}+\dfrac{n^2}{b^2}\right)}\sin\frac{m\pi\alpha}{a}$$

$$R_o = \sqrt{\frac{\rho}{2}}\ \frac{\pi^5 N_o}{32 C\, P_s\, b \displaystyle\sum_{m_{odd}}\sum_{n_{odd}} \frac{1}{mn^2\left(\dfrac{m^2}{a^2}+\dfrac{n^2}{b^2}\right)}\sin\frac{m\pi\alpha}{a}}$$

(36)

Circular Control Chamber with Straight Ridge

The equilibrium equation expressed in cylindrical coordinates is as shown earlier

$$\frac{\partial^2 W}{\partial r^2} + \frac{1}{r}\frac{\partial W}{\partial r} + \frac{1}{r^2}\frac{\partial^2 W}{\partial \theta^2} = -\frac{P(r,\theta)}{N_o}$$

(5)

In this case the pressure (Fig. 6) is

$$P(r,\theta) = \begin{cases} P_1 - P_c, & \alpha < r < a, \ \pi - \cos^{-1}\alpha/r < \theta < \pi + \cos^{-1}\alpha/r \\[2mm] P_2 - P_c, & 0 < r < \alpha, \ 0 \le \theta \le 2\pi \\[2mm] P_2 - P_c, & \alpha < r < a, \ -\pi + \cos^{-1}\alpha/r < \theta < \pi - \cos^{-1}\alpha/r \end{cases}$$

(37)

350

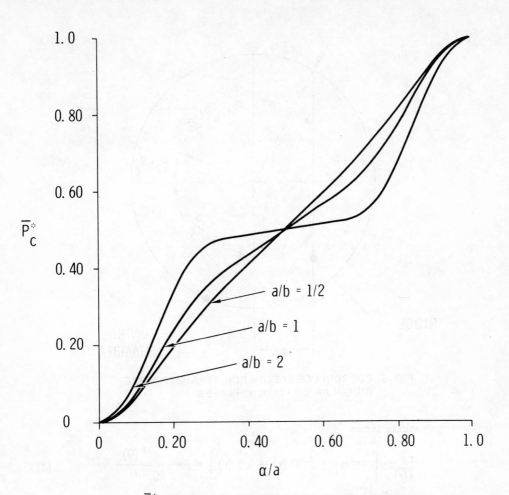

FIG. 5 $\bar{P}_c^*$ VERSUS α/a FOR STRAIGHT RIDGE, CIRCULAR
CONTROL CHAMBER

Due to the form of the boundary conditions, a series solution such as that used in the preceding section (Equations 23, 24) will be necessary. In this case, the associated eigenvalue equation is

$$\frac{\partial^2 \phi}{\partial r^2} + \frac{1}{r} \frac{\partial \phi}{\partial r} + \frac{1}{r^2} \frac{\partial^2 \phi}{\partial \theta^2} = -\lambda \phi \tag{38}$$

with boundary conditions $\phi(a, \theta) = 0$, $\phi(r, \theta) = \phi(r, -\theta)$. Assuming that $\phi(r, \theta)$ can be expressed as

$$\phi(r, \theta) = f(r) g(\theta) \tag{39}$$

leads to the following relation

$$g(\theta) f''(r) + \frac{1}{r} g(\theta) f'(r) + \frac{1}{r^2} f(r) g''(\theta) = -\lambda f(r) g(\theta) \tag{40}$$

351

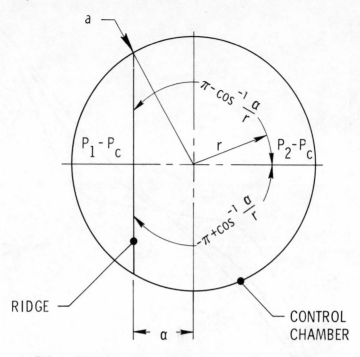

FIG. 6 COORDINATE SYSTEM FOR STRAIGHT RIDGE,
CIRCULAR CONTROL CHAMBER

or upon rearranging terms

$$\frac{r^2}{f(r)} \left[f''(r) + \frac{1}{r} f'(r) + \lambda f(r) \right] = - \frac{g''(\theta)}{g(\theta)} \qquad (41)$$

Since the left-hand side of (41) is independent of θ and the right-hand side is independent of r, it follows that both must be independent of both r and θ, hence, equal to a constant. Also, in order that $g(\theta)$ be single-valued it must be periodic with period 2π. Hence, (41) becomes

$$\frac{r^2}{f(r)} \left[f''(r) + \frac{1}{r} f'(r) + \lambda f(r) \right] = - \frac{g''(\theta)}{g(\theta)} = m^2 \qquad (42)$$

where m is an integer.

Thus,

$$g(\theta) = a \cos m\theta + b \sin m\theta \qquad (43)$$

and $f(r)$ is obtained from

$$r^2 f'' + rf' + (r^2\lambda - m^2) f = 0. \qquad (44)$$

352

Equation (44) is a form of the well known Bessel equation the general solution of which is

$$f(r) = c J_m(\sqrt{\lambda}\ r) + d Y_m(\sqrt{\lambda}\ r) \tag{45}$$

The most general form of $\phi(r, \theta)$ is then

$$\phi(r, \theta) = (a\cos m\theta + b\sin m\theta)\left[c J_m(\sqrt{\lambda}\ r) + d Y_m(\sqrt{\lambda}\ r)\right] \tag{46}$$

The θ boundary condition requires that ϕ be an even function of θ, hence, $b = 0$. Since $Y_m(0)$ is infinite this term must also be discarded, and $d = 0$. The condition $\phi(a, \theta) = 0$ gives

$$\sqrt{\lambda} = \frac{1}{a} K_{mn} \tag{47}$$

where K_{mn} is the nth zero of the Bessel function of order m. Equation (46) thus becomes

$$\phi_{mn}(r, \theta) = J_m(K_{mn}\ r/a)\cos m\theta \tag{48}$$

and

$$W(r, \theta) = \sum_m \sum_n a_{mn} J_m(K_{mn}\ r/a)\cos m\theta \tag{49}$$

$$P(r, \theta) = \sum_m \sum_n b_{mn} J_m(K_{mn}\ r/a)\cos m\theta \tag{50}$$

Now using (49) and (50) in (5) and evaluating for the mn^{th} term leads to the relation

$$a_{mn} = \frac{a^2}{K_{mn}^2\ N_0}\ b_{mn} \tag{51}$$

where b_{mn} determined in the normal manner is

$$b_{mn} = \frac{2}{\pi a^2}\ \frac{1}{J_{m+1}^2(K_{mn})}\ \int_o^a \int_o^{2\pi} P(r, \theta)\ r\ J_m(K_{mn}\ r/a)\cos m\theta\ dr\ d\theta \tag{52}$$

353

and using (37)

$$b_{mn} = \frac{2}{\pi a^2} \frac{1}{J_{m+1}^2 (K_{mn})} \left\{ (P_1 - P_c) \int_\alpha^a r \, J_m(K_{mn} \, r/a) \, dr \int_{\pi - \cos^{-1} \alpha/r}^{\pi + \cos^{-1} \alpha/r} \cos m\theta \, d\theta \right.$$

$$+ (P_2 - P_c) \int_0^\alpha r \, J_m(K_{mn} \, r/a) \, dr \int_0^{2\pi} \cos m\theta \, d\theta$$

$$\left. + (P_2 - P_c) \int_\alpha^a r \, J_m(K_{mn} \, r/a) \, dr \int_{-\pi + \cos^{-1} \alpha/a}^{\pi - \cos^{-1} \alpha/a} \cos m\theta \, d\theta \right\} \qquad (53)$$

Performing the indicated integrations in (53) where possible and simplifying results in

$$b_{mn} = \begin{cases} \dfrac{4(P_1 - P_2)}{\pi a^2 J_1^2(K_{on})} \displaystyle\int_\alpha^a r \cos^{-1} \alpha/r \, J_0(K_{on} \, r/a) \, dr + \dfrac{4(P_2 - P_c)}{K_{on} J_1(K_{on})}, m = 0 \\[20pt] \dfrac{4(P_1 - P_2)}{\pi a^2 m J_{m+1}^2(K_{mn})} \displaystyle\int_\alpha^a r \sin(m \cos^{-1} \alpha/r) \, J_m(K_{mn} \, r/a) \, dr, m \neq 0 \end{cases}$$

$$(54)$$

Using (54) in (51) and the result in (49) gives the following equation of diaphragm deflection

$$W(r, \theta) = \frac{4 P_s (\bar{P}_1 - \bar{P}_2)}{\pi N_0} \sum_{n=0}^\infty \frac{J_0(K_{on} \, r/a)}{K_{on}^2 J_1^2(K_{on})} \int_\alpha^a r \, J_0(K_{on} \, r/a) \cos^{-1} \alpha/r \, dr$$

$$+ \frac{4a^2 P_s (\bar{P}_2 - \bar{P}_c)}{N_0} \sum_{n=0}^\infty \frac{J_0(K_{on} \, r/a)}{K_{on}^3 J_1(K_{on})}$$

$$+ \frac{4 P_s (\bar{P}_1 - \bar{P}_2)}{\pi N_0} \sum_{m=1}^\infty \sum_{n=0}^\infty \frac{(-1)^n \cos m\theta \, J_m(K_{mn} \, r/a)}{m K_{mn}^2 J_{m+1}^2(K_{mn})} \int_\alpha^a r \sin$$

$$\cdot (m \cos^{-1} \alpha/r) \, J_m(K_{mn} \, r/a) \, dr \qquad (55)$$

354

To determine the parameter $\bar{P}_c^*$, Equation (55) is solved for $\bar{P}_c$ under the conditions

$$W(\alpha, \pi) = 0$$

$$\bar{P}_1 = 1$$

$$\bar{P}_2 = 0$$

Hence,

$$\bar{P}_c^* = \frac{\left[\displaystyle\sum_{n=0}^{\infty} \frac{J_o(K_{on}\,\alpha/a)}{K_{on}^2\, J_1^2(K_{on})} \int_\alpha^a r\cos^{-1}\frac{\alpha}{r}\, J_o(K_{on}\, r/a)\, dr + \displaystyle\sum_{m=1}^{\infty}\sum_{n=0}^{\infty} \frac{J_m(K_{mn}\alpha/a)}{mK_{mn}^2\, J_{m+1}^2(K_{mn})} \int_\alpha^a r\sin(m\cos^{-1}\alpha/r)\, J_m(K_{mn}\, r/a)\, dr \right]}{\pi a^2 \displaystyle\sum_{n=0}^{\infty} \frac{J_o(K_{on}\,\alpha/a)}{K_{on}^3\, J_1(K_{on})}}$$

(56)

Equation (56) has been evaluated by use of the digital computer.[1] The resulting values of $\bar{P}_c^*$ are plotted versus ridge position in Fig. 7. For the ridge displaced downstream of the center of the control chamber — i.e., for $\alpha < 0$, Fig. 6 may be used with the transformation

$$\bar{P}_c^*\,(-\alpha/a) = 1 - \bar{P}_c^*\,(\alpha/a)$$

(57)

The parameter R_o is found as before by determining the flow area over the ridge when $\bar{P}_1 = \bar{P}_2 = 1$, and $\bar{P}_c = 0$.

With reference to Fig. 8 the flow area over the ridge is

$$A_o = \int W\, ds$$

(58)

where

$$ds = \sqrt{1 + r^2 \left(\frac{d\theta}{dr}\right)^2}\, dr$$

and

$$\left(\frac{d\theta}{dr}\right)^2 = \left(\frac{\alpha}{r}\right)^2 \left(\frac{1}{r^2 - \alpha^2}\right)$$

---

[1] Program not available outside IBM

355

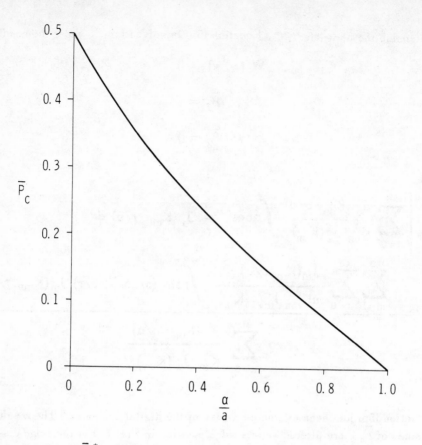

FIG. 7 $\bar{P}_c^*$ VERSUS α/a FOR STRAIGHT RIDGE, CIRCULAR
CONTROL CHAMBER

so that

$$ds = \sqrt{\frac{1}{r^2 - \alpha^2}} \; r\,dr \tag{59}$$

It is known from an earlier section that the deflection of a circular diaphragm
under constant tension and uniform loading is, from Equation (9),

$$W = \frac{P_s}{4N_o} (a^2 - r^2) \tag{60}$$

Using (58) and (59)

$$A_o = \frac{P_s a^3}{3N_o} \left(1 - \frac{\alpha^2}{a^2}\right)^{3/2} \tag{61}$$

and

$$R_o = \sqrt{\frac{\rho}{2}} \; \frac{3N_o}{P_s a^3 C} \left(1 - \frac{\alpha^2}{a^2}\right)^{-3/2} \tag{62}$$

356

Accuracy of Results

First recall that the assumption of constant, uniform tension was utilized in the analyses. This assumption is valid, in general, only where the magnitude of the deflections are such that the initial tension in the diaphragm is substantially unaffected. Recall also that a definition of $\overline{P}_c^*$ was that value to which the normalized control pressure must drop to allow a previously sealed diaphragm to just open. Under this condition, deflections in the diaphragm are relatively small and the constant, uniform tension assumption should be adequate. Furthermore, the tension does not appear in the equations for $\overline{P}_c^*$.

On the other hand, the parameter R_o is determined under conditions of maximum deflection, and the expression for R_o does contain the tension. Hence, the validity of the constant tension assumption in this case would appear to be in question. The use of this parameter in the form derived, however, has been found to be of value in describing the characteristics of diaphragm elements, provided the value used for initial tension is determined empirically.

One method for the determination of the initial tension consists of assembling a diaphragm over a circular cavity in the same manner that the diaphragm element is to be assembled. Then with a pressure in the cavity equal to the supply pressure to be used, the deflection at the center is measured. The empirical value of the initial tension (from Equation 60) is then

$$N_o = \frac{P_s\, a}{4W_o} \tag{63}$$

For a 0.002-in. polyurethane film with a supply pressure of 1 psi, the initial tension, N_o, has been found by this method to be approximately 0.1 lb/in.

Although not reported herein, analyses have also been performed under the assumption of zero initial tension with tension a function of diaphragm strain. Although considerably more difficult to perform, the analysis under this assumption produced results not significantly different from those obtained from the constant tension assumption. Actually, the diaphragm experiences a small initial tension with increasing tension due to deflection, that is, a condition which is somewhere between the assumptions of zero initial tension and constant tension. But, since assumptions of the two extremes produced not significantly different results, it can reasonably be assumed that these results are not significantly different from those that would be obtained in a considerably more complex analysis involving an initial, but not constant, tension.

The assumption of incompressibility limits the use of the characteristic equations to relatively low pressure (1 to 2 psi gage) applications. However, the switch-open points are generally applicable since this analysis was performed for the zero flow condition. To determine the switch-closed point for higher pressure applications the orifice equations for compressible flow [4] should be used.

Finally, consider the comparison of the experimental operating characteristic curve with the analytical, straight-line, characteristic curve shown in Fig. 9. The results shown are quite typical of results obtained for hundreds of elements incorporating all the geometries discussed with a broad range of ridge positions.

357

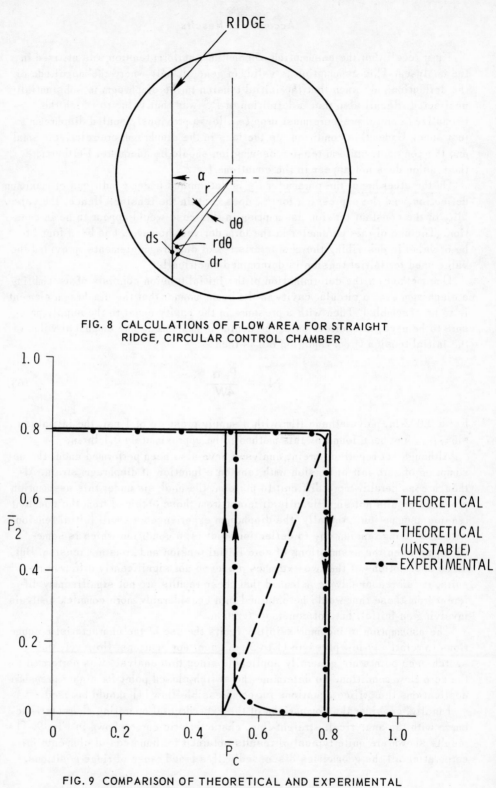

RIDGE

FIG. 8 CALCULATIONS OF FLOW AREA FOR STRAIGHT
RIDGE, CIRCULAR CONTROL CHAMBER

THEORETICAL

THEORETICAL
(UNSTABLE)

EXPERIMENTAL

FIG. 9 COMPARISON OF THEORETICAL AND EXPERIMENTAL
STATIC OPERATING CHARACTERISTICS

The switch-closed point always occurs at a lower control pressure than predicted by the straight-line approximation. This is due to the assumption in the straight-line approximation of negligible elastic forces. Results of the complete analysis, Equations (16) and (17), however, are consistent with the experimental results. The magnitude of this discrepancy is a function of the ratios R_o/R_1 and R_o/R_2, but for most elements is less than five per cent.

The switch-open point generally occurs at a higher value of control pressure than predicted by the analysis. The discrepancy here is due to the implicit assumption that when the diaphragm is on the ridge, the flow is zero. Actually a leakage flow exists which increases as the switch-open point is approached, since the net sealing force on the diaphragm decreases. This leakage flow causes an upward force on the diaphragm downstream of the ridge which produces the premature opening. The magnitude of the discrepancy in the switch-open point has been found to be generally less than ten per cent.

Summary

The static operating characteristics for diaphragm pneumatic logic devices are completely defined by three parameters: the normalized switch-open control pressure $\overline{P}_c^*$; the minimum ridge impedance R_o; and the up and downstream restrictor ratio (R_1/R_2). Most diaphragm elements are designed such that R_o is quite small compared to R_1 and R_2. For this class of elements the much simplified straight-line characteristics may be used where only the parameters $\overline{P}_c^*$ and (R_1/R_2) are required. The restrictor ratio is readily obtained from the orifice dimensions, and the values of $\overline{P}_c^*$ for the most common geometric configurations have been provided.

The diaphragm device thus lends itself to analysis which is quite easily applied and yet reasonably accurate. This characteristic has been, and undoubtedly will continue to be, instrumental in the rapid progress being made in this new technology.

Acknowledgments

The author wishes to thank Mr. D. R. Winner of the Endicott Scientific Computation Laboratory who programmed for machine computation those equations for which analytical solutions were not available. Thanks also to members of the Fluid Technology group, in particular Mr. H. R. Mueller and Mr. R. R. Schaffer for their active interest and support.

References

[1] D. F. Jensen, H. R. Mueller, and R. R. Schaffer, "Pneumatic Diaphragm Logic," to be presented at the Fourth Fluidics Symposium, Chicago, Ill., May 8-11, 1967.

[2] R. Courant and D. Hilbert, "Methods of Mathematical Physics," Interscience Publishers, Inc., New York, 1953, pp. 297-307.

[3] F. B. Hildebrand, "Advanced Calculus for Engineers," Prentice-Hall, Inc., Englewood Cliffs, New Jersey, 1948.

[4] V. L. Streeter, "Fluid Mechanics," Second Edition, McGraw-Hill Book Company, Inc., New York, 1958, p. 101.

Fluidic Pulse Network Hazards

P. Bauer

Bowles Engineering Corporation
Silver Spring, Maryland

Abstract

Fluidic pulse switching networks at relatively high operating speeds present timing problems requiring meticulous consideration of hazards during circuit design. Analyses and simulations are suggested to anticipate and rectify hazards before hardware fabrication. A digital computer simulation of a sample circuit is demonstrated, and design procedure recommendations are given.

Introduction

Fluidic digital systems are firmly established at present and are utilized in increasingly complex forms, operating at higher and higher speeds. As all digital networks, Fluidic circuits are prone to timing hazards. Such effects are particularly apparent at higher operating speeds, when steady-state circuit design loses its validity. When signals become shorter in time than the signal path delays, encountered timing effects must be carefully accounted for in the design process to avoid hazards.

Timing hazards are defined as error signal generating situations resulting from failure to consider timing effects in detail during the circuit design.

Signals or pulses in high speed Fluidic systems can not be represented by the conventional image of square waves. Pulses exhibit rise and fall times of the order of the pulse widths used, and an acceptable short pulse may well be more triangular in shape. The ever-present noise superimposed on such a waveform will modify the triggering instant in an element when fed by such a signal, causing jitter of the passed signal. This jitter not only varies the relative signal occurrence in time but also narrows or widens the resulting pulse.

The orders of magnitude of these effects are such that Fluidic digital circuits with more than a few staged elements, operating at repetition rates of more than a few tens of pps, begin to exhibit significant timing hazards if the design process has not allowed for their avoidance. At higher speeds (shorter pulses) in larger circuits, hazards may well cause complete system malfunctions.

360

Causes of Hazards

Principal causes of hazards in Fluidic networks are the ones already mentioned earlier, namely the following:
1) Relative signal propagation delays through elements and interconnecting paths.
2) Signal jitter.

The latter cause is itself essentially a function of signal noise. Every signal comprises noise, which effects an apparent variation of the instant of switching of every element due to its modulation of pulse rise and fall shape. An element output signal again comprises noise as well as relative jitter with respect to its input signal. Thus, jitter is added during each passage through switching elements. It should be born in mind that jitter accumulated through a larger number of elements will occasionally result in very wide and very narrow pulses. This situation can reach extremes where wide pulses may cause overlaps of successive pulses or narrow pulses may become too narrow to switch the next element. A loss of signal results in either case, even though this occurence may have a low probability. Since even a small probability of a single malfunction is usually not permissible in a digital system, total jitter dispersion must be considered in the design.

Fig. 1 illustrates the jitter generation during a pulse passage through a switching element. The upper waveform represents the assumed jitter-free input pulse to the element and the lower waveform indicates the resulting output pulse. Simplifying assumptions have been made, such as the equality of rise and fall times and the existence of clean waveforms, to facilitate the presentation of the mechanism concerned. However, even under such assumptions, gross effects are immediately detectable. Fig. 1 also indicates usual orders of magnitudes of these effects by the applied time scale.

Circuit Design and Analysis

Conventionally, circuit networks are designed in the following steps:
1) General logic design (steady-state).
2) Logic adaptation to suit available functions.
3) Hardware design.

Even though the above procedure should allow for sequential logic when applicable, this is not sufficient in most cases. All significant component time delays as well as signal jitter should be considered to avoid probable hazard occurences due to these causes. In practice, high speed Fluidic circuits usually *do not* function at all unless such allowances are made. Therefore, it is imperative that a circuit design anticipates and avoids timing hazards by sufficiently detailed and considerate designs and by analyses of such designs before implementation with hardware.

Fundamentally, there are two approaches to circuit analysis with respect to hazards:
1) Simulation of circuit operation.
2) Determination of relevant network characteristics and comparison with established criteria.

361

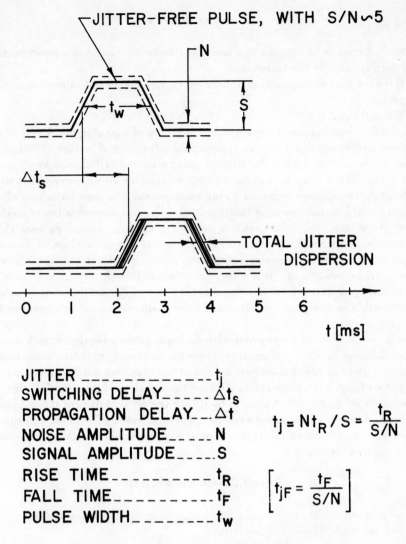

JITTER-FREE PULSE, WITH S/N~5

TOTAL JITTER DISPERSION

t [ms]

JITTER _____ t_j
SWITCHING DELAY_____ Δt_s
PROPAGATION DELAY___ Δt
NOISE AMPLITUDE_____ N
SIGNAL AMPLITUDE_____ S
RISE TIME_____ t_R
FALL TIME_____ t_F
PULSE WIDTH_____ t_w

$$t_j = N t_R / S = \frac{t_R}{S/N}$$

$$\left[t_{jF} = \frac{t_F}{S/N} \right]$$

FIG. 1 – JITTER GENERATION DIAGRAM

A combination of both approaches usually provides the most convenient and economical method. Simulation of circuit and subcircuit operation by multiple graphs of the various signals in relevant positions in the circuits as functions of time in form of tables or waveform diagrams, utilizing the expected delay and jitter values, can be very useful. In this process, many graphs may have to be generated simultaneously. This places considerable strain on the designer. A small plotting error can easily remain undetected and may void this operation. As a result, this approach should be limited to low-complexity circuits or sub-circuits, where inputs and output are easily determined. Network characteristics, such as summations of delays and the respective maximum accumulated jitter dispersion limits in parallel signal paths, may be determined and may, together with some graphical plotting, permit partial analysis.

362

Such procedures, if undertaken before implementation with hardware, will pay for themselves manyfold in saved time and cost.

If system circuits are large and complex, a thorough analysis can become lengthy and tedious. Errors may be unwittingly introduced. This situation may be aggravated by the need for simulation with a large number of different input conditions. Several methods have evolved to improve circuit timing analysis with the aid of a digital computer. Sufficiently general computer programs can be prepared and kept available, permitting analyses with little time expenditure and reducing the chances of errors considerably.

Computer Analyses

The following approaches to computer aided circuit analysis should be generally applicable and should permit implementation with simple software not requiring extensive knowledge of programming.

Input signals can be represented in the form of explicit functions or in the form of conditional statements. For example, a step function may be given by a function of a high odd root of time. Automatic rounding off of values to the closest integer is usually available to take care of the approximation. Combinations of suitable signal representations will be found useful in most cases.

Logical operations, as represented by Boolean symbols, are often limited or not permitted in programming languages, and the following transformations can be used to obtain the basic logic functions by algebraic manipulation of binary signal values ("zero" and "one"):

LOGIC FUNCTION	ALGEBRAIC REPRESENTATION
AND: $A.B$	$A \times B$
NOT: $\overline{A}$	$1 - A$
NOR: $\overline{A + B}$	$(1-A) \times (1-B)$
OR: $A + B$	$1-(1-A) \times (1-B)$

Conditional statements representing truth tables may be utilized in place of the above transformations at the expense of larger programs and increased memory requirements.

Time delays may be accounted for by utilization of the memory capability of the computer, where a signal value at time T is not computed, but is recalled from a result of previous computations at time $T-D$. Signal jitter can be handled in a similar manner. However, it should be remembered that total jitter dispersion must be considered. Since this may require a large number of computations, a network simulation program will be especially appreciated.

It is beyond the scope of this discussion to delve into details of circuit simulation. However, anyone involved in such design should experience few difficulties in simulating other characteristics such as circuit branching, feedback, and feedforward. The present discussion should provide a basis for the preparation of general programs suiting particular needs and applications. It is visualized that a library of compatible routines, covering often applied subcircuit functions, can be kept available. Thereafter, relatively little effort will procure a program for a specific network simulation and will accomplish in a short time, what may otherwise take many days of painstaking manual analysis.

A specific simplified example of simulation is shown in the next section. Its program is written in the Dartmouth College "BASIC" computer language.

Sample Circuit

The simple circuit shown in Fig. 2 represents a common logic function $\overline{A}.B$. For the purpose of this demonstration, it is assumed that the circuit is to perform a binary decoding function, where input A represents the binary state of, for example, 2^1 weighting, and B represents the binary state of 2^2 weighting. A and B are assumed to be repetitive 50% duty cycle pulses of 2:1 frequency ratio and both signals are in phase. The required decoding function searches exclusively for a total input weight of 4.

This decoder subcircuit presents a significant time delay (D) to the passage of signal A through the inverter. This will cause a changed time relationship between signals $\overline{A}$ and B, which has to be anticipated and corrected to avoid hazards.

Fig. 3 shows test results of such a circuit by its input and output waveforms, clearly indicating the hazardous operation.

This circuit is simulated by a sample computer program and its execution shown in Table 1. Time (T) may be interpreted in $\frac{1}{2}$ to 1 millisecond increments per unity step, which would mean an introduced time delay (D) of 1 to 2 milliseconds. Such a time scaling would apply to a realistic example, where the repetition rate of signal A is 125 to 250 pps, and the repetition rate of signal B is one half that of signal A. The plot of the signal values is performed in coarse steps of two time units in Table 1 for the sake of brevity only. Columns 2 and 4 are signal inputs A and B over a time range equivalent to the one given in Fig. 3. The desired output signal $\overline{A}.B$ is given in column 5. However, it is computed on the assumption of an absence of the differential time delay (D) in the path of signal A. Column 6 shows the output when delay (D) is taken into account, as computed using the delayed input signal A, given in column 3. Again the hazard is clearly apparent, just as it appears in the actual output waveform traces in Fig. 3.

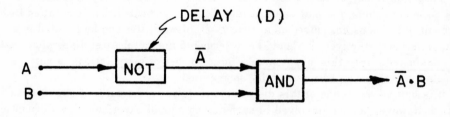

FIG. 2 – DECODER SUBCIRCUIT

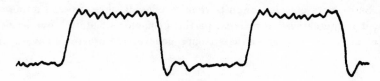

SIGNAL (A)

SIGNAL (B)

OUTPUT

FIG. 3 – DECODER SIGNAL TRACES

Corrective Measures

From the given simple circuit example it appears obvious how to correct the malfunction with a corresponding delay D in the path of signal B. Of course, situations are not as simple normally. However, once an analysis has been performed, hazards can usually be traced to their sources and rectified by changes in the circuitry.

Jitter effects, however, can be reduced only by an improvement of the signal to noise ratio, by an improvement of element switching characteristics and signal path frequency response, and by a reduction in the number of elements in a signal path. The latter is essentially the only means available to the circuit designer who has to work with standard components. Further jitter improvement can be achieved by special component design.

Conclusion

The preceding discussion shows the importance of detailed timing considerations in the course of the design of a Fluidic high speed digital network. Furthermore, it is shown that a circuit analysis with respect to timing hazards should be performed before implementation with hardware. The following sequence of design tasks is recommended to avoid unexpected pitfalls:

365

1) General logic design.
2) Logic adaptation to suit available element functions.
3) Analysis with respect to timing hazards.
4) Rectification of timing hazards.
5) Circuit hardware design.

It is further shown that a simulation of circuit operation can uncover causes of timing hazards and provide clues to their rectification, whether the simulation is with manually plotted graphs, with the aid of a digital computer, or a combination of these. Since more complex circuits require considerable effort in a thorough analysis, it is indicated that at least partial computer simulation can be performed at significant saving in time and cost, once generalized programs have been prepared.

TABLE 1

```
100PRINT"PLOT OF (NOT A).B"
110PRINT"INPUT  (A)  UNDELAYED AND"
120PRINT"INPUT  (A)  DELAYED BY (D)"
130PRINT
140PRINT"TIME","INPUT  DEL.  INPUT  OUT  OUT(DEL)"
150PRINT"T"," A       A      B     N(A)B N(A)B"
160PRINT
170READZ,D,Q,QO,B,P,PO,A(O)
180DATA2,2,2,4,0,2,8,0
190    FORT=OTO26STEP2
200IFT<ZTHEN  220
210LETZ=Z+D
220LETA=A(T+D−Z)
230IFT<QTHEN  260
240LETA(T+D−Z)=1−A(T+D−Z)
250LETQ=Q+QO
260IFT<PTHEN  290
270LETB=1−B
280LETP=P+PO
290PRINTT,A(T+D−Z);A;B;[1−(T+D−Z)]*B;(1−A)*B
300NEXTT
310END
```

PLOT OF [NOT A].B
INPUT [A] DELAYED BY [D]

TIME T	INPUT A	DEL. A	INPUT B	OUT $N[A]B$	OUT[DEL] $N[A]B$
0	0	0	0	0	0
2	1	0	1	1	1
4	1	1	1	1	0
6	0	1	1	1	0
8	0	0	1	1	1
10	1	0	0	0	0
12	1	1	0	0	0
14	0	1	0	0	0
16	0	0	0	0	0
18	1	0	1	1	1
20	1	1	1	1	0
22	0	1	1	1	0
24	0	0	1	1	1
26	1	0	0	0	0

An Experimental Evaluation of Fluidic Transmission Line Theory

Ramesh Krishnaiyer
Thomas J. Lechner, Jr.
Johnson Service Company
Milwaukee, Wisconsin

Abstract

The article describes the known theories for obtaining the complex properties of a fluidic transmission line, and evaluates them in light of experimental data. The frequency response of the transmission line was studied for several lengths, each with various receiving end terminations. The Nichols' theory was found to give the most accurate prediction from a practical point of view. A further improvement has been achieved through a modification of Nichols' theory. An expression for the input or sending impedance of the line and the tests conducted to verify the results have also been included.

Nomenclature

A = Area of Cross Section of Line, in.^{2}

C = Capacitance/Unit Length, $\dfrac{\text{cis-sec}}{\text{psi}}$/in.

D = Inside Diameter of Line, in.

E = Voltage, volt

f = Signal Frequency, cps.

G = Conductance/Unit Length, $\dfrac{\text{cis/in.}}{\text{psi}}$

I = Current, ampere

j = $\sqrt{-1}$, dimensionless

ℓ = Total Line Length, in.

L = Inertance/Unit Length, $\dfrac{\text{psi-sec.}}{\text{cis}}$/in.

P = DC Pressure (Mean), psia

Q = Volume Flow Rate, cis

R = Resistance/Unit Length, $\dfrac{\text{psi}}{\text{cis}}/\text{in.}$

x = Coordinate Indicating Distance from Load, in.

Y = Shunt Admittance/Unit Length, $\dfrac{\text{cis}}{\text{psi}}/\text{in.}$

Z = Series Impedance/Unit Length, $\dfrac{\text{psi}}{\text{cis}}/\text{in.}$

γ = Propagation Constant, dimensionless

γ^* = Ratio of Specific Heats, dimensionless

μ = Viscosity, psi-sec.

ν = Kinematic Viscosity, $\dfrac{\text{in.}^2}{\text{sec.}}$

ρ = Density, $\dfrac{\text{lb}_f - \text{sec}^2}{\text{in.}^4}$

ω = Signal Frequency, rad/sec

Subscripts

c = Line Characteristic Properties

g = Generator or Source Properties

L = Load Properties

r = Receiving end Properties

s = Sending end Properties

t = Transducer Properties

T = Isothermal Properties

Introduction

In recent years a great deal of effort has been exerted on the new technology of fluidics. This technology deals with small pieces of channeled material that have active properties. These devices can be made to operate as amplifiers and switches and can perform operations in a manner analogous to transistor circuits.

As the speed of sound (in air) is roughly 10^{-6} times the speed of light, the transmission of fluid signals over a given length, are confronted with distributed parameter effects at frequencies 10^{-6} times lower than electronic systems. That is, whatever phenomenon occurs in electronic systems at 500 Mc, probably will be encountered in pneumatic systems at about 500 cps. Since the useful frequency range of fluidic devices extend at least to 2,000 cps, we are sure that distributed effects must be considered. This points out the grave need for a confident method of determining the effects of the transmission line that interconnect the various fluidic components.

This paper describes the known theories and evaluates them as to their applicability to this growing technology.

Electrical Theory [2]

An electrical transmission system essentially can be represented as a combination of three separate sections — the energy source, the load, and the link between the two, the transmission line. Four distributed parameters, R, G, L, and C, are required to characterize a transmission line.

We also have to define two other quantities, Z and Y, at this time.

$$Z = R + jwL \quad \text{(See Figure 1)} \tag{1}$$

$$Y = G + jwC \tag{2}$$

We have,

$$\frac{dE}{dx} = ZI \tag{3}$$

and

$$\frac{dI}{dx} = YE \tag{4}$$

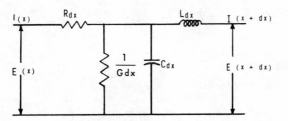

FIG. 1 EQUIVALENT CIRCUIT OF AN ELEMENTARY LENGTH

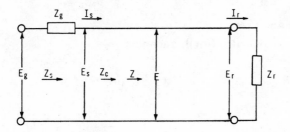

FIG. 2 TRANSMISSION SYSTEM BLOCK DIAGRAM

A block diagram for the transmission system can be drawn as in Fig. 2.

The equations for the receiving end conditions, I_r and E_r are obtained as below.

$$I_r = \frac{2\ Z_c\ \exp(-\gamma\ell)\ E_g}{M} \tag{5}$$

$$E_r = \frac{2\ Z_c\ Z_r\ \exp(-\gamma\ell)\ E_g}{M} \tag{6}$$

where

$$Z_c = \sqrt{\frac{Z}{Y}} = \sqrt{\frac{R\ +\ j\omega L}{G\ +\ j\omega C}} \tag{7}$$

Propagation constant,

$$\gamma = \sqrt{(R\ +\ j\omega L)(G\ +\ j\omega C)} = \alpha\ +\ j\beta\ \text{numeric per unit length} \tag{8}$$

and

$$M = (Z_g + Z_c)(Z_r + Z_c)\ -\ (Z_g - Z_c)\ (Z_r - Z_c)\exp(-2\gamma\ell) \tag{9}$$

Lossy Line Analysis

If E_s is known, we can put $E_g = E_s$ and $Z_g = 0$.

$$\frac{E_r}{E_s} = \frac{2\ Z_r\ \exp(-\gamma\ell)}{(Z_r + Z_c)\ +\ (Z_r - Z_c)\exp(-2\gamma\ell)} \tag{10}$$

Lossless Line Analysis

For a lossless line $R = G = 0$, such that

$$Z_c = \sqrt{\frac{L}{C}}$$

and

$$\gamma = j\omega\sqrt{LC} \tag{11}$$

Substituting (11) into (10) gives,

$$\frac{E_r}{E_s} = \frac{1}{\cos\beta\ell + j\left[\dfrac{Z_c}{Z_r}\right]\sin\beta\ell} \tag{12}$$

Fluidic Theory

A close analogy can be found between a fluidic transmission system and an electrical transmission system.

Lossy Line Analysis

Using the assumptions of small fluctuations and no dc flow, the lossy line analysis of a transmission line containing an ideal gas leads to equations of the form

$$\frac{dP}{dx} = ZQ \tag{13}$$

and

$$\frac{dQ}{dx} = YP \tag{14}$$

which are the same as the electrical system Equations (3) and (4) with the analogous fluidic values. Thus we see that under the assumptions which yield equations (13) and (14) the pressure is analogous to the voltage and the volume flow rate analogous to the current.

Constant Passive Element Theory
The constant fluidic line elements are found to be

$$R = \frac{8\pi\mu}{A^2} \tag{15}$$

$$L = \frac{\rho}{A} \tag{16}$$

$$C = \frac{A}{\gamma^* P} \tag{17}$$

and

$$G = 0 \tag{18}$$

where

$$Z = R + j\omega L$$

and

$$Y = G + j\omega C$$

The heat transfer effects have been neglected in the above analysis. The other assumptions used are 1) rigid line walls which can be shown to be valid for gas filled lines; 2) No mean flow as we have a volume terminated line; 3) Negligible end effects as $\ell/d > 50$; 4) Acoustic signals so that processes may be considered reversible and 5) Adiabatic state changes.[4]

Nichols' Theory
The Nichols' Theory, which uses assumptions similar to those in the constant resistance theory as well as the instantaneous heat transfer effects, is

371

better and more elaborate. A summary of this theory follows, together with some modifications to improve low frequency predictions.

A pair of characteristic frequencies for the fluidic line was defined by Nichols to be;

$$\omega_V = \frac{8\pi\nu}{A} = \text{viscous characteristic frequency} \quad (19)$$

$$\omega_T = \frac{8\pi\nu_T}{A} = \frac{\omega_V}{\sigma^2} \quad (20)$$

where

$$A = \frac{\pi}{4} D^2 \quad (21)$$

and, σ^2 is a dimensionless property of the fluid and is almost independent of both absolute pressure and temperature ($\sigma^2 = 0.708$ for air) and h_v and h_T are related to ω_v and ω_T

$$h_V = 2\sqrt{\frac{\omega}{\omega_V}} \quad (22)$$

$$h_T = 2\sqrt{\frac{\omega}{\omega_T}} \quad (23)$$

Nichols' analysis results in the following equations

$$Z = j\omega L_{s1} + R_{v1}\left[\frac{R_{e1}}{R_{v1}} + j\frac{\omega L_{e1}}{R_{v1}}\right] \quad (24)$$

and

$$Y = j\omega C_{a1} + \frac{j\omega(\gamma^* - 1)C_{a1}}{\frac{(\gamma^*-1)C_{a1}}{C_{e1}} + j\frac{\omega(\gamma^*-1)C_{a1}}{G_{e1}}} \quad (25)$$

where

$$L_{s1} = \frac{\rho}{A} = \text{cross section inertance per unit length} \quad (26)$$

$$C_{a1} = \frac{A}{\gamma^* P} = \text{adiabatic capacitance per unit length} \quad (27)$$

$$R_{v1} = \omega_v L_{s1} = \frac{8\pi\mu}{A^2} = \text{viscous resistance per unit length} \quad (28)$$

372

$$R_{e_1} = R_{v_1} \tag{29}$$

$$L_{e_1} = \frac{1}{3} L_{s_1} \tag{30}$$

$$G_{e_1} = \frac{8\pi\nu_T}{\gamma^* P} \tag{31}$$

$$C_{e_1} = (\gamma^* - 1) C_{a_1} \tag{32}$$

$$\frac{R_{e_1}}{R_{v_1}} = j \frac{\omega L_{e_1}}{R_{v_1}} = j \frac{h_v^2}{4} \left[\frac{1}{1-J\,(h_v\,\sqrt{2})} - 1 \right] \tag{33}$$

$$\frac{(\gamma^*-1)C_{a_1}}{C_{e_1}} + j \frac{(\gamma^* - 1)C_{a_1}}{G_{e_1}} = \frac{1}{J(h_T\,\sqrt{2})} = \frac{1}{J(\sigma\,h_v)} \tag{34}$$

Expanding the Bessel function expressions in Equations (33) and (34) and equating the real and imaginary terms for large h_v and h_T, Nichols shows

$$\frac{R_{e_1}}{R_{v_1}} \approx \frac{3}{8} + \frac{1}{4} h_v + \frac{15}{64} \cdot \frac{1}{h_v} \tag{35}$$

$$\frac{\omega L_{e_1}}{R_{v_1}} \approx \frac{1}{4} h_v - \frac{15}{64} \cdot \frac{1}{h_v} \tag{36}$$

$$\frac{(\gamma^*-1)C_{a_1}}{C_{e_1}} \approx \frac{1}{4} + \frac{1}{2} h_T + \frac{3}{32} \cdot \frac{1}{h_T} \tag{37}$$

and

$$\frac{\omega(\gamma^*-1)C_{a_1}}{G_{e_1}} \approx \frac{1}{2} h_T - \frac{3}{32} \cdot \frac{1}{h_T} \tag{38}$$

Fig. 3 plots the viscous skin effects represented by Equation (33) and Fig. 4 plots the non-adiabatic skin effects represented by Equation (34). [3]

We find that the Equation (35) is only an approximate equation for R_{e_1}/R_{v_1} and does not describe the curve accurately. A similar situation exists in the case of Equations (37) and (38) also. A reasonably accurate set of equations for the different curves has been obtained by means of curve fitting techniques and is given below

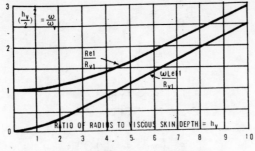

FIG. 3 VISCOUS SKIN EFFECTS

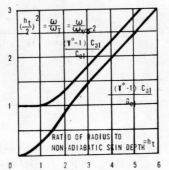

FIG. 4 NON-ADIABATIC SKIN EFFECTS

$$\frac{R_{e_1}}{R_{v_1}} = \frac{3}{8} + \frac{1}{4} h_v + \frac{3}{8} \cdot \frac{1}{h_v} \equiv DR \tag{39}$$

$$\frac{\omega L_{e_1}}{R_{v_1}} = \frac{1}{4} h_v - \frac{15}{64} \cdot \frac{1}{h_v} \equiv DL \tag{40}$$

$$\frac{(\gamma^*-1)C_{a_1}}{C_{e_1}} = \frac{1}{4} + \frac{1}{2} h_T + \frac{1}{4} \cdot \frac{1}{h_T} \equiv DC \tag{41}$$

$$\frac{\omega(\gamma^*-1)C_{a_1}}{G_{e_1}} = \frac{1}{2} h_T - \frac{1}{4} \cdot \frac{1}{h_T} \equiv DG \tag{42}$$

Now, Equations (24) and (25) can be rewritten as:

$$Z = R_{v_1}\left[\frac{R_{e_1}}{R_{v_1}}\right] + j\left[\omega L_{s_1} + R_{v_1}\left(\frac{\omega L_{e_1}}{R_{v_1}}\right)\right] \tag{43}$$

374

and

$$Y = \cfrac{\omega(\gamma^*-1)C_{a1}\left[\cfrac{\omega(\gamma^*-1)C_{a1}}{G_{e1}}\right]}{\left[\cfrac{(\gamma^*-1)C_{a1}}{C_{e1}}\right]^2 + \left[\cfrac{\omega(\gamma^*-1)C_{a1}}{G_{e1}}\right]^2}$$

$$+ j\omega\left\{C_{a1} + \cfrac{(\gamma^*-1)C_{a1}\left[\cfrac{(\gamma^*-1)C_{a1}}{C_{e1}}\right]}{\left[\cfrac{(\gamma^*-1)C_{a1}}{C_{e1}}\right]^2 + \left[\cfrac{\omega(\gamma^*-1)C_{a1}}{G_{e1}}\right]^2}\right\} \tag{44}$$

Substituting Equations (26), (27), (28), (39), (40), (41), and (42) in Equations (43), and (44), we get,

$$Z = \frac{8\pi\mu}{A^2}\ [DR] + j\left[\frac{\omega\rho}{A} + \frac{8\pi\mu}{A^2}\ [DL]\right] \tag{45}$$

$$Y = \frac{\omega(\gamma^*-1)\frac{A}{\gamma^*P}\ [DG]}{[DC]^2 + [DG]^2} + j\omega\left\{\frac{A}{\gamma^*P} + \frac{(\gamma^*-1)\frac{A}{\gamma^*P}\ [DC]}{[DC]^2 + [DG]^2}\right\} \tag{46}$$

Karam [4,5] was mainly interested in high frequencies, i.e., where $\omega \gg \omega_v$, so that his approach was to simplify Equations (35), (36), (37), (38). These simplified equations, however, give large errors when ω is in the neighborhood of ω_v. Therefore it was our purpose to approximate the Bessel function expansion to give an expression that would best describe the performance of the line over a wider frequency range. Our approximations, given in Equations (39), (40), (41), and (42), give a sufficiently accurate prediction for practical application over the frequency range $0.1\,\omega_v < \omega < \infty$, and henceforth will be referred to as Nichols' theory.

The evaluation of Nichols' frequency dependent parameters at $\omega = 0$, will yield the constant parameters given in equation set (15) through (18).

Applying Nichols' theory to the lossy line analysis, we have,

$$\frac{P_r}{P_s} = \frac{2\ Z_c\ Z_r\ \exp(-\gamma\ell)}{Z_c(Z_r+Z_c) + Z_c(Z_r-Z_c)\exp(-2\gamma\ell)} \tag{47}$$

375

where

$$Z_c = \sqrt{\frac{Z}{Y}} \quad \text{(Using Equations (45) and (46))} \quad (48)$$

and

$$Z_r = \frac{Z_t\, Z_L}{(Z_t + Z_L)} \quad (49)$$

Lossless Line Analysis

The lossless line theory is a very convenient theory because of the fact that the characteristic impedance is reduced to a real number, and the propagation constant is reduced to an imaginary number, see Equation (11). This greatly simplifies the form of the equations necessary for the prediction of line behavior. There is, however, a very serious limitation, which is the error encountered in the neighborhood of the resonant frequencies. This error is so large that a modified theory of lossless lines is necessary.

Modified Lossless Line Theory

The modified theory consists in factoring the resistance of the line from each unit element and lumping it at the sending end of the line. The resulting equations of this theory are:

$$\frac{P_r}{P_s} = \frac{1}{\left(1 + \dfrac{R_s}{Z_r}\right) \cos \beta \ell + j \left(\dfrac{R_s}{R_c} + \dfrac{R_c}{Z_r}\right) \sin \beta \ell} \quad (50)$$

where

$$R_s = \frac{8\eta\mu}{A^2} \quad (51)$$

$$R_c = \sqrt{L/C} \quad (52)$$

$$Z_r = \frac{Z_t\, Z_L}{Z_t + Z_L} \quad (53)$$

Procedure

An accurate solution of the system's performance can be obtained by deriving the differential equations for the system, but this approach is not feasible for other than simple systems. One of the methods for predicting and adjusting the system performance without resorting to the actual solving of the system's differential equation is based upon the frequency response analysis of the system. This mainly consists of obtaining two different sets of curves, one connecting the amplitude ratio with the frequency and the other connecting the phase shift with the frequency. By amplitude ratio, we mean the ratio of the signal amplitude at the sending end to the signal amplitude at the receiving end. The phase shift is the difference in phase between the above two signals.

Before going into the actual analysis, the nature of the load presented by the transducer had to be determined. The transducers used were Pace (Model No. P7D) chosen because of their low input capacitance. The input impedance of these transducers was found from experiment to be:

$$Z_t = 0.04 - j \frac{1}{2\pi f (0.0016)} \tag{54}$$

Experimental

Our fluidic transmission line was tygon tubing of 0.0625 in. diameter. The schematic of the experimental set up is shown in Fig. 5. The end of the tubing connected to the tank and hence to the signal generator is the sending end and the end connected to the pressure transducer is the receiving end, the transducer being the load.

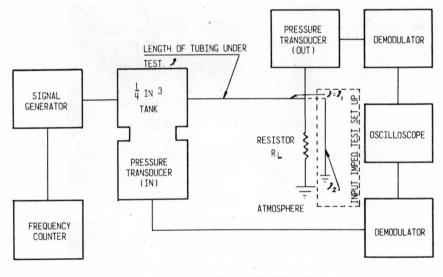

FIG. 5 SCHEMATIC OF TEST SET UP

Figs. 6 and 7 show actual pictures of the experimental set up. Frequency response tests were run for lengths 36, 32, 28, 20, 12, 8, and 4 inches of tubing. These tests were each conducted for four different load resistances, i.e., $R_L = \infty$, 16.02, 4.28 and 0.768. The latter ($R_L = 0.768$) was a 0.025 in. orifice whose resistance was evaluated at the operating pressure level.

Each of the above mentioned lengths and their corresponding loads were experimentally checked for frequencies between 10 and 250 cps, using a Sperry Utah sine wave generator. Typical waveforms of sending and receiving pressures are illustrated in Figs. 8 and 9.

The temperature was constant at 80 F and the mean pressure level was held at 15.7 psia. No attempt was made to hold the amplitude constant and it varied from 0.05 to 0.5 psi.

FIG. 6 EXPERIMENTAL SET UP

FIG. 7 CLOSE UP VIEW OF THE TRANSMISSION LINE
SIGNAL GENERATOR AND THE TRANSDUCERS

Analytical

The IBM 7040 computer at Marquette University was used to analytically check the experimental results. The three theories (constant parameter, Nichols', and the modified lossless) were programmed and solutions were obtained for frequencies between 10 and 1000 cps. Results were obtained for the various lengths and load resistances mentioned.

Figs. 10 and 11 show a sample comparison of these theories for a length of 32 in. and an infinite load resistance.

Fig. 12 shows a sample comparison of the Nichols' theory for the four load resistances at a length of 32 in.

378

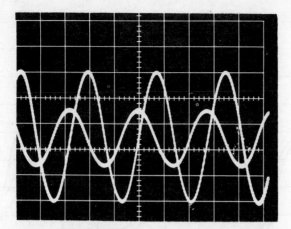

FIG. 8 TYPICAL INPUT-OUTPUT WAVEFORMS FOR
$\ell = 32$ in., $P = 1$ psig, $f = 70$ cps

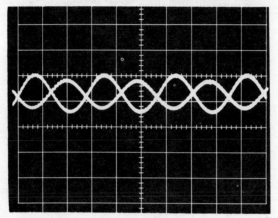

FIG. 9 TYPICAL INPUT-OUTPUT WAVEFORMS FOR
$\ell = 32$ in., $P = 1$ psig, $f = 170$ cps

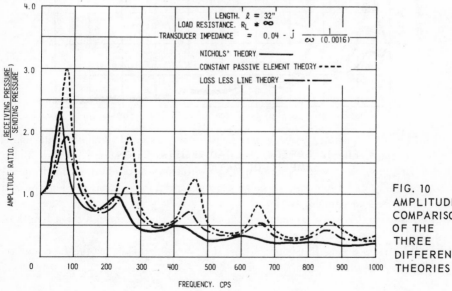

FIG. 10
AMPLITUDE
COMPARISON
OF THE
THREE
DIFFERENT
THEORIES

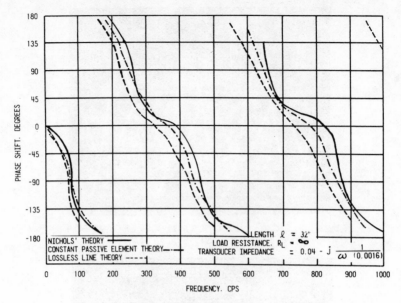

FIG. 11 PHASE COMPARISON OF THE THREE
DIFFERENT THEORIES

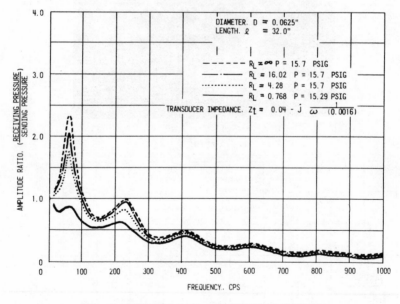

FIG. 12 EFFECT OF LOAD RESISTANCE ON
AMPLITUDE RATIO

TABLE 1

NICHOLS' THEORY PARAMETERS

Frequency cps	Characteristic Impedance $\frac{psi/in.}{cis}$	Propagation Constant dimensionless	Resistance $\frac{psi/in.}{cis}$	Conductance $\frac{cis/in.}{psi}$	Inductance ($\times 10^{-4}$) $\frac{psi\text{-}sec/in.}{cis}$	Capacitance ($\times 10^{-4}$) $\frac{cis\text{-}sec/in.}{psi}$
10.0	0.6510 −j0.4078	0.0058 +j0.0081	0.0071	0.0008	0.4591	2.0595
20.0	0.5878 −j0.2907	0.0070 +j0.0137	0.0073	0.0025	0.5113	1.9300
40.0	0.5547 −j0.1300	0.0087 +j0.0245	0.0080	0.0050	0.4956	1.8038
60.0	0.5423 −j0.0947	0.0010 +j0.0350	0.0087	0.0069	0.4784	1.7440
80.0	0.5353 −j0.0763	0.0111 +j0.0453	0.0094	0.0085	0.4658	1.7081
100.0	0.5307 −j0.0648	0.0121 +j0.0555	0.0100	0.0098	0.4563	1.6837
120.0	0.5273 −j0.0568	0.0130 +j0.0656	0.0106	0.0110	0.4490	1.6657
140.0	0.5247 −j0.0510	0.0138 +j0.0756	0.0111	0.0121	0.4430	1.6518
160.0	0.5226 −j0.0465	0.0146 +j0.0856	0.0116	0.0132	0.4381	1.6407
180.0	0.5208 −j0.0429	0.0153 +j0.0955	0.0121	0.0141	0.4340	1.6315
200.0	0.5194 −j0.0399	0.0160 +j0.1054	0.0125	0.0151	0.4304	1.6237
300.0	0.5144 −j0.0306	0.0190 +j0.1543	0.0145	0.0190	0.4180	1.5975
400.0	0.5114 −j0.0255	0.0216 +j0.2028	0.0162	0.0224	0.4104	1.5820
500.0	0.5094 −j0.0222	0.0238 +j0.2509	0.0177	0.0253	0.4052	1.5714
600.0	0.5079 −j0.0199	0.0259 +j0.2988	0.0191	0.0279	0.4012	1.5637
700.0	0.5067 −j0.0181	0.0278 +j0.3466	0.0204	0.0304	0.3982	1.5577
800.0	0.5058 −j0.0167	0.0295 +j0.3942	0.0215	0.0326	0.3957	1.5528
900.0	0.5050 −j0.0156	0.0312 +j0.4417	0.0227	0.0347	0.3936	1.5488
1000.0	0.5043 −j0.0147	0.0328 +j0.4892	0.0237	0.0367	0.3919	1.5454

Table 1 shows the significance of the Nichols' theory by illustrating how the per unit values of resistance, capacitance, inductance and conductance vary with frequency. The two columns on the left of Table 1 give the values of the characteristic impedance and propagation constant. Note that this table is only a function of mean pressure and temperature, and will not be affected by line length, or loading conditions.

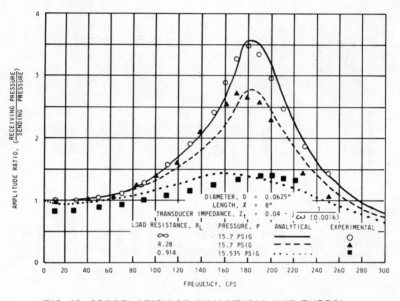

FIG. 13 CORRELATION OF ANALYTICAL AND EXPERI-
MENTAL RESULTS (AMPLITUDE VS. FREQUENCY
PLOT)

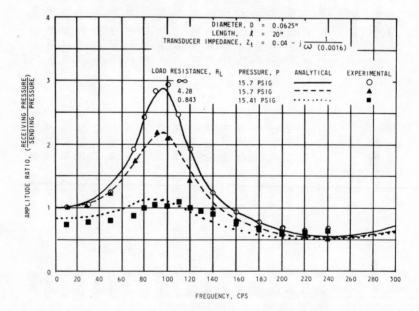

FIG. 14 (SEE FIG. 13)

382

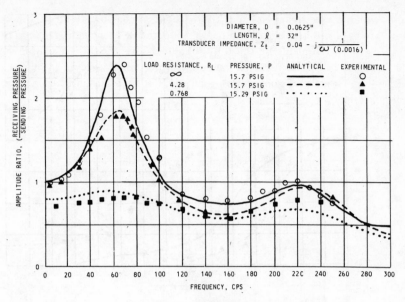

FIG. 15 (SEE FIG. 13)

Correlation of Results

Space requirements prohibit showing all the results but typical examples of 8 in., 20 in., and 32 in. lengths are illustrated in Figs. 13 through 18 where the experimental amplitude and phase are compared with the computer solutions.

In particular Fig. 13 illustrates the correlation of experimental and theoretical (modified Nichols) amplitude ratios, versus frequency of an 8 in. line, for three different load resistances. In each case, the Pace transducer was in parallel with the load. Figs. 14 and 15 present the same information for lengths of 20 in. and 32 in. respectively. Fig. 16 illustrates the correlation of experimental and theoretical (modified Nichols) phase shift, versus frequency of a line terminated in an infinite resistance, for three different lengths. Fig. 17 presents the same information for the lines terminated in a resistance of 4.28 $\frac{\#f \sec}{\text{in.}^5}$, and Fig. 18 for the lines terminated in an 0.025 in. orifice. The inconsistency in graphing form was necessary in order to sufficiently separate the data.

Input Impedance

The input or sending impedance of a transmission line can be shown to be:

$$Z_s = Z_c \frac{(Z_r + Z_c) + (Z_r - Z_c) \exp(-2\gamma \ell)}{(Z_r + Z_c) - (Z_r - Z_c) \exp(-2\gamma \ell)} \tag{55}$$

The transmission line is usually used to connect a fluidic device to its load. In this case it is desirable to know what impedance the device sees, looking into the line. For this reason a set of tests were conducted to verify equation (55) using the modified Nichols' theory.

383

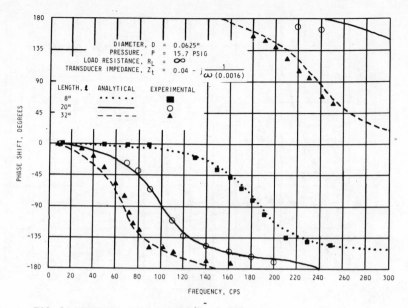

FIG. 16 CORRELATION OF ANALYTICAL AND EXPERI-
MENTAL RESULTS (PHASE SHIFT VS. FREQUENCY
PLOT)

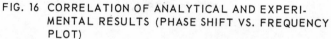
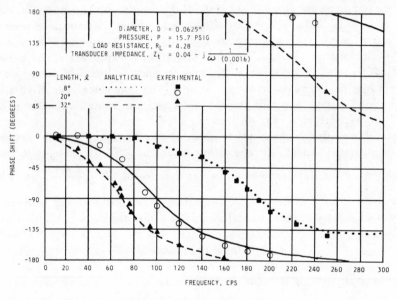

FIG. 17 (SEE FIG. 16)

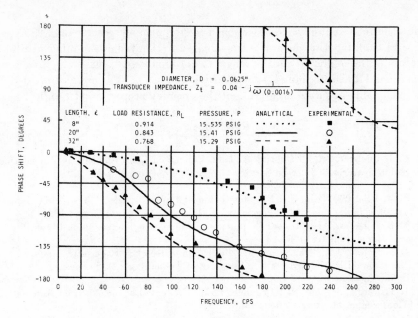

FIG. 18 (SEE FIG. 16)

The sending impedance of the three lengths of lines used were calculated for various frequencies. The experiment devised to verify the input impedance of the line, also checked the transfer equations of the line. A schematic of this set up is shown in the dotted box of Fig. 5. The length $\ell = \ell_1$ is the transmission line and a second length, ℓ_2, serves as the load. The calculated input impedance was combined with the transducer impedance to find the receiving impedance for the first line. With this impedance, the complex amplitude ratio was calculated. The experimental and analytical values of the amplitude ratio and phase shift have been listed in Tables 2, 3 and 4.

The correlation shown by these tables gives an indication of the degree of accuracy that can be achieved from the Nichols' theory.

Conclusions

The assumptions of lossless lines do not allow adequate correlation with the experimental behavior. Constant parameter lossy theory gives a closer correlation but because of the heat transfer effects of the fluid the actual resonant frequencies do not vary as multiples as predicted by the theory (see Fig. 10). The Nichols' theory allows the per unit parameters to vary with frequency to adjust for heat transfer effects. This theory when the Bessel function is properly and sufficiently expanded gives an excellent prediction of the characteristic impedance and propagation constant.

It is interesting to note that one of the assumptions of the analysis has been violated and the equations still produce accurate results. This violation is concerned with the assumption of no mean flow in the tube. The tests run with the orifice terminated line most violates this assumption, but this did not seem to be a detrimental restriction.

The equations still have to be checked for frequencies greater than 250 cps. The Sperry Utah function generator was limited to that range and other available generators in the higher frequency range do not produce adequate waveforms.

Equations (45), (46), and (47) together with equation (55), are sufficient to obtain a reasonably accurate prediction of the complex properties of fluidic lines.

References

[1] T. J. Lechner, Jr., "Effect of Air Line Volume on Controllability in Pneumatic Transmission Systems," Johnson Service Company, Research Report, DER-153B, May 10, 1960.

[2] E. W. Kimbark, "Electrical Transmission of Power Signals," New York, John Wiley and Sons, Inc.; London, Chapman and Hall, Ltd., 1949, pp. 95 and 102.

[3] N. B. Nichols, "The Linear Properties of Pneumatic Transmission Lines," ISA Transactions, January, 1962.

[4] J. T. Karam, Jr., "The Frequency Response of Blocked Pneumatic Lines," Wright-Patterson AFB, Ohio, Air Force Institute of Technology, M.S. Thesis, GAM/ME/66B-3, 1966.

[5] J. T. Karam, Jr., and M. E. Franke, Paper Presented at the 7th Joint Automatic Control Conference, Seattle, August, 1966.

TABLE 2

VERIFICATION OF INPUT IMPEDANCE

First Length Inches	Second Length Inches	Frequency cps	Experimental				Analytical	
			Input Amplitude psi	Output Amplitude psi	Amplitude Ratio	Phase Shift Degrees	Amplitude Ratio	Phase Shift Degrees
8	8	10	0.575	0.570	0.991	—	1.005	− 0.85
		50	0.305	0.325	1.066	—	1.153	− 5.84
		100	0.160	0.290	1.813	− 26.2	1.856	− 23.73
		150	0.145	0.355	2.448	−105.2	2.530	−102.86
		200	0.140	0.130	0.929	−158.0	0.932	−145.32
		240	0.115	0.060	0.522	−169.2	0.526	−152.7
	20	10	0.560	0.560	1.000	—	1.008	− 1.38
		50	0.270	0.325	1.204	− 4.6	1.254	− 11.7
		100	0.175	0.235	1.343	− 86.2	1.452	− 81.45
		150	0.170	0.065	0.382	− 66.5	0.399	− 67.46
		200	0.125	0.100	0.800	− 52.0	0.788	− 45.5
		240	0.100	0.135	1.350	− 86.8	1.327	− 83.48
	32	10	0.555	0.550	0.991	—	1.01	− 1.93
		50	0.235	0.295	1.255	− 28.1	1.296	− 23.53
		100	0.215	0.125	0.581	− 33.8	0.615	− 36.39
		150	0.145	0.175	1.207	− 38.8	1.178	− 36.36
		200	0.130	0.175	1.346	−113.9	1.398	−105.02
		240	0.115	0.070	0.609	−143.1	0.657	−129.41

TABLE 3

VERIFICATION OF INPUT IMPEDANCE

First Length Inches	Second Length Inches	Frequency cps	Experimental				Analytical	
			Input Amplitude psi	Output Amplitude psi	Amplitude Ratio	Phase Shift Degrees	Amplitude Ratio	Phase Shift Degrees
20	8	10	0.565	0.565	1.000	–	1.016	– 2.80
		50	0.265	0.405	1.528	– 18.7	1.590	– 24.99
		100	0.220	0.345	1.568	–133.6	1.473	–130.69
		150	0.165	0.100	0.606	–166.2	0.580	–160.47
		200	0.125	0.050	0.400	174.4	0.393	–172.54
		240	0.095	0.040	0.421	169.2	0.365	177.21
	20	10	0.555	0.555	1.000	–	1.022	– 4.15
		50	0.235	0.385	1.638	– 42.6	1.752	– 49.68
		100	0.230	0.110	0.478	–137.3	0.511	–133.39
		150	0.160	0.045	0.281	– 87.3	0.243	– 95.45
		200	0.120	0.095	0.792	–124.9	0.707	–113.7
		240	0.100	0.070	0.700	–173.3	0.665	–161.44
	32	10	0.545	0.550	1.009	–	1.027	– 5.55
		50	0.250	0.300	1.200	– 74.8	1.251	– 76.85
		100	0.210	0.080	0.381	– 63.1	0.400	– 62.89
		150	0.155	0.160	1.032	–112.5	0.953	–110.25
		200	0.125	0.075	0.600	–169.0	0.536	–158.98
		240	0.100	0.045	0.450	–179.9	0.421	–171.07

TABLE 4

VERIFICATION OF INPUT IMPEDANCE

First Length Inches	Second Length Inches	Frequency cps	Experimental				Analytical	
			Input Amplitude psi	Output Amplitude psi	Amplitude Ratio	Phase Shift Degrees	Amplitude Ratio	Phase Shift Degrees
32	8	10	0.560	0.575	1.027	—	1.030	− 5.58
		50	0.225	0.470	2.089	− 61.6	2.017	− 67.32
		100	0.220	0.150	0.682	−159.6	0.719	−157.97
		150	0.150	0.090	0.600	171.7	0.512	174.76
		200	0.125	0.075	0.600	106.5	0.645	120.56
		240	0.110	0.045	0.409	35.6	0.41	56.36
	20	10	0.555	0.570	1.027	—	1.038	− 7.60
		50	0.270	0.390	1.444	− 93.5	1.433	− 99.82
		100	0.210	0.075	0.357	−163.3	0.353	−151.80
		150	0.150	0.045	0.300	−146.3	0.291	−138.17
		200	0.130	0.070	0.538	155.9	0.573	169.49
		240	0.100	0.080	0.800	94.5	0.733	111.06
	32	10	0.545	0.555	1.018	− 10.7	1.043	− 10.09
		50	0.310	0.255	0.823	−108.9	0.801	−109.93
		100	0.205	0.075	0.366	− 81.6	0.360	− 87.87
		150	0.160	0.115	0.719	−163.6	0.677	−159.05
		200	0.120	0.085	0.708	126.2	0.686	140.84
		240	0.110	0.050	0.455	58.5	0.465	77.22

389

Linear Restriction of Compressible Fluids With Capillary Tubes

Gary L. Roffman

Fluid Systems Branch
Harry Diamond Laboratories
Washington, D. C.

Abstract

An approximate analysis of the flow of compressible fluid in capillary tubes shows that if the downstream pressure is kept constant, a length of capillary tube can be chosen so that the mass flow through the tube is proportional to the pressure difference across the tube. Variation in the ratio of pressure difference to mass flow has been kept to within 3.5% of a constant over a pressure range of 0 to 100 kN/m^2 (15 psid) and to within 1.5% of a constant over a pressure range of 0 to 50 kN/m^2 (7.5 psid). A more exact analysis of the flow in capillary tubes should lead to a further reduction in the variation of the ratio of pressure difference to mass flow.

Nomenclature

H_L = entrance head loss ($m^2/\sec^2$)

K_L = entrance loss coefficient

L = length of tube (m)

L^* = tube length for minimum change of Z (m)

$\dot{m}$ = mass flow ($kg/\sec$)

n = number of tubes in parallel

p = static pressure (kN/m^2)

P_o = static pressure at tube entrance (kN/m^2)

P_1 = static pressure before tube (kN/m^2)

P_2 = static pressure after tube (kN/m^2)

P_L = static pressure at distance L along tube (kN/m^2)

Q = volume flow ($m^3/\sec$)

r = radius of tubes (m)

R = gas constant $(\text{joules}/kg \ {}^{\circ}K)$

T = temperature $({}^{\circ}K)$

V_o = velocity of gas in tube entrance (m/sec)

Z = ratio of pressure drop to mass flow $(kN\text{-sec}/m^2\text{-}kg)$

Z^* = value of Z for minimum change of Z $(kN\text{-sec}/m^2\text{-}kg)$

ρ = density (kg/m^3)

ρ_o = density of gas in tube entrance (kg/m^3)

$\bar{\rho}$ = average density in tube (kg/m^3)

μ = viscosity $(N\text{-sec}/m^3)$

Introduction

In using proportional and digital flueric components to do computation and control functions, a need has arisen for precision passive flueric components. Linear passive components are especially desirable from a circuit analysis standpoint. When passive components are used in feedback circuits with high gain amplifiers, the resulting closed loop transfer function depends only on the passive components. If these components are linear, linear operations such as summing, scaling, differentiation, and integration can be readily performed [1].

One type of passive fluid component is the fluid restrictor. When the working fluid is a gas, which is often the case, capillary tube fluid restrictors have a linear relation between pressure drop and volume flow when the pressure drop is small so that the flow of gases is laminar and density changes are negligible. For large pressure drops where the flow is compressible, fluid restrictors which have a linear relation between pressure drop and mass flow are desired. Observations have been made which indicate that this also can be accomplished with capillary tubes, if the length of the tubes is designed correctly. In this report, an analysis is presented for compressible flow through capillary tubes. From this analysis, a restrictor having the desired linear relation between mass flow and pressure drop can be designed.

Theory

Because of the difficulty of finding solutions for the fluid equations for compressible flow, the problem is separated into two parts. An existing incompressible solution is used and then the effects of compressibility are approximated by assuming a relation between the density of the gas and its pressure.

A linearized solution of the boundary layer equations for incompressible flow in parallel capillary tubes was found by White [2]. He found that the pressure drop from the tube entrance to any point in the tube is given by (see Fig. 1):

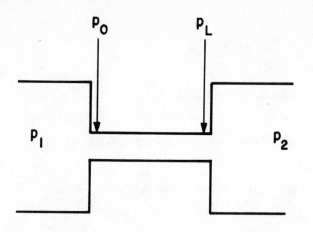

FIG. 1 PRESSURE APPLIED TO CAPILLARY TUBES

$$P_0 - P_L = \left(\frac{8\mu L}{\pi n r^4}\right) Q + \left(\frac{2\rho}{3\pi^2 n^2 r^4}\right) Q^2 \tag{1}$$

as long as the quantity $\dfrac{\mu \pi n L}{\rho Q}$ is greater than 0.3 which insures that a

insures that a series part of the solution is negligible.

If the area change at the end of the tube is large, all the dynamic pressure is lost as the flow leaves the tubes so that the static pressure at the end of the tube P_L equals P_2 (Fig. 1). From the equation of state using the assumption that the process is isothermal:

$$\dot{m} = \overline{\rho} Q = \frac{\rho_{ave} G}{RT} = \left(\frac{P_0 + P_2}{2RT}\right) Q \tag{2}$$

Since $P_L = P_2$ and using the relationships in equation (2), equation (1) becomes:

$$P_0^2 - P_2^2 = \left(\frac{16 RT\mu L}{\pi n r^4}\right) \dot{m} + \left(\frac{4RT}{3\pi^2 n^2 r^4}\right) \dot{m}^2 \tag{3}$$

In Fig. 1 it is seen that as the flow enters the capillary tube there is an abrupt area change which causes a pressure difference between P_1 and P_o. If the area change at the tube entrance is large and the velocity of the gas before the tube entrance is small, a modified form of Euler's equation is written as:

$$H_L + \frac{V_o^2}{2} + \int \frac{dP}{\rho} = 0 \tag{4}$$

Equation (4) can be integrated by assuming isothermal flow, and by writing the head loss as $H_L = K_L V_o^2/2$ and using the continuity relationship $V_o = \dot{m}/\rho_o \pi r^2$ the equation becomes:

$$\frac{\dot{m}^2(1+K_L)}{2\pi^2 r^4} = \rho_o^2 RT \ln \frac{P_i}{P_o} \tag{5}$$

For n tubes in parallel and since $\rho_o = p_o/RT$ equation (5) becomes:

$$\rho_o^2 \ln \frac{P_i}{P_o} = \frac{RT(1+K_L)\dot{m}^2}{2\pi^2 n^2 r^4} \tag{6}$$

K_L is an experimental constant that depends on the geometry of the tube entrance. For the square edged tubes and large area changes, K_L is about 0.5 [3]. Since the total pressure drop across the tube entrance is relatively small, expanding the logarithmic term in equation (6) and neglecting higher order terms changes equation (6) to

$$\rho_o^2 \left[\frac{2\left(\frac{P_i}{P_o}-1\right)}{\frac{P_i}{P_o}+1} + \cdots \right] = \frac{RT(1+K_L)\dot{m}^2}{2\pi^2 n^2 r^4} \tag{7}$$

or

$$P_i^2 - P_o^2 = \frac{RT(1+K_L)\left(\frac{P_i}{P_o}+1\right)^2 \dot{m}^2}{4\pi^2 n^2 r^4}$$

Since the entrance pressure drop is relatively small, $(p_1/p_o + 1)^2$ is approximately equal to 4. Assuming this value of $(p_1/p_o + 1)^2$ and the experimental value (0.5) for K_L, equation (7) can be written as:

$$P_i^2 - P_o^2 = \frac{1.5\,RT\,\dot{m}^2}{\pi^2 n^2 r^4} \tag{8}$$

Combining equations (5) and (8) to eliminate p_o^2 yields:

$$P_i^2 - P_2^2 = \left(\frac{16\,RT\mu L}{\pi n r^4}\right)\dot{m} + \left(\frac{17\,RT}{6\pi^2 n^2 r^4}\right)\dot{m}^2 \tag{9}$$

The transfer relation between the mass flow and pressure drop is defined as:

$$Z = \frac{P_i - P_2}{\dot{m}} \qquad \left(\frac{KN-sec}{m^2-Kg}\right) \tag{10}$$

393

This quantity is not called resistance, since mass flow and pressure drop are not analogous to current and voltage. By using in equation (10) the value of $\dot{m}$ derived from (9), the value of Z for capillaries is found to be

$$Z = \frac{\left(\dfrac{16RT\mu L}{\pi n r^4}\right)}{2(P_1 + P_2)} + \frac{\left\{\left(\dfrac{16RT\mu L}{\pi n r^4}\right)^2 + 4\left[\left(\dfrac{17RT}{6\pi^2 n^2 r^4}\right)\left(P_1^2 - P_2^2\right)\right]\right\}^{1/2}}{2(P_1 + P_2)}$$

(11)

In order to find the conditions that will produce a linear relation between mass flow and pressure drop, it is necessary to find the relationship between the constant terms and the pressures in equation (11) that produces the least change in Z for a change in the pressures. If Z is differentiated with respect to one pressure and the result set equal to zero, the condition for producing the least change in Z with respect to small changes in that pressure is found. If differentiation is performed with respect to the upstream pressure, P_1, the downstream pressure is fixed. By taking the partial derivative with respect to P_1 of equation (11) and setting the results equal to zero, one obtains the following equation:

$$\frac{\left(\dfrac{16RT\mu L}{\pi n r^4}\right)^2}{\dfrac{17RT}{6\pi^2 n^2 r^4}} = 4P_2^2$$

(12)

which is the condition for a minimum change in Z for a change in P_1 when P_2 is fixed. Solving (12) for the length of capillary tube that produces the least change in Z for a change in P_1 gives:

$$L^* = \frac{0.210 r^2 P_2}{\mu \sqrt{RT}}$$

(13)

For air at room temperature

$$R = 2.87 \times 10^2 \ \left(\frac{joules}{Kg - {}^\circ K}\right)$$

$$T = 2.95 \times 10^2 \ ({}^\circ K)$$

$$\mu = 1.82 \times 10^{-5} \ \left(\frac{N\text{-sec}}{m^2}\right)$$

and equation (13) becomes

$$L^* = 39.7 \ r^2 \ p_2$$

(14)

When the tubes are cut to the length to minimize changes in Z, the value of the transfer relation Z^* can be obtained from equations (11) and (12) as:

$$Z^* = \frac{P_1 - P_2}{\dot{m}} = \left(\frac{17RT}{6\pi^2 n^2 r^4}\right)^{1/2} = \frac{\left(\frac{16RT\mu L^*}{\pi n r^4}\right)}{2P_2} \tag{15}$$

The value of Z^* is seen to depend on the terms in the parenthesis and P_2. Since P_2 is held constant, and, for isothermal flow, the terms in the parentheses are constant, Z^* will remain constant for large changes in P_1. Thus, a linear relation exists between the pressure difference across the capillary tubes and the mass flow through the tubes. The terms in parenthesis are the same terms that appear in equation (9), the equation that describes compressible flow in capillary tubes. The linearity of the mass flow and pressure drop depends on the validity of equation (9). If the terms in parenthesis in equation (9) do not accurately describe the compressible flow in capillary tubes because of the approximations used, the value of Z^* will not be constant. If a more exact analysis shows that the flow through the capillary tubes can be described by equation (9) with other values for the terms in parenthesis that are constant, Z^* can still be made constant but a different length of tubing is needed than is given by equation (14).

The first expression for Z^* in equation (15) is:

$$Z^* = \frac{\left(\frac{17RT}{6}\right)^{1/2}}{\pi n r^2} \tag{16}$$

Equation (16) shows that Z^* is inversely proportional to the square of the capillary tube radius. Z^* is independent of p_2, but the length of tubing L^* changes with p_2 (equation 14) such that Z^* for a particular size radius does not change. Thus, for a single capillary tube, there is only one value of Z^* for each radius.

Because it may be difficult to obtain capillary tubes with radii of all sizes, getting a particular value of Z^* may require using similar tubes in parallel and perhaps even tubes of different radii, each cut to the length required.

Fig. 2 shows the variation of Z versus the pressure ratio across the capillary tube for various lengths of tube. When the tube length is the length L^* given by equation (14), the value of Z is the constant Z^*. For lengths of tubing shorter than L^*, the value of Z increases with increases in the pressure ratio. For lengths of tubing longer than L^*, the value of Z decreases with increases in the pressure ratio. For small pressure ratios, the value of Z is approximately proportional to the length. This occurs, since for small pressure drops and flows, the flows approaches the incompressible case given by Hagen-Poiseuille flow. The effect of compressibility is to increase the mass flow through the capillary tubes by increasing the density. The entrance losses and velocity changes in the tubes act to decrease the mass flow through the tubes. For L^*, the effects of compressibility and entrance and velocity changes combine to make Z constant. For lengths greater than L^*, the effects of compressibility dominate and Z decreases with pressure ratio increases. For lengths less than L^*, the effects of entrance losses and velocity changes dominate, and Z increases with pressure ratio increases.

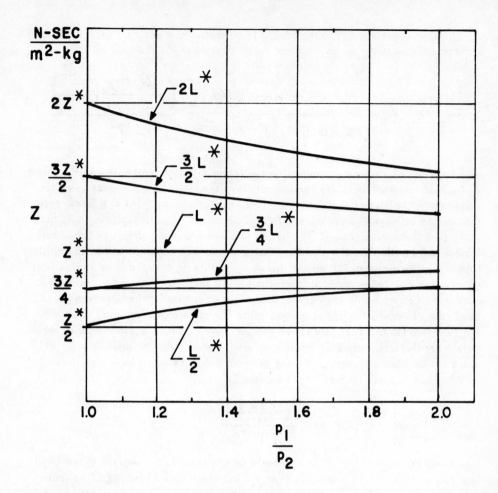

FIG. 2 EFFECTS OF LENGTH ON Z

The equations used to find L^* are not valid if the flow is turbulent. By taking 2000 as the value of the Reynolds number at which turbulence begins and using the value of $\dot{m}$ from equation (15), the pressure difference at which flow becomes turbulent is

$$P_1 - P_2 = \frac{\mu \times 10^3 \left(\frac{17 R 7}{6}\right)^{1/2}}{r} = \frac{8.9}{r} \tag{17}$$

for air at room temperature. The smaller the tube radius, the larger the pressure difference before the flow becomes turbulent and the larger the linear pressure range. If P_1/P_o is as large as 1.5, the approximations used are not accurate. In most cases P_1/P_2 must be much larger than 1.5 before P_1/P_o may differ significantly from unity (see equation 7).

396

Pressures p_1 and p_2 (before and after a combination of parallel tubes) and the mass flow through the tubes were measured. The test setup is shown in Fig. 3. Pressures were measured with a series of calibrated pressure gauges, and all pressure measurements were accurate to within 1%. The flow was measured with a displacement flow calibrator and these measurements were also accurate to within 1%. The mass flow was found by measuring the volume flow at a fixed density and then multiplying by the density. The value of p_2 was raised above ambient pressure by adjustment of a downstream needle valve. The pressures were measured in tanks. The capillary tubes were connected to the tanks by tubing with an area about 30 times the combined areas of the capillary tubes.

The capillary tubes tested were ceramic with eight parallel capillary channels of about 3.05×10^{-4} m (0.012 in.) diameter and ten metal tubes bonded together each with a diameter of about 1.78×10^{-4} m (0.007 in.). These capillary tubes were cut to various lengths for the tests.

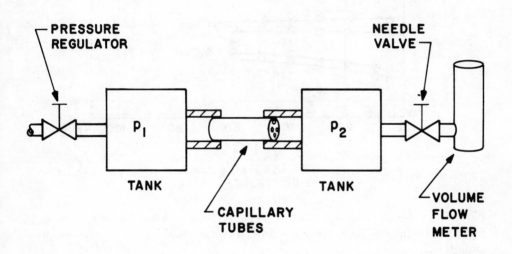

FIG. 3 EXPERIMENTAL TEST SETUP

Experimental Results

In Fig. 4, Z versus pressure difference is shown for three lengths of the eight channel ceramic tubing. For each length of tubing, measurements for two values of p_2 are plotted as points, and the predicted characteristics from equation (11) for various lengths and downstream pressures are plotted as curves. The value of r^4 used in equation (11) was found indirectly because of the difficulty in measuring r and the increased error of raising r to the fourth power. The measurements used to find r were made with small pressure drops; i.e., incompressible flow and for the longest tube length available which made entrance effects negligible. Under these conditions of small pressure drops and mass flows, equation (9) was approximately equivalent to the incompressible equation for Hagen-Poiseuille

397

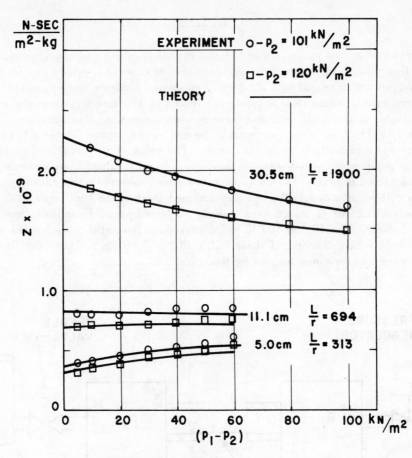

FIG. 4 VALUE OF Z FOR 8 HOLE CERAMIC TUBE VS
PRESSURE DIFFERENCE

flow. The value of r was found using equation (9), and this value of the radius, found for essentially incompressible flow, was used in the equations for compressible flow.

In Fig. 4, equation (11) was quite accurate for the 30.5 cm long tube, but at large pressure differences the experimental values of Z were slightly higher than the analytic ones. As the tubes were shortened, the experimental values of Z deviated even more from analytic ones and especially as the pressure difference increased. The flow in the 5 cm long tube was probably turbulent for pressure differences above 40 kN/m^2.

The radius of the channels in the ceramic tube was found to be 1.60 x $10^{-4} m$. Equation (14) shows that Z is constant if the tube is 10.3 cm long when p_2 is 101 kN/m^2. Since the experimental value of Z was greater than theory predicts, the ceramic tube was first cut to 11.1 cm (about 8% longer than 10.3 cm) to try to compensate for the increase of Z at higher pressure differences. The experimental value of Z for this length, as shown in Fig. 4, increases with pressure differences. The experimental value of Z for a pressure of 60 kN/m^2 was about 4% higher than the initial value of 0.8 x 10^9 N-sec/m^2-kg. The laminar flow range of Z based on equation (17) is 60 kN/m^2. The analytic and experi-

398

mental values of Z for the 11.1 cm long tube agree to about 2% until the pressure difference is greater than 30 kN/m^2.

Figs. 5 and 6 show the test results with the metal tubes. The radius of the metal capillary tubes was found to be 0.903 x 10^{-4} cm. The results for the metal tubes are seen to be similar to those for the ceramic tubes. As the pressure difference increases, the experimental value of Z becomes larger than the theory predicts. A given deviation in experimental Z occurs for smaller values of pressure difference as the tubes are shortened.

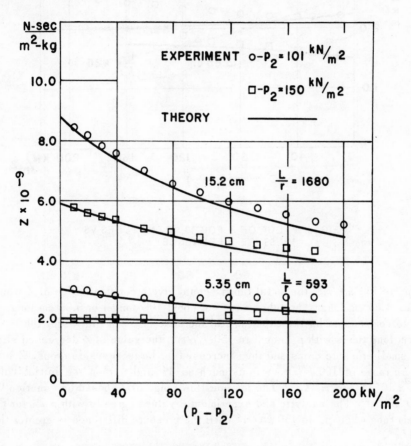

FIG. 5 VALUE OF Z FOR 10 METAL TUBES VS
PRESSURE DIFFERENCE

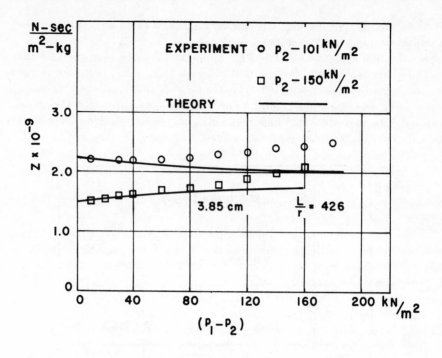

FIG. 6 VALUE OF Z FOR 10 METAL TUBES VS
PRESSURE DIFFERENCE

If p_2 is 150 kN/m^2, the metal tubes should give a constant value of Z when
they are 4.85 cm long. The tubes were cut about 10% longer or 5.35 cm long
to try to compensate for the experimental increase in Z. In Fig. 5, for the
5.35 cm long tubes with p_2 equal to 150 kN/m^2, the value of Z decreased slightly for small pressure drops and then increased for larger pressure drops. Z in the
pressure range of 100 kN/m^2 was as much as 3% higher than the initial value
of 2.1 x 10^9 N-sec/m^2-kg. The laminar flow range of Z, based on equation (17)
is 100 kN/m^2. The analytic and experimental values agree to within 2% for the
5.35 cm tube when p_2 is 150 kN/m^2 until the pressure difference is greater than
50 kN/m^2.

If P_2 is 101 kN/m^2, the metal tubes should give a constant value of Z when
they are 3.27 cm long. The tubes were cut about 20% longer or 3.85 cm long.
In Fig. 6, for P_2 equal to 101 kN/m^2, the value of Z slightly decreases for low
pressure differences and then increases for large pressure differences. Z is about
3.5% higher than the initial value of 2.24 x 10^9 N-sec/m^2-kg over the laminar
pressure range of 100 kN/m^2. The analytic and experimental values agree to
within 3% for pressure differences up to 50 kN/m^2. The value of Z varies by
1.5% from the initial value of 2.24 x 10^9 N-sec/m^2-kg over the pressure range
of 50 kN/m^2. When the tubes are longer than L^*, Z decreases at first for the
low pressures where the analysis is valid. As the pressure increases, additional
losses occur and Z increases. Because Z decreases and then increases, the
value of Z at low and high-pressure differences may be close.

400

To better appreciate the significance of the choice of tube length in making Z relatively constant, it is helpful to see the changes in Z when L is considerably different than the calculated L^*. In Fig. 4, the 30.5 cm long ceramic tube with P_2 equal to 101 kN/m^2, Z changes by 16% in the pressure range of 60 kN/m^2 from the initial value of 2.19 x 10^9 N-sec/m^2-kg. In the same figure, Z changes by 60% in the pressure range of 60 kN/m^2 from the initial value of 0.38 x 10^9 N-sec/m^2-kg measured for the 5 cm long tube when P_2 equals 101 kN/m^2. Similar large changes occur for the metal tubes in Figs. 5 and 6. If a length L^* is chosen for a particular value of P_2 and then P_2 is changed, the length chosen, obviously, no longer provides a constant Z for the new value of P_2. Thus, in Fig. 4, the 11.1 cm long tube with P_2 equal to 120 kN/m^2 instead of 101 kN/m^2 has a change in Z of 10% in the pressure range of 60 kN/m^2 from the initial value 0.69 x 10^9 N-sec/m^2-kg.

The increase in the value of Z as the pressure drop increases could be explained by the term multiplying the mass flow squared in equation (9) increasing as the pressure drop increases. This term contains the entrance losses and velocity-change effects that cause Z to increase for tubes shorter than L^*. It is assumed in equation (9) that the entrance pressure drop is small so that $(P_1/P_o + 1)^2$ is approximately equal to 4.0. This entrance drop term is not completely negligible and may cause as much as a 4% increase in the term $(17\,RT/6\pi^2 n^2 r^4)$ in equation (9) when the maximum pressure difference given in equation (17) for laminar flow is used. However, for the analysis to match the experiments, the increase in $(17\,RT/6\pi^2 n^2 r^4)$ must be much greater than 4%. The experimental values of Z increase with pressure difference and the shortening of the tubes, since both cause the mass flow through the tubes to increase. For large flows and pressure differences, the approximations used for the analysis are not valid.

Conclusions

An approximate solution for the flow of a compressible fluid in capillary tubes shows that there is a length of capillary tube that gives an approximately linear relation between mass flow and pressure difference. Because the analysis is not accurate over the entire laminar flow range, the value of Z (ratio of pressure difference to mass flow) is only constant for about half the laminar pressure range given by eq. (17). If a larger pressure range is needed for a constant value of Z, it is necessary to make the capillary tubes longer than the value found by analysis. Unless a better analysis for compressible flow in capillary tubes is found, the best length of tube to minimize changes in Z will have to be found by trial and error. Based on the measurements taken, tube lengths 10 to 20% longer than the length given by analysis are necessary to maintain the value of Z nearly constant over the entire laminar pressure range given by equation (17).

References

[1] S. Katz and G. Roffman, "Flueric Operations on Pressure Signals," Transactions of the ASME, Journal of Engineering for Industry, Vol. 88, No. 3, August 1966, pp. 274-277.

[2] H. N. White, "Analysis of the Steady-Flow Pneumatic Resistance of Parallel Capillaries," HDL — Proceedings of the Fluid Amplification Symposium, Vol. I, October 1965 pp. 181-213.

[3] J. W. Daily, "Fluid Dynamics," Addison-Wesley Publishing Company, 1966.

Development of High Speed Fluidic Logic Circuitry for a Novel Pneumatic Stepping Motor

William S. Griffin and William C. Cooley

Lewis Research Center
Cleveland, Ohio

Abstract

This paper describes design and development of high speed fluidic logic circuitry used to drive a novel, pneumatic stepping motor. Test results are presented of the circuit driving the stepping motor. The breadboard drive circuitry was able to step the motor at 173 steps per second in either direction and reverse it within one step at 115 steps per second.

Introduction

A result of a continuing program to develop actuator systems compatible with NERVA environments has been a novel, pneumatic stepping motor [1]. A key problem to its application as a practical, working actuator system is that of furnishing properly sequenced pressures to each of its eight bellows. Because of the radiation level at the actuator location, it was considered desirable to develop an environmentally tolerant pressure sequencing system. The advantages of fluid amplifiers were obvious. This paper describes a breadboard no-moving-parts circuit of fluid jet amplifiers to sequence the required bellows pressures. Design and development aspects of one particular circuit are presented along with that circuit's performance when driving the pneumatic stepping motor.

Nomenclature

A,B,C,D	= outputs of counter
$\dot{m}$	= mass flow rate
P	= pressure
R	= reset instruction
S	= set instruction
T	= timing pulse, torque
t	= time
τ	= time delay

402

Subscripts:

a	= atmospheric
b	= backward
c	= control
f	= forward
r	= receiver
s	= supply

Superscript:

–	= denotes logical complement of the quantity

Stepping Motor

Shown schematically in Fig. 1, the actuator motor has only two moving parts: a gimbals supported driving gear free to nutate (wobble) but not to rotate, and an output gear free to rotate but not to nutate. By unequal pressurization of eight bellows attached to its periphery, the driving gear is made to tilt and contact the output gear. As the bellows pressurization pattern is sequenced, the point of contact between the two gears travels around the circumference of the output gear. Since the output gear has 180 teeth and the nutating gear, 181 teeth, the output gear will advance by one tooth, or 2°, for every complete revolution made by the point of contact. Since eight bellows are used for manipulation of the driving gear, the output shaft position can be indexed in increments of 0.25°. Thus, in the absence of excessive load torques which would cause gear disengagement, the actuator motor can accurately position a load to any shaft position which is specified by sequencing of the bellows pressurization pattern. Fig. 2 shows a section drawing of the motor. For a more complete description of the motor and the procedures used in its design, the reader is referred to reference [1].

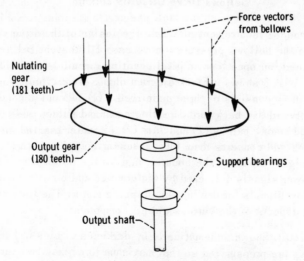

Figure 1. - Schematic of stepping motor operation.

403

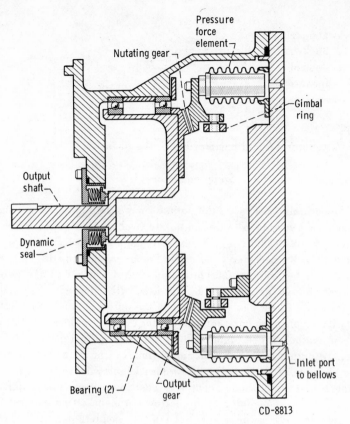

Figure 2. - Cross-section of pneumatic stepping motor.

Bellows Drive Circuitry Design

A key performance requirement affecting the design of the drive circuit was that it sequence the bellows pressures in excess of 160 steps per second. To achieve this speed, an open loop, digital counting circuit using fluid jet amplifiers was developed. Fig. 3 shows a block diagram of the drive circuitry and actuator motor. The circuitry consists of three main parts: (1) two pulse conditioning units which accept forward and backward directing command pulses and convert them into well defined timing pulses (T_f and T_b); (2) a counter circuit which accepts the timing pulses and converts them into a pressurization pattern stored and advanced on the eight outputs of the counter; and (3) the power amplifiers which take the low power signals delivered by the counter and convert them into high pressure and flow signals for driving the stepping motor. The following sections discuss design aspects of the various circuit components.

Counting Circuit. Shown schematically by darkened circles in Fig. 4(a), four adjacent bellows are pressurized so that maximum force may be exerted on the point of contact between the nutating and output gears. To be avoided is a pressurization pattern, such as shown in Fig. 4(b), which shifts the center of force towards the center of the nutating gear and delivers a higher percentage of the bellows output force to the gimbals which support the nutating gear rather than

404

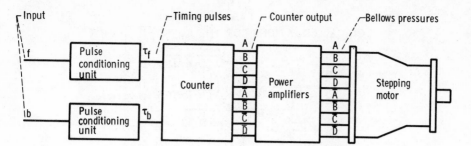

Figure 3. – Block diagram of breadboard actuator system.

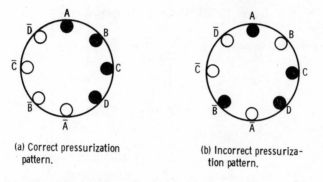

(a) Correct pressurization pattern.

(b) Incorrect pressurization pattern.

Figure 4. – Bellows pressurization patterns.

to the point of contact between the gears. Thus, the counting circuit is required to maintain the pressurization pattern shown in Fig. 4(a) and sequentially index it around the circumference of the nutating gear.

If bellows pressurization is denoted by the logical state, 1, and absence of bellows pressurization by the logical state, 0, then the set of logical equations shown in table I may be used to represent the sequencing of the pressurization pattern. Setting X (S_X) denotes transition of bellows, X, from logical state 0 to logical state, 1, while resetting X (R_X) denotes transition from logical 1 to logical 0: Because of the symmetry of the pressurization pattern, $S_X \longleftrightarrow R_{\overline{X}}$ while $S_{\overline{X}} \longleftrightarrow R_X$. * and + have their usual meaning of logical AND and logical OR, respectively.

These equations contain instructions for both sequencing the pressurization pattern and eliminating any errors in it. The former instructions have either forward (T_f) or backward (T_b) pulses while the latter instructions lack these terms. It is noted that Set and Reset instructions are often given even though the pattern is in a correct state and no need exists for a change in bellows pressure. However, these instructions, under normal operation, are merely redundancies which instruct the affected bellows pressure to remain in the state it is already in.

The counter circuit which was developed to satisfy the logical equations of Table I is shown, schematically, in Fig. 5. The pressurization pattern is stored and advanced on four central bistable fluid jet amplifiers, designated I, II, III and IV. Their outputs are designeted A, $\overline{A}$, B, $\overline{B}$, C, $\overline{C}$, D, and $\overline{D}$, respectively, corresponding to similarly designated bellows in Fig. 4. An active two input OR unit is connected to each control port and furnishes its control signals. To the

405

TABLE I
LOGICAL EQUATIONS FOR THE COUNTER CIRCUIT

$$S_A = T_b *B + T_f *\overline{D} + B*\overline{D} = R_{\overline{A}}$$

$$R_A = T_b *\overline{B} + T_f *D + \overline{B}*D = S_{\overline{A}}$$

$$S_B = T_b *C + T_f *A \qquad = R_{\overline{B}}$$

$$R_B = T_b *\overline{C} + T_f *\overline{A} \qquad = S_{\overline{B}}$$

$$S_C = T_b *D + T_f *B + B*D = R_{\overline{C}}$$

$$R_C = T_b *\overline{D} + T_f *\overline{B} + \overline{B}*\overline{D} = S_{\overline{C}}$$

$$S_D = T_b *\overline{A} + T_f *C \qquad = R_{\overline{D}}$$

$$R_D = T_b *A + T_f *\overline{C} \qquad = S_{\overline{D}}$$

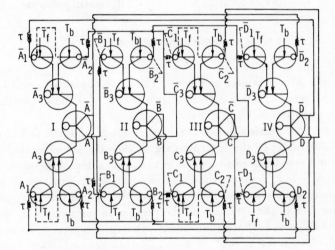

Figure 5. – Schematic of counting circuit for nutator motor.

input of each active OR unit is connected the output of an OR unit acting as a passive AND. These units accept the output of one of the other bistable units as a power supply and a forward (T_f) or backward (T_b) timing pulse as their control signal. Their output is thus the logical product (AND) of the outputs of the central bistable units and the timing pulse. Careful examination of the circuit will show that the logical equations of Table I, including the error correcting terms, are satisfied. The connections which implement the latter are shown as dashed lines.

Operation of the circuit is as follows: Timing pulses of one type only (either T_f or T_b) are applied simultaneously to the control ports of the passive AND units. Those AND units whose power nozzles are pressurized by the outputs of the central bistable amplifiers (I, II, III, IV) will generate output signals of duration

406

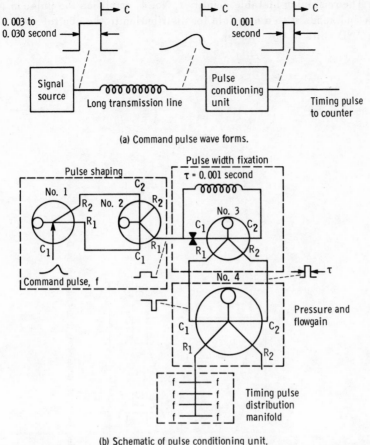

(a) Command pulse wave forms.

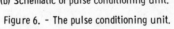

(b) Schematic of pulse conditioning unit.

Figure 6. – The pulse conditioning unit.

approximately equal to the length of the timing pulse. These output signals travel to the control ports of the active OR units, causing them in turn to generate output pulses. The output signals from the active OR units switch the central bistable amplifiers. The outputs of the central bistable units are delayed an amount of time, τ, before they reach the nozzles of the passive AND units. Thus, if the timing pulse is short and has vanished by the time changes in outputs from the bistable amplifiers reach the power nozzles of the passive AND units, nothing further will happen and the counter will be set for the next timing pulse. The sequence is repeated with the application of each timing pulse T_f or T_b.

Pulse Conditioning Unit. As illustrated in Fig. 6(a), the command pulses delivered to the actuator can be highly distorted as a result of propagating down a long transmission line. Their rounded leading edges, low amplitude, and long tails make them unsuitable for direct use as timing pulses. The function of the pulse conditioning unit, shown schematically in Fig. 6(b), is to convert the command pulses into properly shaped timing pulses. The first two elements, No. 1, and No. 2, of the pulse conditioning unit shape the ill-defined command pulse into one with fixed amplitude and sharp leading and trailing edges. The next element, No. 3, is a fluidic one-shot multivibrator which fixes the pulse width at one milli-

407

second. The remaining bistable amplifier, No. 4, amplifies the pulse in pressure and flow and sends it to a manifold for distribution to the control ports of the passive AND units of the counter.

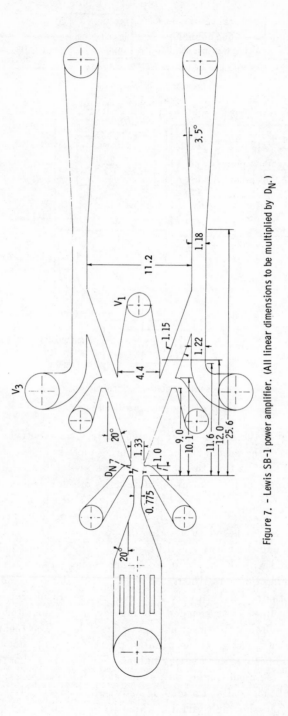

Figure 7. – Lewis SB-1 power amplifier. (All linear dimensions to be multiplied by D_N.)

Power Amplifier. To convert the low pressure and flow outputs of the counter circuit to the high pressures and flows demanded by the stepping motor bellows, a supersonic pressure ratio fluid jet amplifier, shown in outline form in Fig. 7, was used. The receivers are of the "Y" type [2] so that the amplifier could be easily switched into discharging bellows. Although "Y" type receivers have lower output pressures and flows than conventional receivers, their use was necessitated by actuator reversing requirements. Salient characteristics of the power amplifier when driving the stepping motor bellows are listed in Table II.

TABLE II
SPECIFICATIONS OF THE LEWIS SB1 POWER AMPLIFIER

Power nozzle throat size . . . . 0.040 in. wide by 0.060 in deep

Design supply to exhaust pressure ratio 4.0

Maximum normalized receiver pressure . . . . 40 percent of supply

$\quad (P_r - P_a)/(P_s - P_a)$

Maximum normalized receiver flow . . . . 80 percent of supply

$\quad (m_r)/(m_s)$

Mach number of power nozzle. 1.63

Design load volume . . . . 0.576 in.^{3}

Charging time of load volume. . . . . 0.008 sec

Control port switching pressure 0.07

$\quad (P_c - P_a)/(P_s - P_a)$

Control port switching flow. 0.06

$\quad (\dot{m}_c/\dot{m}_s)$

Breadboard Bellows Drive Circuitry

To establish the practicality of the previously discussed bellows drive circuitry, it was implemented in breadboard form and connected to the stepping motor. The complete actuator system is shown in Fig. 8. Except for the power stage, the implementation was made using standard, commercial amplifiers. The design of the circuit and its interconnecting lines, especially the pulsewidth fixation portion of the pulse conditioning unit, is explained in detail in reference [3].

Of interest is an interconnection technique used to reduce signal attenuation in the transmission lines of the counter circuit. For a driving source with an output pressure-flow characteristic typical of most fluid jet amplifiers, it is often possible to find an oversized transmission line in which the pulse reflected by the load is cancelled by the line's driving source impedance. This situation is illustrated in Fig. 9. The larger line has a lower acoustical impedance, Z_2, than the acoustically matched one but the final pressure and flow delivered by the reflected pulse correspond to the final, steady state values (location 3 on the figure). To the load, the combined incident and reflected pulses delivered by the oversized line are indistinguishable from the pulse delivered by an acoustically matched line. Thus, it is possible to deliver a pulse of proper waveform to the load with an oversized line and incur much lower frictional losses than if an acoustically matched line had been used.

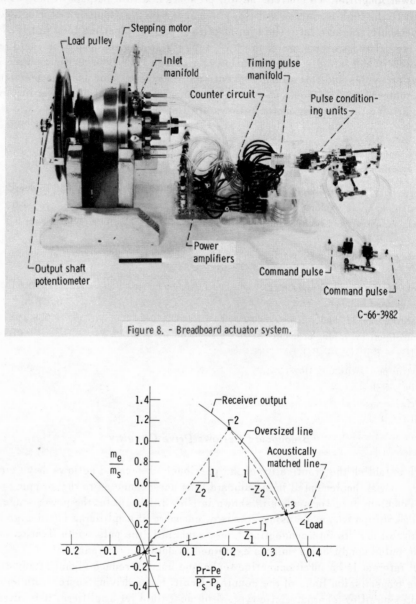

Figure 8. - Breadboard actuator system.

Figure 9. - Illustration of single reflection line termination technique.

This technique was used to size both the lines delivering carry signals from the counter's outputs to the power nozzles of the passive AND units and the lines that distribute the timing pulse from the pulse conditioning unit to the control ports of the passive AND units. Fig. 10 shows a typical carry signal as generated at the counter output (D) and as delivered to the power nozzle of the passive AND unit, (D_{delayed}). As expected, the reflected pulse can be seen at the counter output (signal D) but cannot be seen in the signal delivered to the power nozzle of the passive AND unit. The timing pulse delivered to the control port of the passive

410

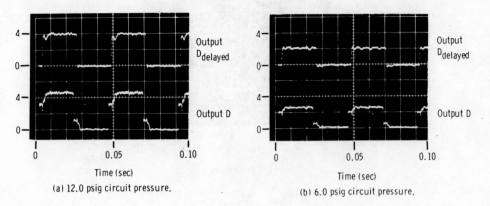

(a) 12.0 psig circuit pressure.

(b) 6.0 psig circuit pressure.

Figure 10. – Counter outputs D and $D_{delayed}$.

AND unit, shown in Fig. 11, is also of proper height and width. Since the pressure transducer which measured this pulse was located approximately two inches from the interaction region of the passive AND unit, the reflected pulse can be seen as a small step in the leading and trailing edges of the timing pulse. This step would not be observed by a transducer located at the junction of the control port and the interaction region.

Experimental Performance of the Breadboard Actuator System. To determine the ability of the bellows drive circuitry to drive the stepping motor, a series of performance tests were conducted on the complete, breadboard actuation system. As shown in Fig. 12, the bellows drive circuitry could step the motor in either direction at 173 steps per second (43°/sec). A more stringent test was to command the drive circuitry to reverse direction every eight steps. As shown in Fig. 13, the stepping motor, which was loaded with an inertia of 28 lbm-in^2, was able to reverse within one step for stepping rates up to 115 steps per second. This performance is roughly comparable to a bandwidth of 7.2 cps at ±1.0° output shaft rotation in a conventional piston actuator.

Maximum output torque was measured by increasing the load torque on the actuator's output shaft until the driving gear would disengage as the actuator was stepped. The results, shown in Fig. 14, indicate a maximum stepping rate of 37°/sec (148 steps/sec) and a maximum output torque of 70 in.-lb$_f$. The decreased maximum actuator stepping rate observed in the output torque tests has not been explained but is believed to result from dynamic interactions between the stepping motor's output stiffness and the high inertia of the pulley used to apply load torques. When the proper load inertia was replaced on the actuator's output shaft, it would be again step at 173 steps per second (43°/sec).

411

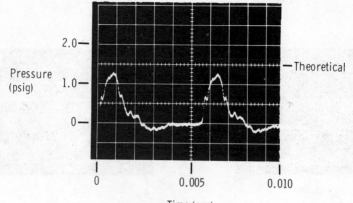

Pressure (psig)

— Theoretical

Time (sec)

Figure 11. - Timing pulse delivered to control
port of passive AND unit. 6.0 psig supply
pressure to pulse conditioning unit.

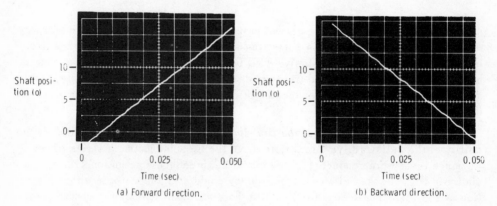

Shaft posi-
tion (o)

Time (sec)

(a) Forward direction.

Shaft posi-
tion (o)

Time (sec)

(b) Backward direction.

Figure 12. - Output shaft position versus
time - 173 steps/sec.

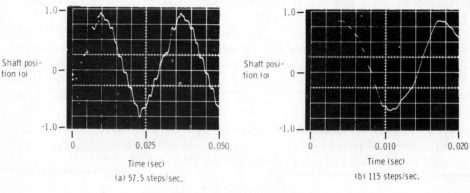

Shaft posi-
tion (o)

Time (sec)

(a) 57.5 steps/sec.

Shaft posi-
tion (o)

Time (sec)

(b) 115 steps/sec.

Figure 13. - Small amplitude response of
breadboard actuator system. Eight
steps each direction.

412

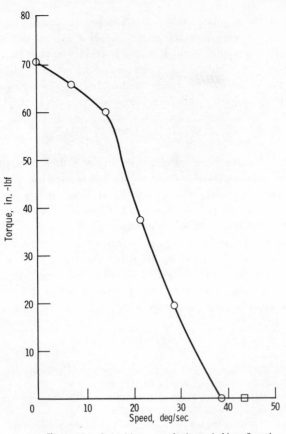

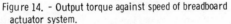

Figure 14. - Output torque against speed of breadboard
actuator system.

Discussion

The maximum rate at which the breadboard circuit could step the motor in one
direction was limited primarily by bellows charging time (cf. Table II), bellows
and gimbal pivot stiffness, and the inertial forces required to move the nutating
gear and its supporting gimbals. The stepping motor was designed to operate with
a 70 psid bellows drive pressure. Thus, internal inertia and stiffness reduced output torque and speed more than they would in a motor designed to operate on the
18 psid drive pressures of the counter circuit. 4.0 psid bellows pressure, alone,
was required to force the nutating gear into contact with the output gear. If the
drive circuitry supply and exhaust pressures are raised to NERVA design values
(200 psia and 50 psia, respectively) output drive pressures will rise to 61 psid
and provide more force for either higher output torque, faster stepping rates, or
faster reversal of slewing direction.

An inherent limitation to circuit speed occurs when the timing pulses are
delivered so rapidly that carry signals from the central bistable units do not have
time to reach the power nozzles of the passive AND units during the quiet period
between timing pulses. If a well defined timing pulse of one millisecond duration
can be delivered to the control ports of the passive AND units (the present case),

413

this limitation will be approximately 500 steps per second. In an integrated circuit reduced pulse dispersion would permit use of a shorter timing pulse and a still higher maximum stepping rate. It would therefore appear that, for most practical cases, the primary limitations to the rate at which the bellows drive circuitry can step the motor will be determined by bellows charging time and motor internal inertia and not by the inherent speed of the circuit itself.

Conclusions

It is concluded that the fluid jet amplifier bellows drive circuitry is sufficiently fast that bellows charging time and motor internal inertia are the primary limitations to the maximum stepping motor system speed. Although it has not been tested at higher rates, it is believed that the current bellows drive circuitry can operate satisfactorily at well above 173 steps per second.

It is also concluded that the improved bellows drive circuitry and the stepping motor constitute a reliable, open-loop stepping actuator system with inherently high output stiffness, reasonable slewing speeds, and small step size. Further improvements in both the actuator and the power valves of the bellows drive circuitry should increase system performance beyond that reported in this paper.

References

[1] G. R. Howland, "Pneumatic Nutator Actuator Motor", Report No. BPAD-863-16719R (NASA CR-54788), Bendix Corp., Oct. 17, 1965.

[2] W. S. Griffin, "Design of a Fluid Jet Amplfier with Reduced Receiver-Interaction-Region Coupling", Tech. Note D-3651, Oct. 1966.

[3] W. S. Griffin, "A Breadboard Fluidic Controlled Pneumatic Stepping Motor System", Proposed NASA Technical Note.

[4] W. E. Gromen, "A Transition Map Method of Counter-Synthesis", Report No. EDC 1-65-35 (NASA CR-61056), Case Inst. of Tech., 1965.

[5] K. N. Reid, Jr., "Static and Dynamic Interaction of a Fluid Jet and a Receiver-Diffuser", ScD Thesis, Mass. Inst. of Tech., Sept. 1964.

[6] F. T. Brown, "Pneumatic Pulse Transmission with Bistable-Jet-Relay Reception and Amplification", ScD Thesis, Mass. Inst. of Tech., May 1962.

[7] P. Blaiklock and R. Sidel, "Development of a Pneumatic Stepping Motor System", Summer Course Notes 2.73, Mass. Inst. of Tech., Dept. of Mech. Engrg., July 1966.

An Automatic Flueric Gain Changer Circuit for Flight Control Systems

W. G. Beduhn

Honeywell Inc.

Abstract

The development of an automatic flueric gain changer circuit for flight control systems is described. The problem to be solved was two-fold: 1) to develop a flueric device capable of changing gain, and 2) to develop a flueric gain scheduler device which would supply the required intelligence to the gain changer, in a predescribed manner, as a function of an altitude pressure signal. This flueric circuit was mechanized from selected types of fluid amplifiers and a number of orifices. Flight test of this unique circuit integrated into a complete fluidic system was successfully demonstrated in an F-101B jet aircraft.

Introduction

This paper describes the development of a flueric gain changer circuit and its use in a fluidic yaw stability augmentation control system. The control system was designed and successfully flight tested in an F-101B high-performance aircraft.

Autopilots designed for high performance aircraft such as the F-101B require complex gain scheduling to obtain optimum augmentation performance over a large flight envelope. This is due to a reduction of inherent aircraft damping and rudder effectiveness as a function of altitude and Mach number. In this application, the autopilot gain was scheduled in a non-linear manner with ambient pressure.

The gain changer performance requirements were defined by an analog computer simulation of the F-101B aircraft performance at 33 different flight conditions. The nominal requirements, along with an acceptable tolerance band, indicate a constant gain between sea level and 35,000 ft altitude with a minimum gain change ratio of 1.4:1 between 35,000 ft and 45,000 ft. (See Fig. 1.)

The development of the gain changer circuit was divided into two parts: 1) development of a flueric gain changer; and 2) development of a flueric gain control circuit to supply the required intelligence to the gain changer.

415

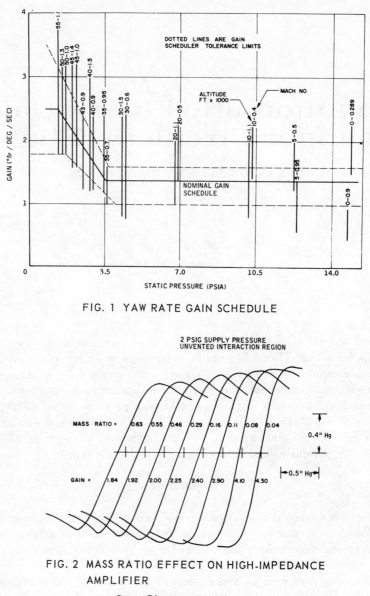

FIG. 1 YAW RATE GAIN SCHEDULE

FIG. 2 MASS RATIO EFFECT ON HIGH-IMPEDANCE
AMPLIFIER

Gain Changer Development

A high input impedance fluid amplifier has been developed which exhibits a significant pressure gain change with changing input mass ratio, (i.e., control mass flow divided by power mass flow), when operated with an unvented inter-action region. Fig. 2 illustrates this phenomenon. Observation has shown that changing the interaction region pressure of certain types of fluid amplifiers changes their output mass flow. Many different amplifier combinations were tested in an effort to utilize these two characteristics to achieve a practical gain changer. It became evident that for stable operations a center-dump-type amplifier was needed to "feed" the high impedance amplifier because of the high-loading, low-output flow required.

416

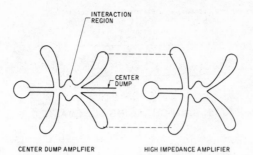

CENTER DUMP AMPLFIER   HIGH IMPEDANCE AMPLIFIER

FIG. 3 AMPLIFIER SCHEMATIC OF GAIN CHANGER

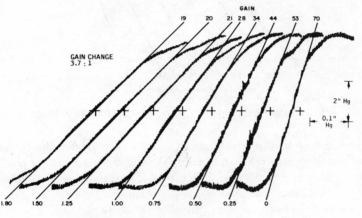

INTERACTION REGION PRESSURE (INCHES Hg)

FIG. 4 GAIN CHANGER WITH UNVENTED HIGH-
IMPEDANCE AMPLIFIER

The gain changer is operated by varying the interaction region pressure on the "feeding" center-dump-type amplifier. An amplifier schematic of the gain changer is shown in Fig. 3. When the pressure in the interaction region of the center-dump amplifier is increased, more flow goes out the output legs. This increases the control flow to the high impedance amplifier and decreases the total gain. Conversely, lowering the pressure in the center-dump amplifier interaction region results in a decrease in control flow to the high impedance amplifier and an increase in total gain. The total gain change is expected to be about 2 to 1.

To ensure complete isolation of the gain changer, another center-dump-type amplifier was used ahead of the two gain changing amplifiers for the yaw damper system application. Impedance and performance matching of these three amplifiers is critical for proper operation. The overall gain change results of this circuit are shown in Fig. 4. The resultant gain change is greater than expected (3.7 to 1 instead of 2 to 1).

Initial test results indicated that the input-impedance of the high-impedance amplifier also varied with changes in mass ratio. This changed the loading condition on the center-dump amplifier, causing its gain and range to change. This phenomenon, combined with the mass ratio gain change in the high-impedance amplifier, explains the larger than expected total gain change.

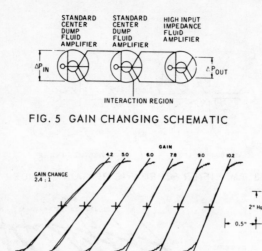

FIG. 5 GAIN CHANGING SCHEMATIC

FIG. 6 COMPLETE GAIN CHANGER CHARACTERISTICS

Although a more than adequate gain change was achieved, the circuit was too noisy and matching was critical. Venting the interaction region of the high-impedance amplifier had the desirable effect of reducing amplifier output noise and reducing matching problems, but also resulted in less overall gain change. A schematic of this finalized gain changing circuit is shown in Fig. 5. The pressure gain curves from this finalized circuit are plotted in Fig. 6 for different interaction region pressure of the feeding center-dump amplifier.

The performance of the gain changer was adequate to meet the fluidic damper system requirements.

Gain Control Development

A gain control circuit is required to supply the intelligence to operate the gain changer.

The gain-control circuit requirements were established by replotting the gain changer results (Fig. 6) in such a manner as to produce a curve of pressure gain ratio versus interaction region pressure. The resultant curve (Fig. 7), when cross plotted with a normalized version of the gain changer circuit requirements (Fig. 8), defines a curve of the interaction region pressure level required for different ambient pressures (P static). This curve is shown in Fig. 9.

The flueric gain control circuit is required to provide a constant pressure signal for ambient pressures greater than 3.5 psia (from 0 ft to 35,000 ft) and to provide a pressure signal approximately proportional to P_{static} for ambient pressures less than 3.5 psia (Fig. 9). The circuit connects into and controls the interaction region pressure of the center-dump amplifier, which provides the desired gain change (i.e., constant gain up to 35,000 ft, then increasing gain up to 45,000 ft).

The non-linear pressure signal required was produced by a four-stage proportional amplifier cascade. The pressure output of one side of the fourth stage in

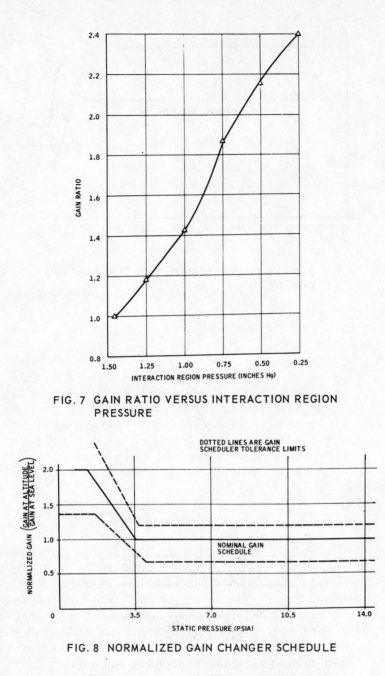

FIG. 7 GAIN RATIO VERSUS INTERACTION REGION
PRESSURE

FIG. 8 NORMALIZED GAIN CHANGER SCHEDULE

the gain control cascade was "teed" into the interaction region port of the gain changer. The cascade was held in saturation until the ambient pressure (P_{static}) was reduced to the "break point" value of 3.5 psia. (It should be noted that the cascade was designed to exhibit negligible signal reversal when driven into saturation.) Further reduction in P_{static} brings the amplifier cascade out of saturation to provide the desired change of interaction region pressure level. A schematic of the gain control cascade, along with a typical gain curve, is shown in Fig. 10.

419

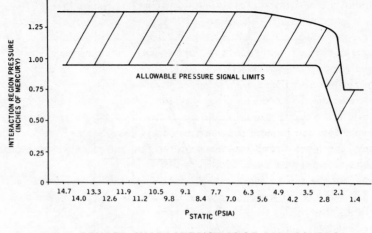

FIG. 9 DESIRED CHARACTERISTICS OF GAIN CONTROL
CIRCUIT

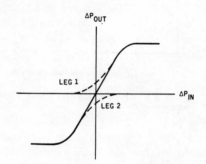

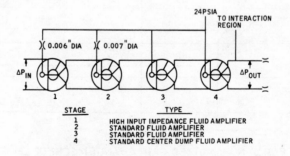

STAGE	TYPE
1	HIGH INPUT IMPEDANCE FLUID AMPLIFIER
2	STANDARD FLUID AMPLIFIER
3	STANDARD FLUID AMPLIFIER
4	STANDARD CENTER DUMP FLUID AMPLIFIER

FIG. 10 SCHEMATIC AND GAIN CURVE FOR GAIN
CONTROL CASCADE

The above cascade would produce the desired non-linear pressure signal, provided a means of varying cascade control pressure (ΔP_{in}) could be devised. The control pressure (ΔP_{in}) must bring the amplifiers out of saturation at the required P_{static}.

The first attempt to produce the desired control characteristics used straight orifices in the input network. One gain control cascade input port was supplied with a fixed pressure (18 psia) while the other input was "teed" in an orifice

420

string sensing a constant pressure source (damper system supply pressure of 24 psia) at one end and ambient pressure (with a static probe) at the other. The complete circuit is shown in Fig. 11. As the static pressure is reduced, the pressure levels between each of the orifices in the network are consequently reduced, provided no orifice approaches its critical pressure ratio (0.528 for air).

A large number of orifices were required to assure that no orifice approached its sonic condition. The source supply pressure for the orifice input network was 24 psia while the static pressure could be as low as 1.4 psia. This pressure ratio 1.4/24 is very low and is more than sufficient to choke any one orifice. To solve this problem, the input circuit was designed so that the pressure ratio across each orifice in the network was never less than 0.90.

Orifice R_1 of the orifice input network (see Fig. 11) was adjusted such that at $P_{static} = 3.5$ psia the pressure P_1 was at a value only slightly more than 18 psia (P_2). At this value of P_1, the control pressure ($P_1 - P_2$) has the gain control amplifier cascade at the "break point" of its gain curve. Any further reduction in P_{static} reduces P_1 which brings the cascade out of saturation. Conversely, any increase in P_{static} increases P_1, which drives the gain control cascade back into saturation. This circuit provided the desired results, as shown in Fig. 12. However, further testing indicated certain difficulties due to supply air variations.

Jet engine compressor bleed air was used as the pressure source for the fluidic damper system. The large pressure and temperature variation of the bleed air presented various component design problems (i.e., amplifier null shift, amplifier gain change, orifice pressure ratio change).

Tests indicated that compensation of an input pressure regulator as a function of temperature (to keep mass flow rate constant) would provide consistent damper system performance. The gain changer circuit had to exhibit the same pressure-temperature relationship to avoid the necessity of a second input regulator. This in turn required that the breakpoint of the gain control cascade remain at approximately the same P_{static} value over the temperature and pressure ranges expected.

Although the gain control circuit shown in Fig. 11 achieved the desired results at a given pressure and temperature, the position of the breakpoint was extremely sensitive to supply pressure variations. This appeared to be inherent in this particular circuit; i.e., any small changes in supply pressure would cause $P_1 - P_2$ to change, since P_2 is fixed.

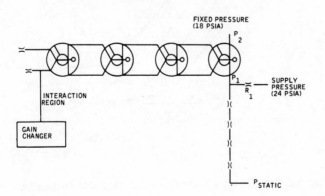

FIG. 11 INITIAL GAIN CONTROL CIRCUIT

421

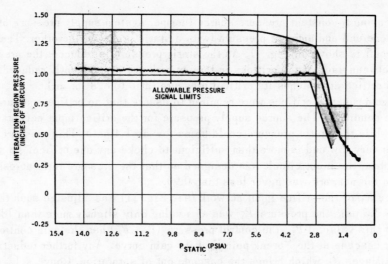

FIG. 12 INITIAL GAIN CONTROL CIRCUIT RESULTS

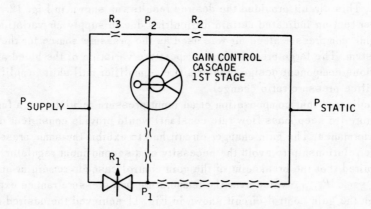

FIG. 13 BALANCED INPUT GAIN CONTROL CIRCUIT

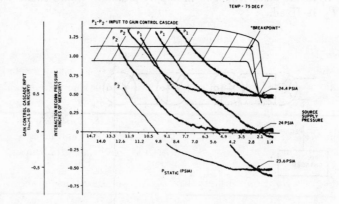

FIG. 14 PRESSURE SENSITIVITY OF RESTRICTOR LEGS

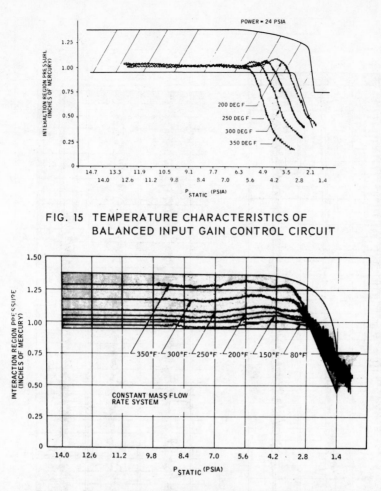

FIG. 15 TEMPERATURE CHARACTERISTICS OF
BALANCED INPUT GAIN CONTROL CIRCUIT

FIG. 16 STABILIZED TEMPERATURE CHARACTERISTICS
OF BALANCED INPUT GAIN CONTROL CIRCUIT

A balanced input orifice network was designed to reduce supply pressure sensitivity of the breakpoint. This circuit is shown in Fig. 13. Circuit orifices R_2 and R_3 were selected so that the pressure ratio across R_2 became critical as P_{static} was reduced to 6 psia and pressure P_2 was at the proper control level for the gain control cascade input. The sonic restrictor (R_2) prevents pressure P_2 from reducing as P_{static} is reduced from 6 psia to 1.4 psia. Pressure P_1 was lowered and adjusted (by selection of orifices and adjusting the variable orifice R_1) to reach a value slightly higher than P_2 at 3.5 psia (P_{static}). This is the approximate position of the required "breakpoint" in the gain scheduling curve. The ΔP_{in} $(P_1 - P_2)$ is applied to the first-stage amplifier and brings the amplifier cascade out of saturation at $P_{static} = 3.5$ psia as in the original input network circuit.

Supply pressure effect on the output of the two orifice legs is shown in Fig. 14, together with the output of the gain control cascade at the nominal supply pressure. Although the ambient level of the orifice legs changes, the crossover point, and, hence, the breakpoint of the schedule curve, remains nearly insensitive to supply pressure changes.

423

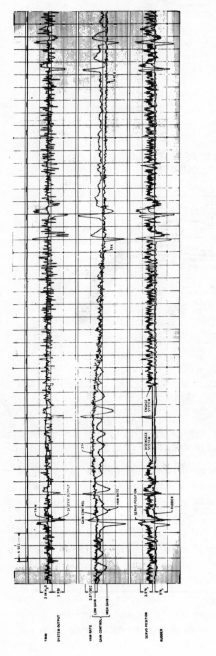
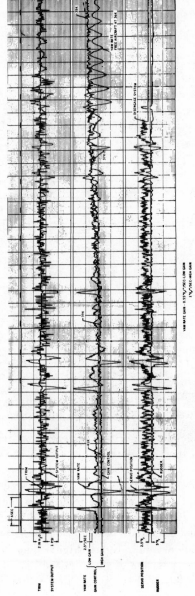

FIG. 17 FLUID YAW DAMPER GAIN SCHEDULER
PERFORMANCE – 35K FT TO 41K FT,
MACH 0.9 – FLIGHT NO. 10

424

Temperature tests were conducted on the balanced input gain control circuit. The results, shown in Fig. 15, indicate a significant change in the breakpoint position over the range of temperature tested. The sensitivity to temperature changes of the balanced input gain control circuit had to be reduced.

Temperature stability was achieved by selecting restrictor R_2 (see Fig. 13) to give approximately the same mass flow in legs one and two at the cross-over point. This reduced the temperature sensitivity and enabled the gain control signal to stay within the required limits over the entire temperature range, as shown in Fig. 16. These results are for stabilized temperature conditions and a constant mass flow system. Tests showed that the breakpoint position of the gain control signal tended to vary with rapidly changing supply temperature.

However, the large mass of the pressure chamber header and the low flow of air through it prevented rapid changes of supply air temperature and the system performed properly during flight test.

Flight Test of Gain Changer Circuit

The yaw stability augmentation control system was successfully flight tested in the F-101B aircraft. The gain changer circuit functioned properly. Fig. 17 shows flight test data of the gain control signal controlling the yaw rate gain in the pre-described manner. Aircraft yaw rate and damper system output (both fluidic output and servo output) were also recorded to describe the overall damper performance.

Summary and Conclusions

The major accomplishments of the program were:

1) A flueric gain changer circuit was developed, integrated into a complete fluidic flight control system, and successfully flight tested in an F-101B aircraft.

2) The flueric gain changer circuit functioned properly from jet engine bleed air, and, during lab tests, over a stabilized temperature range of 70 F to 350 F.

As a result of this program it is concluded that the complex requirement for scheduling gain as a function of altitude, as required by high-performance aircraft controls, can be accomplished by a flueric subsystem.

Acknowledgment

This program was sponsored by the Air Force Flight Dynamics Laboratory under Project 8226, Task 822604, Contract AF33(165)-2533. Mr. J. F. Hall was the technical director for the program.

A Method of Air Gauge Circuit Analysis

H. M. Eckerlin
D. A. Small
Corning Glass Works
Raleigh, North Carolina

Abstract

A non-contact-type air gauge circuit is analyzed, and the result is compared with experimental data. The method of analysis is quick, and the experimental correlation is very good.

Nomenclature

A = nozzle exit area

C = nozzle coefficient

G = gap distance

g = gravitational constant

P = pressure

Q = volume flow rate

R = restriction – square root function

W = weight flow rate

w = specific weight

$\overline{R}$ = restriction – linear function

Subscripts

s = supply

p = gauging pressure

a = atmospheric

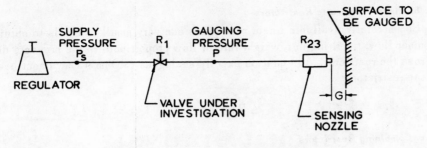

FIG. 1 TYPICAL AIR GAUGE CIRCUIT

Introduction

Air gauging is a technique for covering a small dimensional change into a change in air pressure.

The operation of simple air gauges may be improved considerably by amplifying the output signal with fluidic systems. It is therefore important that circuit equations be developed to provide insight into the problems of interconnection of air gauges and fluidic circuits. In this analysis a simple air gauge circuit will be studied and the results compared with experimental data. The analysis may be extended to complex gauging circuits and fluidics interconnection problems.

Analysis

A typical circuit is shown in Fig. 1. The important circuit components are: 1) a regulated air supply, 2) an intermediate restrictor R_1, 3) gauging pressure P, which is read on a manometer or recorder, 4) the gauging head — in this case a .040 in. nozzle, 5) measured piece — results in creating a gauging gap G.

I. Before proceeding into the circuit analysis, the concepts of restriction must be developed.

a. Square Root Function Restrictor

A nozzle, orifice, or valve may be used for this type of restrictor, and is well described analytically by Bernoulli's equation and a simple form of the continuity equation. Combining these two leads to

$$\Delta P = \frac{w^2 \, R^2}{w} \tag{1}$$

where

$$R \equiv \frac{1}{CA\sqrt{2g}} \tag{2}$$

This new definition of R is convenient because it is independent of pressure level and pressure drop across the restrictor. Equation (1) is analogous to Ohm's Law for electrical resistance.

b. Linear Pneumatic Restrictors

Commercially available linear restrictors use very small channels to obtain a laminar flow; resulting in a weight rate of flow proportional to the pressure drop across the restrictor. An equation exactly analogous to Ohm's Law describes these restrictors:

$$\Delta P = W\bar{R}$$

c. Combining Restrictors

Square root function restrictors in series or parallel may be combined into an equivalent resistance by

$$\text{Series:} \quad R_T^2 = R_1^2 + R_2^2 + \ldots$$

$$\text{Parallel:} \quad \frac{1}{R_T} = \frac{1}{R_1} + \frac{1}{R_2} + \ldots$$

These relations are easily shown by a method similar to that found in any college freshman physics text on combining electrical resistances.

Linear restrictors may also be combined by a method similar to that used for electrical resistors. In particular,

$$\text{Series:} \quad (R_\ell)_T = (R_\ell)_1 + (R_\ell)_2 + \ldots$$

$$\text{Parallel:} \quad \frac{1}{(R_\ell)_T} = \frac{1}{(R_\ell)_1} + \frac{1}{(R_\ell)_2} + \ldots$$

d. Restrictor Values

The value of R_2 in the gauging circuit (the nozzle) may be calculated directly from equation (2)

$$R_2 = \frac{1}{(.82)\,(\pi)\,(.02)^2\,\sqrt{64.4 \times 12}} = 35\,\frac{\text{sec}}{\text{in}^{5/2}}$$

$$R_2 = 35\,\frac{\text{sec}}{\text{in}^{5/2}} \tag{3}$$

R_3 (the gap) may be calculated from equation (2) and a slight stretch of the imagination. It has been determined that the gauging circuit is only effective for gaps which are a small fraction of the nozzle diameter. Therefore, the area between the gauging head and gauged surface is small compared to the nozzle exit area. This situation is similar to orifice flow. Therefore

$$R_3 = \frac{1}{CA_3\sqrt{2g}}$$

$$R_3 = \frac{1}{\pi\,(.04)\,(G)\,\sqrt{64.4 \times 12}}, \quad \text{where C is assumed} = 1.$$

$$R_3 = \frac{.286}{G}\,\frac{\text{sec}}{\text{in}^{5/2}} \tag{4}$$

428

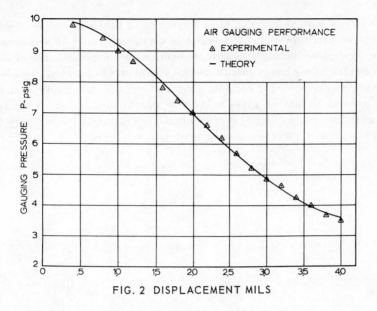

FIG. 2 DISPLACEMENT MILS

Thus R_{23} may be calculated as a function of gap distance, G.

II. Circuit Analysis:

By equating the flow rate through R_1 to that through R_{23}, an expression with P is obtained

$$W_1 = W_{23}$$

$$\frac{(P_s - P)}{R_1^2} w_P = \frac{(P - P_a) w_a}{R_{23}^2}$$

Also, by the perfect gas law, $w = \dfrac{P}{RT}$

$$\therefore \quad \frac{(P_s - P)}{R_1^2} \frac{P}{RT} = \frac{(P - P_a)}{R_{23}^2} \frac{P_a}{RT}$$

This equation may be solved for P

$$P = \frac{-\beta + \sqrt{\beta^2 + 4R_{23}^2 R_1^2 P_a^2}}{2R_{23}^2} \tag{5}$$

where

$$\beta = R_1^2 P_a - R_{23}^2 P_s$$

The only variable on the right hand side of equation (5) is R_{23} for an operating system, and R_{23} in turn is a function of gap, G.

429

Therefore, P may be calculated as a function of G. This is shown on Fig. 2 along with experimental data. Agreement is very good, which is somewhat of a surprise, since several questionable assumptions are present in the analysis.

This method of air gauge circuit analysis is useful because it provides a quick, easy way of studying not only air gauge circuits, but fluidic restrictor circuits in general. It may be expanded to very complicated resistor circuits containing both linear and non-linear restrictors. The mathematics becomes tedious, but digital computer programs may be written to handle them.

Fluidic Cigarette Inspection

Gilbert A. Cotta

Corning Glass Works
Raleigh, North Carolina

Abstract

An inspection system is developed using fluidic elements to sense a flow resistance through cigarettes. A pressure sensitive trigger, whose threshold can
be set between .5 and 2 in. of water, performs the inspection. The inspection
period is limited by a timing signal. The system produces a pneumatic signal sufficient in magnitude to eject cigarettes falling below a set flow resistance.

Introduction

Resistance to air flow is an important parameter in cigarette quality control.
Leaks, crumpled ends, and slight variations in weight result in different resistances. To detect these defects, a pressure threshold level is established, below
which a cigarette is rejected.

Until the advent of fluidics, cigarette manufacturers used electro-mechanical
devices for inspection. Although these perform adequately, maintenance is a
problem due to tobacco entrainment and pressure transducer diaphragm breakage.
In this system, back-pressure techniques using a fluidic trigger have been adapted
to leak detection and quality control on a high speed cigarette manufacturing
machine.

Basic Problems

The system was required to integrate three functions dynamically:
1) Applying pressure to the cigarette,
2) Sensing the pressure at an appropriate time,
3) Establishing a threshold for acceptance.

Back-pressure sensing has been associated with air gauging and extremely low
frequencies, near DC. Through static and dynamic tests on a cigarette manufacturing machine, it was determined clearly that back-pressure sensing could be

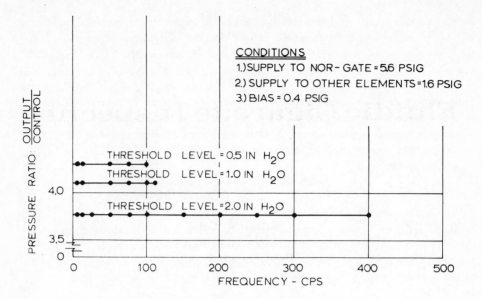

FIG. 1 DYNAMIC BEHAVIOR OF THRESHOLD TRIGGER

used effectively at least to 40 cps. The two ends of cigarette rods were pressurized to 0.4 psig through nozzles having an inside diameter of 0.237 and 0.157 in. Dynamic signals were recorded with a threshold level of 1.0 in. of water to distinguish acceptable cigarette rods from rejects. This level was made variable between .05 −2.0 in. of water for possible variation in the inspection drum mechanical seals.

For the pneumatic trigger, a two stage biased flipflop was initially incorporated but was replaced later because of high sensitivity to small changes in bias pressure, drift, and oscillations. Instead, a standard Corning Schmitt trigger was used. The trigger consists of three proportional fluidic elements followed by two stages of digital elements. The first proportional receives a bias pressure on one side and the inspection signal on the other. The third proportional drives a flipflop cascaded to an Or-gate. Dynamic behavior of this device is demonstrated in Fig. 1. In an additional test, the device was found to switch with a pulse of 0.1 in. of water. If the bias and control threshold signal is metered and controlled effectively, it is capable of switching at 0.25 in. of water at up to 50 cps.

Control Circuit

The design required a digital output signal, switched on only when an inspected cigarette was to be rejected. With the output amplified to 4.0 psig, it is sufficient to overcome a 2.0 psig vacuum holding the cigarette rod, and detach it from the inspection drum. Fig. 2 shows the organization of the inspection system. It comprises a Schmitt trigger, two Nor-gates, a bistable element, and a power amplifier. A timing signal (B) is required to index each inspection cycle. The timing signal was generated by a back-pressure probe and a slotted disc mounted on the same shaft as the inspection drum, which holds 14 cigarettes on its outer periphery. One timing pulse was provided for each inspection cycle. The inspected cigarette signal (A) is connected to the control of the Schmitt trigger. The

432

outputs of this device (C) and (D) are connected to the two Nor-gates. The timing signal (B) is divided through a wye divider and fed to the second inputs of the two Nor-gates. The outputs of the Nors (E) and (F) are in turn fed to a bistable element. The last element is simply a power amplification stage. Waveforms from the system are shown in Fig. 3. In columns (1), (2), and (4), signal (A) represents acceptable cigarettes. In column (3), a slight deviation in pressure indicates a rejected cigarette. Signal (G), which is the output of the inspection control, is continuously OFF but is turned ON when a rejected cigarette passes by. It then stays ON until an accepted cigarette is sensed which turns (G) OFF.

Test Results and Discussion

The system was breadboarded with Corning standard elements and tested both in our Laboratory and on a manufacturing machine. One air manifold supplies all the elements. Constant restrictors were placed as shown to provide regulated pressures to each supply input. One needle valve is required to adjust the bias to the pressure threshold level required for triggering.

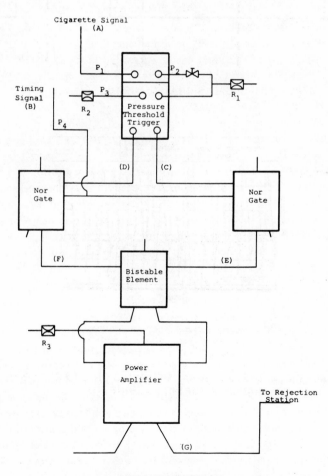

FIG. 2 CIRCUIT DIAGRAM

433

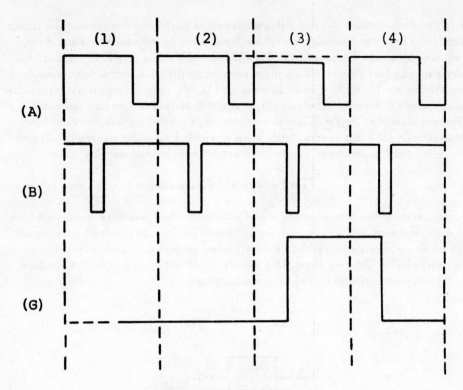

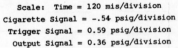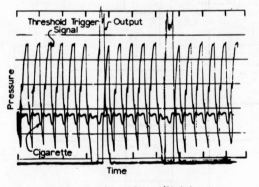

FIG. 3 SIGNAL DIAGRAM

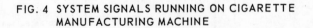

Scale: Time = 120 mis/division
Cigarette Signal = -.54 psig/division
Trigger Signal = 0.59 psig/division
Output Signal = 0.36 psig/division

FIG. 4 SYSTEM SIGNALS RUNNING ON CIGARETTE
MANUFACTURING MACHINE

The output of the system was tested with the output terminal held at 2 psig vacuum. This had no effect on system stability. The system was installed on a manufacturing machine and tested. Results are shown in Fig. 4.

The cigarette pressure magnitude was 0.4 psig with a threshold level of 0.95 in. of water. Output of the system was as high as 2.1 psig, overcoming the vacuum hold on the cigarette. Time delay of the output signal was 55 m.s. when the system ran at the rate of 16.6 cps. By placing the rejection station next to the inspection station, the pressure output of the system rejected low-flow-resistance cigarettes by brute force without the need of further delay on the output. This system was also tested in our laboratory and found to operate up to 40 cps.

The concept of high-speed fluidic leak inspection has been successfully demonstrated. The system designed is applicable to inspection of tubular products of a wide variety.

Acknowledgments

The author extends sincere appreciation to L. W. Langley for assistance in the design and to David Pridgen for his diligence in testing and operating this system.